A Few Nice

"This is the best book out in my opinion."
—Peri Solder
Peri & Ed's
Mountain Hideaway

"Thank you for offering such a great guide. It is a wonderful service to our guests."
—Stacie LeVack
Red Eagle Mountain
Bed & Breakfast

"As every Colorado innkeeper knows, your book is the source of many of our guests from all parts of the state. We are sure your new edition will be the best on the shelves!"
—Sharon Smith and
Wendy Goldstein
Two Sisters Inn

"Thank you Toni and Travis. We've had terrific response from your book."
—Peggy Hahn
Cliff House Lodge
Bed & Breakfast Inn

"We want to commend you on this excellent B&B guide— used by most all of our guests as we keep one at their fingertips."
—Kathy Bates
Ouray 1898 House

"If it hadn't been for your B&B book and our car phone, our honeymoon and vacation would have been a disaster."
—Lea Gaydos, RN

*Absolutely Every**

BED & BREAKFAST

in

COLORADO

almost

FOURTH EDITION

ALAN STARK, EDITOR

Special Contributors

CARL HANSON

TRAVIS ILSE

THE ROCKY MOUNTAIN SERIES

TRAVIS ILSE
PUBLISHERS

POST OFFICE BOX 583
NIWOT, COLORADO 80544

COVER ART
© John Fielder
Denver, Colorado

PRODUCTION BY
Alan Bernhard
ARGENT ASSOCIATES
Boulder, Colorado

PRINTED BY
Data Reproductions,
Rochester Hills, Michigan

ISBN 1-882092-19-8

Printed in the United States of America

1 2 3 4 5 6 7 8 9

Distributed to the trade by
PUBLISHERS GROUP WEST

To Dick & Nana Ilse

You may not be here

with us now, but we

wanted you to know

that this book

is your fault

THE ROCKY MOUNTAIN SERIES

ABSOLUTELY EVERY° *BED & BREAKFAST IN ARIZONA*
(°ALMOST)*
SECOND EDITION

ABSOLUTELY EVERY° *BED & BREAKFAST*
IN CALIFORNIA, MONTEREY TO SAN DIEGO
(°ALMOST)*
FIRST EDITION

ABSOLUTELY EVERY° *BED & BREAKFAST IN NORTHERN CALIFORNIA*
(°ALMOST)*
FIRST EDITION

ABSOLUTELY EVERY° *BED & BREAKFAST IN COLORADO*
(°ALMOST)*
FOURTH EDITION

ABSOLUTELY EVERY° *BED & BREAKFAST IN NEW MEXICO*
(°ALMOST)*
SECOND EDITION

ABSOLUTELY EVERY° *BED & BREAKFAST IN TEXAS*
(°ALMOST)*
SECOND EDITION

ABSOLUTELY EVERY° *BED & BREAKFAST IN WASHINGTON*
(°ALMOST)*
FIRST EDITION

THE MISSISSIPPI RIVER SERIES

ABSOLUTELY EVERY° *BED & BREAKFAST IN ILLINOIS*
(°ALMOST)*
FIRST EDITION

Contents

Directory of Colorado Bed & Breakfasts

INTRODUCTION

Welcome to the diverse and interesting world of bed & breakfasts in Colorado. In this book you will find everything from the traditional Victorian B&B to a castle to a seriously upscale ranch, described in an easy-to-use format that gives you precisely the information you need to decide on a B&B and call for a reservation. A bit later in this introduction we will define our terms, but we think that you will see by thumbing-through this book that there is a great deal of information to consider.

We have structured our book in this way so that if you are looking for particular features and facts, such as an architectural style or price range or the size of the breakfast or any number of other criteria, you can quickly scan our entries to find the information that you need without wading through endless descriptions that often read like advertising copy.

And speaking of advertising copy, we need to make it clear that *no one at this publishing house accepts any money or free rooms or services from the B&B innkeepers.* There are too many B&B books whose authors charge a fee for a B&B to be included. These same authors then write advertising copy and flowery descriptions for their book that may or may not be true. The only way to judge if a book is advertising copy or not is to look for a disclaimer similar to ours in the introduction.

So, start the adventure now, look up some B&Bs, call for a reservation and hit the road with that lover, best friend, husband or wife.

Do it now, don't wait!

WRITING A COLORADO BED & BREAKFAST BOOK

This fourth edition of *Absolutely Every° Bed & Breakfast in Colorado (°Almost)* offers you a choice of 407 B&Bs in 128 cities, towns, villages and wide places in the road. This is the eighth book in our *Absolutely Every° Bed & Breakfast* series, which includes individual books on Arizona (Second Edition), California (Monterey to San Diego), Northern California, Colorado (Fourth Edition), Illinois, New Mexico (Second Edition) and Washington. There is ordering information in the back of the book, but try your local bookstore first.

We build our books by checking telephone directories, chambers of commerce, B&B associations, other books and tourism brochures until we have developed a relatively large list of what may or may not be B&Bs. In the case of *Absolutely Every° Bed & Breakfast in Colorado (°Almost)*, we had an initial list just under 500 B&Bs from Steamboat

Springs in the north to Trinidad in the south and from Burlington in the east to Grand Junction in the west.

After compiling the list, we mailed a four-page survey to the innkeepers. When the survey came back we entered the information into our database from which we published the book. These surveys are signed by the innkeeper and kept on file with the publisher.

We received about 300 responses and from those surveys wrote 286 full entries. Then we started working the phone, making about 200 phone calls to confirm or delete those B&Bs who did not respond to the survey. Admittedly, our method of confirmation was arbitrary, we seldom left messages on answering machines, we called back later in the day and deleted the B&B if we got the answering machine a second time. If an innkeeper was rude or suspicious, we deleted them. If an innkeeper hesitated, when we asked if, at the minimum, a Continental breakfast was included in the price of the room, we deleted them, and obviously, if the phone was disconnected or if there was no answer after two tries we deleted them. All in all, we made at least three attempts to contact B&Bs, i.e., the survey and at least two telephone calls.

We make an extreme effort to have the most accurate, timely and complete information in our book at press time. If we have missed a B&B or made a mistake, let us apologize here and now—it will get into the next edition if we get a note or letter with an address on it. In fact, we love to get letters and appreciate any comments on our books or on B&Bs. Our address is Travis Ilse Publishers, PO Box 583, Niwot, CO 80544.

This gets to the reason for (*Almost) in our title. Given that we tentatively identified just under 500 B&Bs and could confirm 407, we have fallen short on our goal of Absolutely Every*. But, our decision will always be to get accurate information to our readers. If we don't have a fairly high confidence level in the existence and efficacy of a B&B, we simply don't put it in the book.

But there are other reasons for the (*Almost): Innkeepers are busy people who forget to return their survey forms with the information that gets them listed, even after a reminder or two. Innkeepers are also independent folks who may not want to be listed in any book in general, or our book in particular.

Some Reservation Service Organizations (RSOs) don't want their client B&Bs listed with information that could allow a traveler to call the B&B directly, thus endangering the RSO's commission; kind of small-time thinking, but ours is not to wonder why. If any B&B represented by an RSO wishes to be in the next edition, please write us. We simply need an innkeeper's name and the address to include the B&B, using the RSO's phone number is fine with us.

Some homestays are located in areas that are zoned for residential use only. These homestays are frowned on by the local bureaucrats (and sometimes neighbors). To have information widely disseminated by a book might cause legal problems for these homestay innkeepers.

And then there is the "Goathead Factor" where someone has been rude or arrogant on the phone. If they are rude to us, there's a chance that they'll be rude to you. Here we exercise our right under the First Amendment to take them off the list and out of the database.

CAVEATS

(1) Because of the breadth of coverage of our books, we depend on the honesty of the innkeepers. We know as a fact that these are some of the most hard working, interesting and nicest people in the world. We admire their hard work. But there is always the exception. Please write us if an innkeeper has treated you badly or misrepresented their inn.

(2) We can't stress this too much, so we'll repeat it: *No one at Travis Ilse Publishers benefits in any way from the B&Bs in this book.* We don't accept free rooms or request or receive payment for entries in the book. This book is a service to our readers, not the Colorado bed & breakfast industry; *no Innkeeper ever pays anything to be listed in the book.*

(3) The bed and breakfast industry is volatile; openings, closings and changes in prices and ownership occur regularly. That's why it is always advisable to call ahead and ask questions before you make reservations. Dropping-in is chancy and seldom welcome.

(4) We wish to make it perfectly clear that the editor, contributors and Travis Ilse Publishers make no warranty, implied or specific, about operations or policies of bed & breakfast establishments, or trade associations mentioned in this book.

BED & BREAKFAST DEFINITIONS

Our guide is essentially an annotated database of small and medium-sized bed & breakfast inns, hotels and host homes that include a proper breakfast in the price of the room. However, we have exercised our right as editors, writers and data entry clerks to be inconsistent by including a few "grand" inns with more than 50 rooms (our maximum) because we felt their location and quality warranted inclusion. Though neither absolutely concise nor agreed upon by everyone in the industry, the following definitions may help you determine differences between types of establishments in order of size.

HOST HOME (or Homestay): The original B&B. Here the resident owner rents from one to three spare bedrooms, typically with shared bathroom, although private bathrooms are becoming more common. With professionalism and competition on the rise, host homes can offer the best of all worlds in terms of rates, services and personal touches.

SELF SERVE: Usually a separate cottage or cabin where the innkeeper has stocked the refrigerator. Not exactly a B&B where breakfast is served, but the typical privacy of these small places makes them worth mentioning.

GUESTHOUSE: A separate unit — cabin, carriage house, etc. Breakfast is either served in the main house or delivered to the guesthouse. Sometimes B&Bs have a guesthouse in addition to rooms in the main building. Clearly, these are the most private of B&B accommodations.

INN: The largest and fastest growing category in the B&B industry — five to fifteen rooms, generally with private bathrooms, larger staff and outstanding hospitality.

COUNTRY INN: Usually located in the "country"—rural areas far from the maddening crowd. Rooms number between five and twenty-five and a restaurant or dining hall serves other meals besides breakfast.

HOTEL: Usually small or historic hotels—between twenty-five and fifty rooms, that have been renovated to preserve their historic past and charm.

LODGE OR WORKING RANCH: A country inn located in a resort or remote area. While breakfast is always included in the price of the room, complete meal packages are frequently offered as well, along with all sorts of activities.

OUR GUIDEBOOK DEFINITIONS

Our guide is organized in a clear, friendly format that avoids codes, symbols and endless gibbering narrative (except for this introduction). Our goal is to provide you with more information than you need to make an informed decision about a B&B and ask the right questions when you call for reservations. Each town for which there are complete B&B listings is covered with a thumbnail sketch of information on sights, festivals and strange, little-known facts, followed by brief instructions on how to get there.

In addition to 286 survey-based listings, there are 121 short listings that include the B&B name, address, telephone number, innkeeper's name and sometimes a KUDOS/COMMENT. These listings are based on a telephone conversation where the person answering the phone confirmed that the number called was a functioning B&B and that breakfast is included in the price of the meal. For these short listings, no one signed a survey warranting that all the information was correct. We assume honesty on the part of the innkeepers; but *always call first*.

The B&B name is set in large type followed by the address, telephone number, toll-free number, FAX number, and names of the innkeepers and languages other than English spoken by the staff. Note that there are some towns in Colorado where the post office does not deliver to street addresses. Always ask the innkeeper for a mailing address; never assume that mailing to an address in the book will get your deposit to the B&B.

Digression #1 . . . 800 numbers followed with cute words, e.g., 800-INN-FOOL. One of the worst marketing ideas ever, because it is inconvenient to look for all those letters on the key pad. In fact, wasn't it the TELEPHONE COMPANY in the '50s that changed all the old word exchanges to numbers for just that reason? Dumb, stupid, a waste of time and inconvenient for B&B guests. By the way, there are digressions throughout the book that are always marked by ellipses followed by initials (...TI). Most of these come from Travis himself on the final edit, but a good number come from the editor (...AS), the other editor, (...CH), or the production type (...AB).

LOCATION: Where the B&B actually is relative to the town or area it is in (i.e., directions and miles from the center of town, a highway exit or nearest landmark). It's a good idea to carry the book along with you or keep the B&B telephone number in your daybook just in case you are direction-impaired.

OPEN: Most B&Bs in Colorado are open all year, but there are some seasonal B&Bs, particularly in winter sports areas. Note that some B&Bs close for a week or two randomly when the innkeeper decides that someplace else like Orcas Island or Abaco sounds like a pretty good idea.

DESCRIPTION: On our survey form that the innkeeper completes for this book, we ask when a building was built, the architectural style, type of furnishing and whether it is on the Colorado or National Historic Registers. With this book we have let some notes on landscaping and surroundings slip in. Tell us if this helps in your decision.

NUMBER OF ROOMS: This is a notation of the rooms with private bathrooms and with shared bathrooms. Also noted here are the availability of suites and guesthouses that are assumed to have private bathrooms, *but always ask*. We also ask the innkeepers to name a favorite room. While it is not surprising that the room named is often the most expensive room in the house, it is usually a very special room with extra amenities, such as a tub for two and a terrific view.

RATES: This may be the most confusing section of our book, simply because there is no standard in the B&B industry for setting rates. We have simply tried to reprint the innkeeper's range of rates, which vary by private or shared bathroom, season and rooms. Use the rates in the book as a guideline only. Ask the innkeeper for a specific rate for a specific room. Ask about lower mid-week rates, extended stay rates, seniors' rates, corporate rates, and government rates. There are some very good deals out there. We also note minimum stay requirement and cancellation policies. Digression #2 . . . Innkeepers need the protection of cancellation policies, but anything more than two weeks notice for a full refund is just dumb. Charging a fee to process a cancellation seems spiteful. Excessive cancellation policies and fees for cancellation are counterproductive to the bed & breakfast industry.

BREAKFAST: The second most important reason (think about it) for staying in a B&B is the breakfast that is *always* included in the price of the room. So we ask the innkeepers for an accurate description of their morning fare: a *full breakfast* ranges from the familiar eggs, pancakes, meats, fruits and beverages to three courses formally served to a full buffet. *Continental* is usually fresh coffee, fruit, fresh juices and assorted baked goodies, usually homemade; *Continental Plus* is somewhere in between, more than Continental and less than a full breakfast. Digression # 3 . . . We are seeing more and more "B&Bs" just offer a loaded refrigerator instead of a real breakfast. This makes us wonder when some motel is going to offer a certificate for breakfast burritos at the local jiffy mart and then try to call itself a B&B.

CREDIT CARDS: Whether or not credit cards are accepted is listed here. But be prepared — bring a checkbook or travelers checks. Some B&Bs do not accept credit cards because the local bank is run by morons or because of the added expense to the innkeeper. Note also that some innkeepers will accept credit cards for a reservation confirmation but not for payment when you check-out.

AMENITIES: All the "extras" that make a B&B vastly different from other accommodations. These may include: a hot tub, fireplaces, afternoon wine and cheese, nature trails, a llama petting zoo. . . .

RESTRICTIONS: Things you can't do or bring to a B&B, which usually involve smoking, children and pets.

Most B&Bs do not allow smoking inside the establishment, although a good number have outside smoking areas.

Children are problematical. While some B&Bs welcome them, others do not; and most set an age limit. Be considerate. If you take your children to a B&B make sure that they are under voice command. One Colorado Innkeeper said it best, "Children of responsible parents are always welcome."

A good number of B&Bs have resident pets and would rather not have dog fights every time a guest rolls up with a pack of Poodles in the back of his Land Cruiser; so leave you best friend at the kennel. We also list the names of resident pets because we believe that pets are an integral part of a home away from home and good fun to have around. Not to worry if you are allergic to pets as most Innkeepers do not allow their pets in the guest rooms. *A good rule is to always ask about restrictions when you call for a reservation.*

AWARDS: Any awards given an inn that are recognized and significant to the hospitality industry or historic preservation organizations.

REVIEWED: Books in which a B&B has been reviewed. We have made an effort to include only those B&B books that are truly "review" publications, where the writer and publisher receive no compensation of any kind (including free rooms and meals) for their review.

Digression # 4 . . . Fee-based bed & breakfast books . . . while no one really cares about the standards of another industry, there is a clear distinction in book publishing between the author and publisher who assume all risks for a book and the author or publisher who solicit a fee for including a B&B in a book—the former is called publishing, the latter is called advertising.

RATED: Indicates whether a B&B has been rated by the American Automobile Association, American Bed & Breakfast Association or Mobil Travel Guides. These ratings are a good indication of the quality of a B&B, *but* please don't infer that a nonrated B&B is inferior. There are many great B&Bs that are not rated.

MEMBER: Membership in professional associations recognized by the hospitality industry.

KUDOS/COMMENTS: These are comments from other innkeepers and inveterate B&B guests. We welcome your comments too; write us at Travis Ilse Publishers, PO Box 583, Niwot, CO 80544.

A FINAL NOTE

We'd like to hear your thoughts on any B&B that you visit. Just copy the form on the following page and fold a bunch of them into the book so that they'll be handy when you travel. If you give us permission to use some or all of your comments in the next edition of this book, we'll send you a free copy of this or any other book in the series (AZ, CA, Northern CA, IL, NM, TX, WA).

Let us know what you think. Write to us at Travis Ilse Publishers, PO Box 583, Niwot, CO 80544. We love to get letters.

—*Travis Ilse*
—*Alan Stark*
—*Carl Hanson*

B&B Guest Comment Card

B&B VISITED: _____

LOCATION: _____

DATES VISITED: _____

COMMENTS, KUDOS, QUIBBLES: _____

_____

_____

_____

_____

_____

❏ I/we grant Travis Ilse Publishers permission to incorporate some or all of our comments in future editions of this book.

❏ I/we prefer not to be quoted, but here are our comments anyway.

NAME_____ DATE _____

ADDRESS (CITY, STATE, ZIP)_____

_____ PHONE _____

Please mail to: Travis Ilse (CO4), PO Box 583, Niwot, CO 80544

B&B Guest Comment Card

B&B VISITED: _____

LOCATION: _____

DATES VISITED: _____

COMMENTS, KUDOS, QUIBBLES: _____

_____

_____

_____

_____

_____

❏ I/we grant Travis Ilse Publishers permission to incorporate some or all of our comments in future editions of this book.

❏ I/we prefer not to be quoted, but here are our comments anyway.

NAME_____ DATE _____

ADDRESS (CITY, STATE, ZIP)_____

_____ PHONE _____

Please mail to: Travis Ilse (CO4), PO Box 583, Niwot, CO 80544

ALAMOSA

One of the states most productive agricultural areas in the center of the San Luis Valley, it's a gateway to Great Sand Dunes National Monument and home to Adams State College. Browse the Rio Grande Art Market, and check out the Sunshine Festival in June and Gallery & Artists Home Tour in November. Dune trekking and exploring the trails of the Sangre de Cristos are the main attractions here. But don't overlook a visit to the Alamosa-Monte Vista National Wildlife Refuge and the spactacular Crane Festival in March. From Denver, 200 miles southwest via I-25 and Highway 160 or 28 miles from the New Mexico border.

COTTONWOOD INN & GALLERY— A BED & BREAKFAST INN

123 San Juan Avenue, Alamosa, CO 81101   719-589-3882
Julie Mordecai, Resident Owner   800-955-2623
Spanish spoken.   FAX 719-589-6437

LOCATION	Three blocks north of Main Street on the corner of Second and San Juan.
OPEN	All year.
DESCRIPTION	A 1908 Four Square with Craftsman interior, filled with antiques and artwork, apartment suites next door.
NO. OF ROOMS	Seven rooms with private bathrooms. Two rooms share one bathroom. Julie Mordecai's favorite room is the Azul room.
RATES	High season rates range from $65-93 and off season rates are $48-79 for a double. Additional children are $10 and adults are $15. There is a minimum stay on special weekends and cancellation requires one week's notice with a $15 per night cancellation fee regardless of time frame.
CREDIT CARDS	American Express, Diners Club, Discover, MasterCard, Visa
BREAKFAST	Full breakfast using local produce served in the dining room. Three breakfast seatings at 7:15, 8:15 and 9:15 a.m. Tea & cookies are served in the afternoon. Dietary restrictions will be met.
AMENITIES	Robes, desks, telephones in some rooms, TV/VCR in common room, thick towels and Neutrogena bath products, fresh cookies and beverages; golf, scenic railway, hot spring and horseback riding packages.
RESTRICTIONS	No smoking, the resident dog, Sula, is "respectful, well-trained and kind."
REVIEWED	*America's Wonderful Little Hotels, Inns & Guesthouses, The Colorado Guide, Frommer's Colorado 1995, Recommended Country Inns of the Rocky Mountain Region, 22 Days in the American Southwest, Country Inn's magazine*
MEMBER	Bed & Breakfast Inns of Colorado, Professional Association of Innkeepers International

ALLENSPARK

The gemlike setting of this little hamlet is at the southeast corner of Rocky Mountain National Park, in Roosevelt National Forest, 16 miles south of Estes Park on Scenic Highway 7. The Longs Peak Scottish Festival in September is a major event.

ALLENSPARK LODGE AND CRYSTAL SPRINGS CABINS

184 Main, Allenspark, CO 80510   303-747-2552
Mike & Becky Osmun, Resident Owners   FAX 303-747-2552 (call first)

LOCATION	Downtown Allenspark
OPEN	All year.
DESCRIPTION	A 1933 three-story "classic mountain log lodge" with eclectic furnishings. The lodge was built by my grandfather...TI
NO. OF ROOMS	Five rooms with private bathrooms and eight rooms share three bathrooms. The best room is the Hideaway.
RATES	Year-round rates for a single or double with a private bathroom are $70-90, for a room with a shared bathroom, $45-60. The entire lodge rents for $850-2,000. There is no minimum stay in the lodge and a 15-day cancellation policy with a $15 fee.
CREDIT CARDS	MasterCard, Visa
BREAKFAST	Continental plus is served in the dining room and includes selections of teas and juices, hot and cold cereal, something fresh-baked such as muffins, coffeecake or nutbread, coffee, a small fruit basket and various jams and breads for toasting. During busier times the lodge offers soups and breads, sandwiches, nacho plates, etc. Lunch and dinner are also available.
AMENITIES	Complimentary coffee, cookies and teas, hot tub, ping pong, pool table, a library, picnic tables, grills and games. Small receptions (70 or under), seminars and retreat groups can be accommodated.
RESTRICTIONS	No smoking, no pets, children over 14 are welcome in the lodge. The resident cats, who aren't allowed downstairs, are Esmeralda and Katie Ann Calico.
REVIEWED	*Frommer's Colorado, Bed & Breakfasts of the Rocky Mountains, The Best Selected Inns*
MEMBER	Colorado Association of Campgrounds, Cabins and Lodges
RATED	Mobil 2 Stars

Sunshine Mountain Inn

18078 Colorado Highway 7, Allenspark, CO 80510   *303-747-2840*
Marge Hoglin, Resident Owner

Antonito

Cumbres & Toltec narrow-gauge Scenic Railroad, Platora Reservoir, Great Sand Dunes National Monument

Conejos River Guest Ranch

25390 Highway 17, Antonito, CO 81120   *719-376-2464*
Ms. Shorty Fry, Ranch Foreman
Some Spanish spoken.

LOCATION	Thirteen miles west of Antonito on Highway 17 between mile markers 25 and 26.
OPEN	Mid-May to January 2nd
DESCRIPTION	An 1893/1982 ranch house with western ranch decor and wraparound deck, set along the banks of the Conejos River in the Rio Grande Forest.
NO. OF ROOMS	Eight rooms with private bathrooms. Best view: the Riverview room. Most romantic: the Loft room.
RATES	Seasonal rates are $69-85 for a single or double with private bathroom and $85 for a suite or guest house with a private bathroom. "Early Bird" discount of 10% available mid-May through early June. There is a minimum stay of two nights and cancellation requires 72 hours' notice.

Conejos River Guest Ranch, Antonito

CREDIT CARDS	MasterCard, Visa
BREAKFAST	Full breakfast, served in the dining room, includes beverages and choice of four hot meals or a light breakfast of oatmeal, muffin and toast. Dinner is also available and box lunches if ordered in advance.
AMENITIES	Lawn games, volleyball, children's playground, hiking, private fishing on property, fireplace in common den, deck facing river, campfires on weekends, horse boarding and rentals, meeting and retreat facilities, catering, cook-out facilities, and handicapped access to several rooms.
RESTRICTIONS	None. Resident pets include one Quarter horse named Rambo; a burro named Sadie; two mix-breed dogs, Rex and Ginger; a black-faced sheep named Elvira; and two standard Poodles, Sheba & Sam.
MEMBER	Bed & Breakfast Innkeepers of Colorado

ARVADA
(DENVER)

This thriving community offers first rate cultural events through the Arvada Center for the Arts and Humanities. Fifteen miles northwest of downtown Denver.

ON GOLDEN POND BED & BREAKFAST

7831 Eldridge Street, Arvada, CO 80005　　　　　　303-424-2296
Kathy & John Kula, Resident Owners　　　　　　　　800-682-0193
German spoken.

LOCATION	From I-70 take exit #266 (Ward Road) north to 72nd Street, go left to Alkire, then right to 78th and left on Eldridge.
OPEN	All year.
DESCRIPTION	A 1977 two-story contemporary country inn with eclectic furnishings on 10 acres.
NO. OF ROOMS	Five rooms with private bathrooms. Kathy suggests the Peacock as her best room.
RATES	Year-round rates are $60-120 for a single or double with a private bathroom, the entire inn rents for $450. There is no minimum stay and a seven-day cancellation policy with a $15 fee.
CREDIT CARDS	American Express, Discover, MasterCard, Visa
BREAKFAST	Full breakfast, served in dining room, includes bread puddings with fruit or German potato eggnests or homemade muffins and cinnamon breads.

AMENITIES	Swimming pool, hot tub, horseback riding and boarding nearby, pond with gazebo, air conditioning and meeting rooms, Jacuzzi tubs in all rooms, two rooms with fireplaces, and one room handicapped accessible.
RESTRICTIONS	No smoking indoors, one room is designated for children and pets. The resident critters are an outside dog, Mocki; two barn cats, Max and Moritz; two horses, Heidi and Silver; two goats, Loui and Lenny; and five peacocks.
REVIEWED	*Arvada Sentinal, Denver's Mile High Magazine, Western Stock* magazine.
MEMBER	Bed & Breakfast Innkeepers of Colorado
KUDOS/COMMENTS	"Eclectic with grand hosts." (1994)

THE TREEHOUSE

6650 Simms Street, Arvada, CO 80004   303-431-6352
LeAnne & Todd Thomas, Resident Owners   FAX 303-456-1414

LOCATION	Located fifteen minutes northwest of downtown Denver. From I-70, exit Kipling northbound. Kipling will wind into 64th Street. Turn north on Simms. Go two blocks.
OPEN	All year.
DESCRIPTION	A 1945 two-story European chalet with country and antique decor on a 10-acre forest.
NO. OF ROOMS	Five rooms with private bathrooms. Todd and LeAnne's favorite is the Burgandy room.
RATES	Year-round rates are $69-109 for a single or double with a private bathroom and $435 for the entire B&B. No minimum stay is required and cancellation requires seven days' notice.
CREDIT CARDS	MasterCard, Visa
BREAKFAST	Full breakfast is served in the dining room and guestrooms, includes fresh fruit, yogurt, homemade granola, homemade muffins or cinnamon rolls, beverages, plus a hot entree like quiche or omelets. Lunch and special meals are available for small meetings and seminars.
AMENITIES	Flowers, robes, redwood Jacuzzi on back deck, afternoon tea and cake, homemade cookies and milk always available, private fireplaces in guestrooms, brass beds.
RESTRICTIONS	No smoking, no pets.
REVIEWED	*Recommended Country Inns (Rocky Mountain Region)*
MEMBER	American Bed & Breakfast Association, Bed & Breakfast Innkeepers of Colorado
RATED	AAA 3 Diamonds, ABBA 3 Crowns

ASPEN
(CARBONDALE)

Historic silver-mining boom town and world-class resort with alpine skiing on a four-mountain complex, celebrates Winterskol in January and hosts the World Cup Giant Slalom in March. Summer comes alive with the acclaimed Aspen Music Festival, the Food and Wine Classic in June, Beer Festival in July and hangliders that swarm over the town like moths. Other nice things to do: hiking around the Maroon Bells, fishing the Gold Medal Roaring Fork River, a visit to nearby Ashcroft and sled dog rides at Krabloonik's Kennels, aspen-viewing in the fall, and (if you care) celebrity-watching all year. As for shopping — bring money and perspective. From Denver, 200 miles west via I-70 and Highway 82. Or try a summer-only, white-knuckle shortcut over Independence Pass.

ALPINE LODGE

1240 East Cooper, Aspen, CO 81611   *970-925-7351*
Jim & Christina Martin, Resident Owners   *FAX 970-925-5796*
Spanish, French and German spoken.

LOCATION	First place on the right after city limit sign when arriving from Independence Pass and last place on the left when coming from town.
OPEN	All year.
DESCRIPTION	An 1890 two-story Bavarian lodge with Victorian to rustic furnishings and four cottages.
NO. OF ROOMS	Four rooms and four cabins with private bathrooms, three rooms share two bathrooms. Christina recommends Room 3.
RATES	Winter rates are $100-105 for a single or double with private bathroom, $88 for a single or double with shared bathroom and $118 for a cottage. Off season rates are $50-68 for a single or double with private bath and $35-49 for a single or double with shared bathroom and $68-78 for a cottage. There is a minimum stay during Christmas and 30-day cancellation policy subject to a $25 fee.
CREDIT CARDS	American Express, Discover, MasterCard, Visa
BREAKFAST	Continental Plus is served in the dining room and includes fresh-baked muffins, yogurt, fresh fruit, cereal, coffee, tea and juice. Dinner available during the winter season only.
AMENITIES	Outdoor hot tub, down comforters, fresh flowers in all rooms, teddy bears, TV in lobby and airport pick-up.
RESTRICTIONS	No smoking, children welcome. Bear is the "official lodge dog and takes his job seriously."
REVIEWED	*The Colorado Guide, Colorado Handbook, Let's Go USA, B&B of the Rockies*

ASPEN BED & BREAKFAST LODGE

311 West Main Street, Aspen, CO 81611　　　　970-925-7650
Apryl Beckingham, Resident Manager　　　　　800-362-7736
　　　　　　　　　　　　　　　　　　　　　　　FAX 970-925-5744

CHALET LISL

100 East Hyman Avenue, Aspen, CO 81611　　　970-925-3520
Carol & Al Blomquist, Resident Owners　　　　FAX 970-925-3580

CRESTHAUS LODGE

1301 East Cooper, Aspen, CO 81611　　　　　　970-925-7081
Jeff Stafford, Resident Owner　　　　　　　　800-344-3853
Spanish and some French spoken.　　　　　　　FAX 970-925-1610

LOCATION	East end of town at the base of Independence Pass.
OPEN	All year.
DESCRIPTION	A 1950s/1980s contemporary country inn with European country furnishings.
NO. OF ROOMS	Thirty-one rooms with private bathrooms. Melinda likes the Southwestern Suite.
RATES	Winter has three rate schedules for a single or double with private bathrooms: Low season, $95-180; Regular season, $170-255; and Holiday season, $235-325. Summer has two schedules: Low season, $80-175; and Regular season, $120-205. There is a minimum stay on holidays and holiday weekends. There is a reservation/cancellation policy.
CREDIT CARDS	American Express, Diners Club, MasterCard, Visa
BREAKFAST	Continental Plus is served in the dining room. Special meals by arrangement only.
AMENITIES	Summer: mountain bike rentals, hammock and heated pool in garden area. Winter: complimentary hot drinks, desserts and appetizers, hot tub. Year round: laundry facilities, ample parking and airport transport.
RESTRICTIONS	No smoking in common areas, smoking rooms available. There is a $10 fee for pets. The cat, Smudge, likes to visit rooms and the dog, Geze, is "friendly but shy."
REVIEWED	*America's Wonderful Little Hotels & Inns 1994, ACCESS Guide*
RATED	Mobil 3 Stars

HEARTHSTONE HOUSE

134 East Hyman, Aspen, CO 81611   970-925-7632
Irma Prodinger, Resident Owner   FAX 970-920-4450

HEATHERBED MOUNTAIN LODGE

1679 Maroon Creek Road, Aspen, CO 81611   970-925-7077
Marie Marx, Resident Manager   800-356-6782
    FAX 970-925-6120

LOCATION	Across the street from Aspen Highlands Ski Area, two miles outside of town on the way to the Maroon Bells.
OPEN	All year (closed part of October and April).
DESCRIPTION	A 1960 A-frame with European and country furnishings.
NO. OF ROOMS	Twenty rooms with private bathrooms.
RATES	Seasonal rates are $79-179 for a single or double with private bathroom. The suite rents for $150-250. There is a two-night minimum stay over weekends during prime season. Cancellation requires 30 days' notice.
CREDIT CARDS	MasterCard, Visa
BREAKFAST	Continental Plus is served in the sunroom.
AMENITIES	Swimming pool, hot tub and sauna, down comforters, TV and phone in the rooms, microwave in the lobby, ski storage, excellent ski access, plenty of beautiful views, laundry room, complimentary refreshments and full apres ski.
RESTRICTIONS	Smoking limited, no pets.

HOTEL DURANT

122 East Durant, Aspen, CO 81611   970-925-8500
Rhonda Ardis, Resident Manager   FAX 970-925-8789

LOCATION	On the corner of Durant Avenue and Aspen Street.
OPEN	All year.
DESCRIPTION	A contemporary French country inn.
NO. OF ROOMS	Twenty-one rooms with private bathrooms.

RATES	Seasonal rates are broken into five categories that range from $55-285 for a single or double with a private bathroom. There are minimum stay requirements and cancellation requires 30 days' notice.
CREDIT CARDS	MasterCard, Visa
BREAKFAST	Continental Plus served in the lobby.
AMENITIES	Hot tub, new deck, cable TV and phones in rooms, apres ski, and most rooms have microwaves.
RESTRICTIONS	No smoking, no pets. Children are welcome.

HOTEL LENADO

200 South Aspen Street, Aspen, CO 81611   970-925-6246
Daniel Delano, Frank Peters, Jayne Poss, Resident Owners 800-321-3457
Spanish spoken.   FAX 970-925-3840

LOCATION	From Glenwood, turn right at the first light in town, the hotel is one block toward Aspen Mountain on the left.
OPEN	All year.
DESCRIPTION	A 1983 two-story contemporary lodge with elegant rustic interior and country furnishings.
NO. OF ROOMS	Nineteen rooms with private bathrooms. The best room in the house might just be #18.
RATES	Depending on the season...and there appear to be seven of them...TI, rates are $85-440 for a single or double with a private bathroom. You can bet on a minimum stay during the holidays and cancellation requires 30 days' notice.
CREDIT CARDS	American Express, Diners Club, MasterCard, Visa
BREAKFAST	Full breakfast includes a variety of egg dishes, waffles, blueberry pancakes and beverages. There is also a light bar menu available all day.
AMENITIES	Robes, hot tub, library, concierge services, bellman/houseman, conference room, TV screening room, TV and phones in all rooms, Markham's Bar.
RESTRICTIONS	Smoking limited, no pets.
REVIEWED	*The Colorado Guide, Best Places to Stay in the Rockies, Recommended Country Inns of the Rocky Mountain Region, America's Wonderful Little Hotels & Inns*
RATED	Mobil 3 Stars

INDEPENDENCE SQUARE BED & BREAKFAST

404 South Galena Street, Aspen, CO 81611   970-920-2313
Jami Ryan, Resident Manager   800-633-0336
                                          FAX 970-925-1233

LOCATION	Center of Aspen on the mall.
OPEN	November 22nd to April 14th and June 1st through September 30th.
DESCRIPTION	Victorian B&B hotel with French country furnishings.
NO. OF ROOMS	Twenty-eight rooms with private bathrooms.
RATES	June 1st to September 30th rates are $99-205 for a room with private bathroom. Winter rates (November 27th to April 13th) range from $99-350 for a room with a private bathroom. Ask about specials and minimum stays. There is a reservation/cancellation policy.
CREDIT CARDS	American Express, MasterCard, Visa
BREAKFAST	Continental Plus buffet served in the library.
AMENITIES	Rooftop Jacuzzi and sundeck, complimentary use of The Aspen Club health and racquet facilities, TV, phone, wet bar and refrigerator in the rooms, individual ski lockers, airport transportation, turndown service on request and air conditioning.
RESTRICTIONS	Limited smoking, no pets.
REVIEWED	America's Wonderful Little Hotels & Inns.
MEMBER	Colorado Hotel and Lodging Association

INNSBRUCK INN

233 West Main, Aspen, CO 81611   970-925-2980
Heinz Corrdes, Resident Owner   FAX 970-925-6960

LITTLE RED SKI HAUS

118 East Cooper, Aspen, CO 81611   970-925-3333
Marjorie Babcock & Derek Brown, Resident Owners   FAX 970-925-4873
Spanish, German and some French spoken.

LOCATION	Two blocks from the mall area of Aspen and 1-1/2 blocks from the ski lifts.
OPEN	All year except for April 20 to May 20 and the month of October.
DESCRIPTION	An 1888 two-story Victorian lodge with Victorian furnishings.
NO. OF ROOMS	Four rooms have private bathrooms and 16 rooms share eight bathrooms. The best room is the Silver Bell.
RATES	The winter rates are $124 for a double with private bathroom and $88 for a double with shared bathroom. Summer rates are $70 for a double with private bathroom and $58 for a double with shared bathroom. There is a 30-day cancellation policy.
CREDIT CARDS	MasterCard, Visa
BREAKFAST	During the winter, full breakfast is served every day but Saturday when expanded Continental is served. During the summer, full breakfast is served on weekends and expanded Continental is served on weekdays.
AMENITIES	Apres ski party, organized sleigh rides, cross-country ski trips, skimobile rides and picnics on the mountain during the winter. In the summer, music students perform live music in the parlor. Retreats and seminars in the summer.
RESTRICTIONS	None

MOLLY GIBSON LODGE

101 West Main Street, Aspen, CO 81611   970-925-2580
Dave Tash, Resident Manager   800-356-6559
       FAX 970-925 2582

MOUNTAIN HOUSE LODGE

905 East Hopkins, Aspen, CO 81611   970-920-2550
P.J.Sullivan & Syd Devine, Resident Owners   FAX 970-920-3440/ext.532

LOCATION	One block off Highway 82, on the corner of Hopkins and West End Street
OPEN	All year.
DESCRIPTION	A 1987 two-story western lodge with "light" southwestern furnishings.
NO. OF ROOMS	Twenty-four rooms with private bathrooms. P.J. suggests the Aspen Suite.
RATES	There are SIX rate schedules for the year and the range is considerable, from $40-250. Please call for details...to break down the rates here would require a separate chapter...CH. There is a minimum stay and 45-day cancellation policy and a substantial cancellation fee.
CREDIT CARDS	American Express, Diners Club, Discover, MasterCard, Visa
BREAKFAST	Full buffet breakfast is served in the dining room in winter and "generous" Continental is served in the summer.
AMENITIES	Hot tub, phone, cable TV, refrigerators, indoor ski lockers, lounge with fireplace and laundry.
RESTRICTIONS	No pets.

SARDY HOUSE

128 East Main Street, Aspen, CO 81611   970-920-2525
Daniel Delano, Frank Peters, Jayne Poss, Resident Owners   800-321-3457
Spanish spoken.   FAX 970-920-3840

LOCATION	When coming from Glenwood Springs, the inn is located at the first light inside town on the left-hand side.
OPEN	All year.
DESCRIPTION	A restored 1892 two-story Queen Anne Victorian inn with Victorian furnishings.
NO. OF ROOMS	Twenty rooms with private bathrooms. Jayne Poss recommends the Atkinson Suite.
RATES	There are eight seasons at this inn. The cheapest room in the heart of "mud season" is $95 and the most expensive room at Christmas is $750. Bring your big wallet...TI. There is a minimum stay on weekends. Cancellation requires 30 days' notice.

CREDIT CARDS	American Express, Diners Club, MasterCard, Visa
BREAKFAST	Full breakfast, with specials each morning, is served in the dining room or by room service. Dinner is served in the restaurant.
AMENITIES	Robes, hot tub, outdoor heated pool, sauna, concierge service, bellman/houseman, conference room, TV in all rooms, suites have VCR and stereo, full service dining room and Jack's Bar.
RESTRICTIONS	Limited smoking, no pets.
REVIEWED	*Official Guide to American Historic Inns, The Colorado Guide, America's Wonderful Little Hotels & Inns 1994, Best Places to Stay in the Rockies, Recommended Country Inns of the Rocky Mountain Region*
MEMBER	Distinctive Inns of Colorado
RATED	Mobil 4 Stars
KUDOS/COMMENTS	"Friendly, polite hosts, truly interested in their guests, historic landmark with modern amenities, special ambiance." (1997)

SNOW QUEEN VICTORIAN BED & BREAKFAST

124 East Cooper Avenue, Aspen, CO 81611   970-925-8455
Norma Dolle & Larry Ledingham, Resident Owners   FAX 970-925-7391
Some Spanish, German spoken.

LOCATION	Greater downtown Aspen on the corner of Cooper and South Aspen Streets.
OPEN	All year except April 15 to approximately May 25.
DESCRIPTION	An 1890 Victorian inn with Victorian furnishings.
NO. OF ROOMS	Six rooms with private bathrooms. Norma recommends the Best Friend Room.
RATES	Summer rates are $70-95 for a double with private bathroom. Winter rates are $90-160 for a double with private bathroom. Christmas rates are slightly higher. There is a 30-day cancellation policy and a $20 handling charge.
CREDIT CARDS	MasterCard, Visa
BREAKFAST	Continental Plus is served in the kitchen area. May change to full breakfast.
AMENITIES	TV in most rooms and the parlor, phones in most rooms, outdoor hot tub, wine parties.
RESTRICTIONS	No pets, the resident cat is called "Maya."

STAPLETON SPURR BED & BREAKFAST

1370 Owl Creek Road, Aspen, CO 81612   970-925-7322
Sam & Elizabeth Stapleton, Resident Owners   FAX 970-925-7322

LOCATION	Four miles west of Aspen, 1-1/4 mile off of Highway 82, just behind the airport on top of the hill.
OPEN	June through October and November through April.
DESCRIPTION	A 1968 ranch home with simple ranch furnishings and beautiful views.
NO. OF ROOMS	Two rooms share one bathroom.
RATES	Year-round rates are $50-60 for a single or double and $120 during the Christmas holidays. There is a two-night minimum stay, one week during Christmas and a reservation/cancellation policy.
CREDIT CARDS	MasterCard, Visa
BREAKFAST	Continental breakfast is served in the dining room or on the deck.
AMENITIES	TV, radio, phone and fireplace in the living room, walking or bicycling on long bike path.
RESTRICTIONS	No smoking, no pets (resident dogs and cats), children over three are welcome.

ULLR LODGE BED & BREAKFAST

520 West Main Street, Aspen, CO 81611   970-925-7696
Anthony Percival, Resident Owner   FAX 970-920-4339
Dutch spoken.

LOCATION	On the corner of Fifth and Main Streets on the residential west end of Aspen.
OPEN	All year.
DESCRIPTION	A small, privately owned (for 18 years) 1968 two-story Swiss chalet. "We encourage a quiet atmosphere."
NO. OF ROOMS	Fourteen rooms with private bathrooms.
RATES	Winter season (December through March) rates are $70-100 for a double with bath and $165 for a suite. Off season rates are $50-70 for a double with bath and $89-100 for a suite. Rates will fluctuate somewhat during the ski and summer seasons. There is a five-night minimum stay in the winter and a 45-day cancellation policy. Summer cancellation is 14 days.
CREDIT CARDS	American Express, Diners Club, MasterCard, Visa
BREAKFAST	Full breakfast in the winter and Continental in the summer.
AMENITIES	TV, phones, game room, indoor & outdoor whirlpool and a swimming pool in the summer.
RESTRICTIONS	Limited smoking and no pets.
REVIEWED	AAA 2 Diamonds

BAILEY

On the South Platte River in the Pike National Forest, this is a prime spot for trout fishing. Or visit McGraw Historical Park for a trip back in time. Only 35 miles southwest of Denver on Highway 285.

GLEN-ISLE RESORT

PO Box 128, Bailey, CO 80421   303-838-5461
Gordon & Barbara Tripp, Resident Owners

LOCATION	One-and-seven-tenths miles west of Bailey on Highway 285.
OPEN	B&B only June 4 through September 5, cabins all year.
DESCRIPTION	A 1900 slab and shingle lodge with cabins, furnished with antiques, located on 160 acres, and listed on the National and State Historic Registers.
NO. OF ROOMS	Fourteen rooms share seven bathrooms. The best room is room J.
RATES	Year-round rates are $55 for a double with shared bathroom. There is no minimum stay and a 30-day cancellation policy.
CREDIT CARDS	No
BREAKFAST	Full breakfast, served in the dining room, includes pancakes, French toast, bacon and sausage, fruit and beverages. Special chuckwagon dinners are served once a week.
AMENITIES	Fireplaces in cabins, children's playground, ping-pong, billiards, shuffleboard, sing-a-longs, square dancing, horseshoes, movies, bingo games, library, trout fishing, horseback riding, meeting facilities.
RESTRICTIONS	None. The resident critters include two cats, two dogs, one llama, one horse, and one burro.

BASALT

Once a booming railroad town (the Chamber of Commerce is in a red caboose), this choice spot is halfway between Glenwood Springs and Aspen/Snowmass, on the Gold Medal waters of the Frying Pan and Roaring Fork Rivers, and down the road from 1000-acre Ruedi Reservoir. Handy to the best of skiing, and the Mountain Festival in July is pure fun. From Denver, 160 miles west via I-70 and Highway 82.

ALTAMIRA RANCH BED & BREAKFAST

24384 Highway 82, Basalt, CO 81621   970-927-3309
Martha Waterman, Resident Owner

LOCATION	One mile south of Basalt exit on Highway 82.
OPEN	All year.
DESCRIPTION	A 1906 ranch house rebuilt in the style of Frank Lloyd Wright with antique and contemporary furnishings on a working ranch.
NO. OF ROOMS	Two rooms with shared bathroom.
RATES	The year-round rate is $75 for a double with a shared bathroom. There is a three-night minimum stay on July 4th and Christmas and a one-week cancellation policy.
CREDIT CARDS	No
BREAKFAST	Full breakfast is served in the dining room and includes a choice of entree, homemade pastries and fruit. Special dietary needs can be met.
AMENITIES	Antique shop.
RESTRICTIONS	No smoking, no pets, children over six are welcome. The resident Golden Retriever is called Ginger Snap.
MEMBER	Bed & Breakfast Innkeepers of Colorado

Shenandoah Inn, Basalt

SHENANDOAH INN

0600 Frying Pan Road, PO Box 560, Basalt, CO 81621   *970-927-4991*
Bob & Terri Ziets, Resident Owners   *FAX 970-927-4990*
French and Spanish spoken.

LOCATION	From greater downtown Basalt, go 0.3 mile up Midland Avenue to inn.
OPEN	All year.
DESCRIPTION	A 1964 two-story country inn with "country/southwest/eclectic" furnishings located on the Frying Pan River.
NO. OF ROOMS	Two rooms with private bathrooms and two rooms share one bathroom.
RATES	High season (February, March, June through September) rates are $95 for a single or double with a private bathroom, $85-90 for a single or double with a shared bathroom, $165 for a suite. Off season rates are $10 less. There is a minimum stay on weekends and holidays and cancellation requires 14 days' notice, 30 days' for holidays.
CREDIT CARDS	MasterCard, Visa
BREAKFAST	Full gourmet breakfast is served in the dining room and includes five courses with specialty coffees and teas, freshly squeezed juice, homemade breads and preserves, a hot entree, fresh fruit and beverages.
AMENITIES	Fresh flowers, turndown service, hot tub on riverfront deck, robes, TV/VCR in library, fireplace in living room, catering and large dining room for meetings and retreats.
RESTRICTIONS	No smoking, no pets, children over 12 are welcome.
REVIEWED	*American Mornings Cookbook, Pure Gold Colorado Treasures Cookbook, Inn for the Night*
MEMBER	Bed & Breakfast Innkeepers of Colorado

BELLVUE

This small community is great is a great jumping-off spot to the Cache la Poudre (Poo der)-North Park Byway and the Wild and Scenic Cache la Poudre River, also known as the "trout route" bring your fly rod. Twenty miles west of Fort Collins via Highway 14.

GYPSY TERRACE BED & BREAKFAST

4167 Poudre Canyon Highway, Bellvue, CO 80512   970-224-9389
Bernie Alexy & Barb Gibbens, Resident Owners

LOCATION	From Highway 287, take Highway 14 west up the Poudre Canyon for four miles, the B&B is on the left just past the first bridge.
OPEN	All year.
DESCRIPTION	A restored 1910 ranch, "modified dance hall," with a colorful past and a mixture of antique and modern furnishings.
NO. OF ROOMS	Two rooms with private bathrooms. Barb recommends the Loft.
RATES	Year-round rates are $65-75 for a double with private bathroom. There is no minimum stay and cancellation requires seven days' notice and a $15 fee.
CREDIT CARDS	MasterCard, Visa
BREAKFAST	Full breakfast, served in the dining room, includes a choice of entree, fresh homemade bread and beverages.
AMENITIES	Great Room with a woodburning stove, skylights, oversized showers and towels, flannel sheets in winter, loft has a brass bed and small deck leading to a hot tub which is available to all guests.
RESTRICTIONS	No smoking, no pets, children over five are welcome. Jack, the resident Australian Shepherd, loves to play Frisbee and Banjo the cat is "seldom seen."

THE RAINDROP BED & BREAKFAST

6901 McMurry, Bellvue, CO 80512   970-493-0799
Tara Parr, Resident Owner

LOCATION	Call for directions.
OPEN	All year.
DESCRIPTION	A 1978 passive solar host home with eclectic furnishings, modern art, fine crafts and many plants.
NO. OF ROOMS	One room with a private bathroom and two rooms share one bathroom.

RATES	Year-round rates are $95 for a single or double with private bathroom and $75 for a single or double with shared bathroom. The whole house rents for $300 a night. There is no minimum stay and a first night deposit is appreciated.
CREDIT CARDS	No
BREAKFAST	Full breakfast is served just about anywhere and includes eggs, fruit, home grown vegetables and beverages. Special meals are available.
AMENITIES	Outdoor hot tub, large greenhouse, massage therapy room, fresh flowers, facilities for small group retreats or training.
RESTRICTIONS	No smoking, no pets. There are two resident Labs and a crowd of chickens and turkeys.

SCORCHED TREE B&B

31601 Poudre Canyon Highway, Bellvue, CO 80512   *970-881-2817*
Brenda Wray & Roland Treiber, Resident Owners   *FAX 970-881-2475*
Spanish spoken.

LOCATION	On Highway 14 (Poudre Canyon) exactly 31.6 miles from the intersection of Highway 287 and Highway 14 on the Cache La Poudre River.
OPEN	All year.
DESCRIPTION	A 1925 Northwestern Indian-style log host home with rustic Indian furnishings on the Cache La Poudre River.
NO. OF ROOMS	Two rooms with private bathrooms. The best room: Saddle Blanket
RATES	Year-round rates are $110 for the Saddle Blanket, the Scarlet is $95. There is no minimum stay and a seven-day cancellation policy.
CREDIT CARDS	Discover, MasterCard, Visa
BREAKFAST	Full breakfast, served in the dinng room, includes eggs benedict, fresh fruit, fresh muffins, assorted pastries and beverages. Lunch and dinner are available with reservations. Holiday and wild-game dinners are available by reservation.
AMENITIES	Fresh flowers, hot tub, board games, wine and hors d'oeuvres, in-house chef, picnic lunches and hunting and fishing outfitting available.
RESTRICTIONS	No smoking, no pets, children over eight are welcome if renting both rooms. The resident cats are known by Retta and Buckskin.

Berthoud

A small, peaceful farming village halfway between Boulder and Fort Collins. Go out to Carter Lake for some fishing, water skiing or sailing.

Berthoud Bed & Breakfast

444 First Street, Berthoud, CO 80513
Janey & Gary Foster, Resident Owners

970-532-4566
FAX 970-532-4566

Berthoud Bed & Breakfast, Berthoud

LOCATION
From I-25, take exit 250 and go exactly five miles on Colorado 56, the B&B is on the left.

OPEN
All year.

DESCRIPTION
A three-story Victorian with each room decorated according to a different theme, e.g., French, Oriental, tropical.

NO. OF ROOMS
Seven rooms with private bathrooms. Janet suggests the Egyptian room.

RATES
Year-round rates for a single or double with a private bathroom are $78-135. There is no minimum stay and cancellation requires five days' notice.

CREDIT CARDS
American Express, Discover, MasterCard, Visa

BREAKFAST
Full breakfast is served in the dining room or on the South lawn in the spring. Dinner is also available.

AMENITIES
Outside hot tub in the flower and vegetable garden, parking on site, afternoon tea, local phone calls and FAX available, Victorian-style meeting room, shuttle to and from airport, Stearman PT17 airplane rides available...is that the airport shuttle, a Stearman? Sign me up!...TI

RESTRICTIONS
No smoking, the dogs are Orville and Yeti, named after two well-known pilots; the llamas are Sebastian and Niki, named after two well-known spitoons. There are also three sheep.

REVIEWED
Rocky Mountain Region Bed & Breakfasts, American Historic Inns, Plane Bargains, Mountain Flyer

BEULAH

A delightful little town in the beautiful and scenic Beulah Valley, on the eastern edge of the Wet Mountains and San Isabel National Forest, 25 miles southwest of Pueblo via I-25 and Highway 72. It's worth a detour.

BEULAH HOUSE

8733 Pine Drive, Beulah, CO 81023   *719-485-3201*
Harry & Ann Middelkamp, Resident Owners

LOCATION	From Pueblo, southwest on Highway 78 for 24 miles. Turn left in Beulah at the junction of Central Avenue and Pine Drive. One mile up on the right side, big rock and stone fence.
OPEN	All year.
DESCRIPTION	A 1910 Spanish Mission-style lodge with Spanish and antique furnishings, some rooms in Chinese and African themes, located on 6 wildlife-filled acres.
NO. OF ROOMS	Four rooms with private bathrooms and three rooms share one bathroom. Number six is the honeymoon suite.
RATES	Year-round rates for a double with a private bathroom are $105-up and $175 for a suite. No cancellation policy unless it is at the last minute...Nice, reasonable policy...TI
CREDIT CARDS	No.
BREAKFAST	Continental breakfast is served in the room and a lunch/brunch by the pool. Dinner and special meals are also available.
AMENITIES	All rooms have stocked bars, TVs if wanted and robes. Heated swimming pool, outdoor Jacuzzi, sauna, chapel, library, exercise room, golfcart transportation around estate, golf at private country club, tennis close by, Jeep picnics, stables for horse boarding, meeting facilities, and airport pickup available.
RESTRICTIONS	None, smoking and non-smoking rooms available, pets depend (as we have raccoons, skunks, sometimes bear and fox, and resident German Shepherds, King and Foxy, plus Giz the alley cat). Children of all ages are welcome and we have babysitting.
REVIEWED	*The Colorado Guide*

DANIEL'S BED & BREAKFAST

8927 Grand Avenue, Beulah, CO 81023   *719-485-3426*
Daniel L. Garcia Sr., Resident Owner

KK RANCH & CARRIAGE MUSEUM

8987 Mountain Park Road, Beulah, CO 81023   719-485-3250
Katherine Keating, Resident Owner

LOCATION	Take Highway 78 west from Pueblo 20 miles to Beulah Valley. At the first fork in the road keep left and continue past three roads, at the fourth intersection take a hard right onto Mountain Park Road (just off South Pine Drive).
OPEN	All year.
DESCRIPTION	Authentic 1870 homestead ranch house with an interior that includes antiques, fireplaces and wood-burning stoves. The homestead and carriage museum are situated on 67 wooded acres with streams, adjacent to a 600-acre mountain park.
NO. OF ROOMS	Three rooms share one bathroom. Katherine Keating, Captain USN (Ret.), favors the room with the fireplace.
RATES	Year-round rates are $32 for a single with a shared bathroom and $40 for a double with a shared bathroom. The deposit is $25 and refund requires 48 hours' notice.
CREDIT CARDS	No. Personal checks are OK.
BREAKFAST	Continental breakfast is served in the kitchen that looks out over mountains and pasture. Breakfast includes hot breads or rolls, cereal, fruit or juice and coffee. Kitchen privileges can be arrranged.
AMENITIES	Barns and corrals are available, but the owner does not rent horses.
RESTRICTIONS	No smoking, children of all ages are welcome, children under 12 stay free in parents' room. Resident dogs, cats, horses, donkeys and mules.
REVIEWED	*The Colorado Guide, Great American Guest House*

RAVEN'S ROOST BED & BREAKFAST

6174 Pennsylvania Avenue, Beulah, CO 81023   719-485-3227
Darla Ewing, Resident Owner

BLACK HAWK

This Victorian mountain town and National Historic District was the site of Colorado's richest gold strike. Now it's possible to strike it rich in the town's many casinos. Handy to Golden Gate State Park and it's a pretty drive 29 miles west of Denver on Highway 6 and 119.

AFTER SUPPER B&B

PO Box 237, Black Hawk, CO 80422   303-582-5787
Dixie & Bill Lovingier, Resident Owners

CHASE MANSION BED & BREAKFAST

201 Chase Gulch, Black Hawk, CO 80422   303-582-0112
Debra Start, Resident Owner   FAX 303-582-5869
French spoken.

LOCATION	Drive one block north of second light on Highway 119 and turn left at Chase. Big blue house on the left.
OPEN	All year.
DESCRIPTION	An 1879 Victorian Mansard with "Victorian clutter" furnishings.
NO. OF ROOMS	One room with a private bathroom and one room shares a bathroom. Check out the Victorious.
RATES	High season rates, May through December, are $65 for a single with private bathroom, $75 for a double with private bathroom, $55 for a single with shared bathroom and $65 for a double with a shared bathroom. Additional person is $10, an additional couple is $15. Cancellation requires 24 hours' notice; however, there is a $20 fee.
CREDIT CARDS	MasterCard, Visa
BREAKFAST	Continental breakfast is served in the dining room.
AMENITIES	Social director on premises, videos, books, games, refrigerator and kitchen use, wedding and special party arrangements.
RESTRICTIONS	None

The Shamrock Inn, Black Hawk

THE SHAMROCK INN

351 Gregory Street, Black Hawk, CO 80422   *303-582-5513*
Susan Knecht, Resident Owner

LOCATION	West on Highway 6 or I-70 to Highway 119. Upon entering Black Hawk city limits, take left at 2nd light (Bullwackers Casino on corner). Go up three blocks. The Inn is the yellow house on the right.
OPEN	All year.
DESCRIPTION	An 1880 two-story Victorian inn with some antique furnishings. Listed on the National and State Historic Registers.
NO. OF ROOMS	Three rooms with private bathrooms. One room shares one bathroom. Room B has a clawfoot tub.
RATES	Seasonal rates are $65-75 for a single or double with a private bathroom and $50-60 for single or double with shared bathroom. No minimum stay requirements. Cancellations require 24 hours' notice.
CREDIT CARDS	Discover, MasterCard, Visa
BREAKFAST	Guests serve themselves a full breakfast including homemade pastries, fruit, biscuits and homemade sausage gravy, beverages, oatmeal and cold cereals.
AMENITIES	Porch and balcony overlook "main drag" of downtown Black Hawk, 30 casinos within walking or free-shuttle distance, cable TV in rooms, private entrances.
RESTRICTIONS	Children over 12 are welcome and pets with manager's approval. Lakota, a Husky/Lab mix, is the resident dog.
REVIEWED	*The Colorado Guide*
MEMBER	Gilpin County Chamber of Commerce

BLANCA

MT. BLANCA GAME BIRD & TROUT

PO Box 236, Blanca, CO 81123   719-379-3825
Bill Binnian, Resident Manager   FAX 719-379-3589

BOULDER

This beautiful small town is home to the University of Colorado, the National
Center for Atmospheric Research, Celestial Seasonings (tea and tours available),
home of the Bolder Boulder 10K and an 8000-acre system of mountain parks and
greenbelts. For the record, there will be no Boulder bashing in this book — so
what if a good number of us come to work in running shoes — work hard, play
hard, etc...TI. Close to Rocky Mountain National Park and Denver, Boulder is
also home to Celestial Seasonings and the University of Colorado and offers
extensive outdoor recreational opportunities, plus shopping and dining on the
Pearl Street Mall.

THE ALPS BOULDER CANYON INN

38619 Boulder Canyon Drive, Boulder, CO 80302   303-444-5445
John & Jeannine Vanderhart, Resident Owners   800-414-2577
                                                       FAX 303-444-5522

LOCATION	In Boulder Canyon, 1.8 miles west of downtown.
OPEN	All year.
DESCRIPTION	An 1870-1906 remodeled country inn with Adirondack Camp and English country furnishings.
NO. OF ROOMS	Twelve rooms with private bathrooms. The best room in the house is the Wallstreet Room.
RATES	Year-round rates are $80-250 for a single or double with a private bathroom. The entire B&B may be reserved for $1650/night. There is a minimum stay during special events and some holidays. Ask about cancellation policy.
CREDIT CARDS	American Express, Carte Blanche, Diners Club, Discover, JCB, MasterCard, Visa

The Alps Boulder Canyon Inn, Boulder

BREAKFAST	Full breakfast, prepared by onsite chef and served in the dining room (or, seasonally, in gardens and on patio), includes a varied selection of homemade granola and yogurt, hot strudels, crepes and quiches, fresh fruit platters, fresh-baked croissants, rolls, bagels, breads and beverages. Special meals are available for picnics and catering.
AMENITIES	Six rooms with double Jacuzzi tubss, all rooms with antique fireplaces, radio, phones, down comforters and pillows in most rooms, robes, complimentary afternoon and evening refreshments, meeting facilities for up to 40, gardens, and handicapped access.
RESTRICTIONS	No smoking, no pets, children over 12 are welcome. The resident Gordon Setter is Maggie and the resident cats are Sid and S.K. who are..."good question." Please don't feed the animals; they are talented beggars.
REVIEWED	*Westword* magazine, *Frommer's, Recommended Country Inns of the Rocky Mountain Region*
MEMBER	Colorado Hotel and Lodging Association.
RATED	AAA 3 Diamonds, Mobil 3 Stars
AWARDS	"Best Inn in Colorado 1995" by Westword magazine.
KUDOS/COMMENTS	"...a dream come true, beautiful setting, spacious rooms with double Jacuzzi and fireplace!" (1994)

The Boulder Victoria Historic Inn, Boulder

THE BOULDER VICTORIA HISTORIC INN

1305 Pine Street, Boulder, CO 80302   303-938-1300
Matthew Dyroff and Jeffrey White, Resident Owners   FAX 303-938-1435

LOCATION	Downtown on the northeast corner of Pine and 13th two blocks from the Pearl Street Mall.
OPEN	All year.
DESCRIPTION	An elegantly restored 1889 two-story Victorian inn with period antique furnishings. Listed on the State Historic Register.
NO. OF ROOMS	Seven rooms with private bathrooms. The best room in the house is the White-Dyroff suite.
RATES	High season, May through September, rates are $114-$164 for a single or double with a private bathroom and a suite is $139-184. Off season, October through April, rates are $94 for a single or double with a private bathroom and suites are $144-164. There is a two-night minimum stay on weekends and cancellation requires seven days' notice.
CREDIT CARDS	American Express, MasterCard, Visa
BREAKFAST	Continental Plus is served in the dining room or guest rooms and includes homemade granola & meusli, fruitbreads, muffins, yogurt, bagels, croissants and fresh fruit.
AMENITIES	Fresh and dried roses in the rooms, robes, TV, phones, steam showers, down comforters, private entrance or balcony, afternoon tea with scones, cookies and port, special event and meeting space.

RESTRICTIONS	No smoking, no pets, children over 12 are welcome.
REVIEWED	America's Wonderful Little Hotels & Inns, Recommended Country Inns of the Rocky Montain Region, Frommer's Denver, Boulder and Colorado Springs, Best Places to Stay in the Rocky Mountain Region, The Colorado Guide
MEMBER	Distinctive Inns of Colorado, Professional Association of Innkeepers International.
RATED	AAA 3 Diamonds
AWARDS	Historic Preservation Award from Historic Boulder 1991; Landscape Award, Commercial Division, City of Boulder 1994
KUDOS/COMMENTS	"An exquisite Victorian mansion, very professional, attentive young staff; guest oriented. Though the breakfast is Continental Plus, it was superb with wonderful presentation; a great location." (1997)

BRIAR ROSE BED & BREAKFAST

2151 Arapahoe Avenue, Boulder, CO 80302   303-442-3007
Margaret & Bob Weisenbach, Resident Owners   FAX 303-786-8440
French and Spanish spoken.

| LOCATION | Coming into town on Highway 36, turn left at the second light (Arapahoe Avenue), go west about 0.5 mile to 22nd Street. The inn is on the corner. |
| OPEN | All year. |

Briar Rose Bed & Breakfast, Boulder

DESCRIPTION	An 1890 two-story red-brick "country cottage" Queen Anne and carriage house with "light" Victorian furnishings surrounded by shaded lawn and gardens.
NO. OF ROOMS	Nine rooms with private bathrooms. Margaret suggests the Anniversary Room.
RATES	High season, May through December, rates are $97-139 for a single or double with private bathroom. Off season rates are $79-129 for a single or double with a private bathroom. There is a minimum stay during major University of Colorado events and cancellation requires 48 hours' notice...good policy, some mountain B&Bs should take note...TI
CREDIT CARDS	American Express, Diners Club, MasterCard, Visa
BREAKFAST	Continental Plus is served in the dining room or on the sunporch and includes fresh fruit compote, yogurt with berries, croissants and fresh-baked breads, homemade jams and granola, "waffles and crepes when the spirit moves us."
AMENITIES	TV and telephones in rooms, down comforters, fresh flowers, robes, tea trays and homemade cookies.
RESTRICTIONS	No smoking, no pets.
REVIEWED	*Non-Smokers Guide to Bed & Breakfasts, America's Wonderful Little Hotels & Inns, Country Inns and Back Roads, Frommer's Denver, Boulder & Colorado Springs, Recommended Country Inns of the Rocky Mountain Region*
MEMBER	Distinctive Inns of Colorado, Bed & Breakfast Innkeepers of Colorado, Professional Association of Innkeepers International, Boulder Hotel and Motel Asociation, Colorado Hotel and Lodging Association
RATED	AAA 3 Diamonds, Mobil 3 Stars
KUDOS/COMMENTS	"Warm and comfortable." ... "Convenient, spotless, excellent food and service, friendly innkeepers who make you feel right at home." ... "Cozy, restored Victorian with great hosts; good food and a warm atmosphere." (1997)

COBURN HOTEL

2040 16th Street, Boulder, CO 80302   303-545-5200
Derek Wood & Wendy Smith, Resident Managers   800-858-5811
Some Spanish spoken.   FAX 303-440-6740

LOCATION	From Denver, take Highway 36 west into Boulder. Turn left on Canyon and go to 16th Street. Turn right, the hotel is a 1/2 block beyond Pearl Street on the right.
OPEN	All year.
DESCRIPTION	A 1994 two-story (plus garden level) "eco-hotel" with elegant western decor.
NO. OF ROOMS	Twelve rooms with private bathrooms. Best rooms are #11 and #12.
RATES	Year-round rates are $134-167 for a single or double with private bathrooms. There is no minimum stay and cancellation requires 48 hours' notice.
CREDIT CARDS	American Express, Discover, MasterCard, Visa
BREAKFAST	Continental Plus, served in the dining room, includes fresh-baked breads, muffins, granola, waffles, pancakes, quiches, stratas, organic coffees and teas, and seasonal fruit.
AMENITIES	Individually controlled A/C and heat, four rooms with Jacuzzi tubs, seven rooms with fireplaces, four rooms with king-sized beds, three rooms with balconies, three rooms with French doors, 100% cotton linens, meeting facilities, FAX and copier.
RESTRICTIONS	No smoking, no pets
REVIEWED	*The Insiders Guide to Boulder And the Rocky Mountain National Park*
MEMBER	Professional Association of Innkeepers International, "Green" Hotels Association, Boulder Hotel & Motel Association

GUNBARREL GUEST HOUSE

6901 Lookout Road, Boulder, CO 80301
Carolann Evans, Innkeeper

303-530-1513
800-530-1513
FAX 303-530-4573

LOCATION	Seven miles northeast of downtown Boulder off Highway 119 and 63rd Street.
OPEN	All year.
DESCRIPTION	A 1986 contemporary country inn featuring European-style lodging. Rooms are located around a central courtyard/patio.
NO. OF ROOMS	Thirteen rooms with private bathrooms. Try the Evergreen Suite.
RATES	Year-round rates are $94-134 for a single or double with private bath. Cancellation requires 48 hours' notice.
CREDIT CARDS	American Express, Diners Club, MasterCard, Visa
BREAKFAST	Continental Plus, served in the dining room, includes coffee, tea, juice, cream cheese, cereals, homemade granola, coffeecakes, muffins and fruit. Specialized catering is available.
AMENITIES	Fireplaces and kitchenettes in every room, two-person Jacuzzi in the Evergreen Suite, conference room for 45, boardroom for 10, handicapped access, phones, data jack and TV in every room. FAX and parking on site.
RESTRICTIONS	No pets, children over 12 are welcome, please ask about exceptions.
MEMBER	Professional Association of Innkeepers International

INN ON MAPLETON HILL

1001 Spruce Street, Boulder, CO 80302   *303-449-6528*
Jacque Traeger, Resident Owner

LOCATION	One block north of the Pearl Street Mall at 10th Street.
OPEN	All year.
DESCRIPTION	An 1899 brick Victorian Four Square with Victorian interior.
NO. OF ROOMS	Five rooms with private bathrooms and two rooms share one bathroom.
RATES	Year-round rates are $120-135 for a single or double with private bathroom, $88-102 for a single or double with shared bathroom and $135 for a suite. There is a 48-hour cancellation policy.
CREDIT CARDS	MasterCard, Visa
BREAKFAST	Continental Plus with homemade bread and muffins is served in the dining room.
AMENITIES	Complimentary sherry and tea, great room with piano, fireplace and TV, parlor and game room, meeting/wedding space for 35 people.
RESTRICTIONS	No smoking, no pets. The resident canary is called Goldie.
MEMBER	Boulder Hotel & Motel Association
AWARDS	Historic Boulder, 1992 Historic Preservation Award.

PEARL STREET INN

1820 Pearl Street, Boulder, CO 80302   303-444-5584
Patrece, Resident Manager   800-232-5949
German and Spanish spoken.   FAX 303-444-6494

LOCATION	Center of Boulder, three blocks east of the Pearl Street Mall.
OPEN	All year.
DESCRIPTION	An 1895 two-story Victorian with 1985 addition with contemporary Victorian furnishings and central courtyard.
NO. OF ROOMS	Seven rooms with private bathrooms. Try the suite.
RATES	Year-round rates are $95-105 for a single or double with a private bathroom and $115-125 for the suite. There is no minimum stay and there is a reservation/cancellation policy.
CREDIT CARDS	MasterCard, Visa
BREAKFAST	Continental breakfast, served in the dining room, guest rooms or courtyard, is cooked to order and includes four choices. Dinner is also available.
AMENITIES	Fresh flowers, TV, phone and fireplaces in rooms, turndown service, conference and banquet rooms, full bar, concierge service, complimentary afternoon refreshments, reserved parking, handicapped access.
RESTRICTIONS	No smoking, no pets, all children are welcome.
REVIEWED	America's Wonderful Little Hotels & Inns, Frommer's Denver, Boulder and Colorado Springs, Recommended Country Inns of the Rocky Mountain Region.
MEMBER	Colorado Hotel and Lodging Association

THE SANDY POINT INN

6485 Twin Lakes Road, Boulder, CO 80301   303-530-2939
Juanita Miller, Resident Owner   800-322-2939
                                      FAX 303-530-9101

KUDOS/COMMENTS	"Great place to go with a family; Nice staff, would be great for business travelers also." (1996)

BRECKENRIDGE

Summer-long music festival at the Riverwalk Performing Arts Center, jazz festivals on Maggie Pond during the summer, snow sculpting and wood carving competitions in fall and winter and several historic gold mining sites. Breckenridge features access to three world class ski areas: Keystone, Breckenridge and Copper Mountain. The summer months bring the Westfest, performances by the River-walk National Reporatory Orchestra, and outdoor activities on Lake Dillion. There is also shopping at factory outlet stores. From Denver 70 miles west on I-70.

ALLAIRE TIMBERS INN

9511 Highway #9 / South Main Street,   970-453-7530
PO Box 4653, Breckenridge, CO 80424   800-624-4904
Jack & Kathy Gumph, Resident Owners   FAX 970-453-8699

LOCATION	From Denver, take I-70 west to Frisco (exit 203). Take Highway 9 south to Breckenridge. We are 0.2 mile past the Conoco gas station on the right.
OPEN	All year.
DESCRIPTION	A 1991 two-story contemporary log-and-stone inn with southwestern, contemporary and rustic interior.
NO. OF ROOMS	Ten rooms have private baths (tiled showers). Kathy Gumph likes the Summit Suite.
RATES	High season (December through March) rates are $135-185 for a single or double with private bathroom and $185-245 for suites. Low season rates are $120-135 for a single or double with a private bathroom and $185-205 for suites. There is a minimum stay during Christmas and the ski season and a reservation/cancellation policy.
CREDIT CARDS	American Express, Discover, MasterCard, Visa
BREAKFAST	Full breakfast is served in the dining room and includes a buffet sidebar of coffees, teas, juices, cereals, fruit, yogurt and baked goods, plus a hot entree served at your table.
AMENITIES	Robes and slippers, early morning coffee service, afternoon refreshments and snacks, evening desserts, stone fireplace in Great Room, phones in every room, hot tub on main deck, private hot tub and fireplace in suites, wheelchair accessible and considerations for hearing impaired.
RESTRICTIONS	No smoking, no pets (resident Airedale is named Cassie), two guests per room maximum and children over 12 are welcome.
REVIEWED	*America's Wonderful Little Hotels & Inns, Recommended Country Inns of the Rocky Mountain Region, Special Places for the Discerning Traveler, Distinctive Inns of Colorado, The Colorado Guide*

MEMBER	Distinctive Inns of Colorado, Independent Innkeepers Association, Professional Association of Innkeepers International
RATED	AAA 3 Diamonds, ABBA 3 Crowns, Mobil 3 Stars
AWARDS	1993 Top 10 New Inns in America by Inn Marketing Review, 1995 national winner in ABBA's Bed & Breakfast Chefs Competition.
KUDOS/COMMENTS	"An excellent example of what innkeeping is all about." ... "The ultimate in hospitality, decor and service." ... "What a hot tub view!" (1994)

BED & BREAKFAST ON NORTH MAIN STREET

303 North Main Street, PO Box 2454,   970-453-2975
Breckenridge, CO 80424   800-795-2975
Diane Jaynes & Fred Kinat, Resident Owners

LOCATION	In the first block of Main Street on the west side of the street.
OPEN	Closed three weeks in May, two weeks in October and one week in November.
DESCRIPTION	An 1885 1-1/2-story "boom-town" Victorian inn with an 1880 one-story Victorian cottage, "decorated romantically" with antiques.
NO. OF ROOMS	Five rooms in main house with private bathrooms. One room in Victorian Cottage. Owners recommend the Victorian Cottage.
RATES	High season (December, February, March) rates are $95-185 for a single or double in the main house with private bathroom and $175-235 for the cottage. There is a minimum stay requirement during ski season, summer and autumn. There is a 45-day cancellation policy and a $30 charge.
CREDIT CARDS	American Express
BREAKFAST	Full breakfast, served in the dining room, varies daily but will include a theme entree such as a breakfast taco, frittata, quiche or Polynesian delight.
AMENITIES	Outdoor hot tub with view, two parlors with Victorian mantled fireplaces, afternoon refreshments, assorted area guidebooks and menus, lock-up ski and bike racks. The cottage has a Victorian mantled fireplace, Jacuzzi for two and a small kitchenette.
RESTRICTIONS	No smoking, no pets, children over 14 are welcome.
REVIEWED	*The Travel Channel's "Romantic Inns of America" series, The Colorado Guide, Frommer's Colorado, Best Places to Stay, Recommended Country Inns, America's Wonderful Little Hotels & Inns, The Non-Smokers Guide to Bed & Breakfasts*

Bed & Breakfast on North Main Street, Breckenridge

MEMBER	Bed & Breakfast Innkeepers of Colorado, Professional Association of Innkeepers International, Breckenridge Bed & Breakfasts, Summit County Bed & Breakfasts, Colorado Hotel & Motel Association
RATED	AAA 2 Diamonds, Mobil 3 Stars

THE EVANS HOUSE BED & BREAKFAST

102 South French Street, PO Box 387,   *970-453-5509*
Breckenridge, CO 80424
Pete & Georgette Contos, Resident Owners
French and Greek spoken.

LOCATION	Two blocks east of Main Street and Lincoln stoplight in the Historic District.
OPEN	All year.
DESCRIPTION	An 1886 two-story Victorian with the decor of the era, listed on the National Historic Register.
NO. OF ROOMS	Two rooms with a private bathroom and two rooms with shared bathroom.
RATES	Seasonal rates from November through May are $82-95 for a single or double with a private bath and $80-85 for a single or double with shared bath. Off season rates are $55-70 for a single or double with a private bath and $55-60 for a single or double with shared bath. There is a minimum stay during the winter ("but please call, we're flexible"). A two-night deposit is required, which is non-refundable unless the room is rebooked.

CREDIT CARDS	No
BREAKFAST	Full breakfast is served in the dining room from a seven-day menu and includes "a wide variety of hearty portions."
AMENITIES	Fresh flowers in the rooms, robes, cable TV, VCR, books and games in the common room. Telephone in the lobby, ski and bicycle storage, complimentary afternoon refreshments. On-site parking and free ski bus at front door.
RESTRICTIONS	No smoking, no pets (resident parrot, Alex). Supervised, well-behaved children are welcome but $20 extra or $5 for a crib.
REVIEWED	*America's Wonderful Little Hotels & Inns, Recommended Country Inns*
MEMBER	Bed & Breakfast Innkeepers of Colorado, Professional Association of Innkeepers International, National Bed & Breakfast Association, Breckenridge Bed& & Breakfast Association
RATED	AAA 2 Diamonds, ABBA 2 Crowns, Mobil 2 Stars
KUDOS/COMMENTS	"Small but friendly, historic, great hosts." (1996)

FIRESIDE INN

114 North French Street, PO Box 2252,　　　　970-453-6456
Breckenridge, CO 80424　　　　　　　　　FAX 970-453-9577
Mike & Mary Keeling, Resident Owners

LOCATION	One block north of the stoplight in the center of town (Ski Hill Road light), then east two blocks; blue house with picket fence on the corner of French and Wellington.
OPEN	All year except May 1 until the Friday prior to Memorial Day.
DESCRIPTION	An 1879/1979 converted miner's cabin listed on both the National and State Historic Registers. The furnishings are Victorian.
NO. OF ROOMS	Four rooms with private bathrooms and five rooms share three bathrooms. Best room: Brandywine Suite.
RATES	Winter rates, January through March, are $85-105 for a single or double with a private bathroom, $120 for a suite, and the guesthouse rents for $1,000 a week. Low season rates, May through December, are $60-80 for a single or double with a private bathroom, $85 for a suite, and $500 per week for the guesthouse. There is a minimum stay during ski season and cancellation requires 30 days' notice and a fee of $25 per person.
CREDIT CARDS	American Express, Discover, MasterCard, Visa
BREAKFAST	Full breakfast is served in the dining room. "Award winning" French toast available daily.

Fireside Inn, Breckenridge

AMENITIES	Hot tub, TV/VCR in private rooms, discount lift tickets and rentals, fireplace in parlor, guest refrigerators, ski and bicycle storage, extensive local knowledge of mountain bike trails.
RESTRICTIONS	No smoking, no pets
REVIEWED	*Recommended Country Inns of the Rocky Mountain Region, Mountain Biking in Summit County, Hiking the Colorado Trail*
MEMBER	Breckenridge Bed & Breakfast Association, Summit County Bed & Breakfast Association, Colorado Hotel and Lodging Association

HIGH COUNTRY LODGE

5064 Ski Hill Road, Peak 7, PO Box 7957, 970-453-9843
Breckenridge, CO 80424 800-497-0097
Donald Lake, Resident Owner FAX 970-453-7595

LOCATION	Five minutes from downtown at the base of Peak 7.
OPEN	All year.
DESCRIPTION	A recently remodeled 1969 Lindal-cedar A-frame vacation lodge on 10 acres with views of the Continental Divide.
NO. OF ROOMS	Eight rooms with private bathrooms and four rooms share four bathrooms. Room 204, check it out.
RATES	High season, major holidays and January 5 through April 1, rates are $100 for a single or double with a private bathroom, $90 for a single or double with a shared bathroom, $120 for a suite and $120 for the loft apartment. Off season rates are $60-80 less. There is a three-night minimum stay during holidays and a cancellation policy.
CREDIT CARDS	Discover, MasterCard, Visa

BREAKFAST	Full breakfast, served in the dining room, includes crepes, pancakes, muffins and beverages.
AMENITIES	Afternoon snacks, ten-seater Jacuzzi, workout room, game room, three fireplaces, can sleep up to 36. Wedding and honeymoon packages available.
RESTRICTIONS	No smoking, no pets.
MEMBER	Bed & Breakfast Innkeepers of Colorado

HUMMINGBIRD HOUSE BED & BREAKFAST

217 Hummingbird Drive, PO Box 1354,   970-453-6957
Breckenridge, CO 80424
Bob & Betty Flint, Resident Owners

LOCATION	From I-70 take exit 203 and travel 10 miles to Breckenridge. Drive through town, turn on Boreas Pass Road ('T' intersection at the Conoco station), go 1.5 miles to Hummingbird Road, go straight about 50 feet, two-story brown cedar-sided house on the left.
OPEN	All year except the last two weeks of November and May.
DESCRIPTION	A 1980 two-story host home with early American antiques.
NO. OF ROOMS	Two rooms with private bathrooms. Pick the Green Room.
RATES	Winter rates, December 15 to March 31, are $75-85 for a single or double with a private bathroom. Low season rates, April 1 through December 15, are $45-60 for a single or double with a private bathroom. There is a two-night minimum stay during Christmas and cancellations made less than five days prior to stay incur a $15 charge.
CREDIT CARDS	No
BREAKFAST	Full breakfast, served in the dining room, includes (on alternating days) an egg dish, breakfast meats, French toast, waffles, always fresh fruit and homemade pastry.
AMENITIES	Common room has TV/VCR, books, stereo, wood-burning stove. The hot tub is on the deck. The wet bar has a refrigerator, microwave and coffeemaker.
RESTRICTIONS	No smoking, no pets. A crib is available and all children are welcome.

The Hunt Placer Inn, Breckenridge

THE HUNT PLACER INN

275 Ski Hill Road, PO Box 4898, Breckenridge, CO 80424 971-453-7573
Carl & Gwen Ray, Resident Owners 800-472-1430
German spoken. FAX 970-453-2335

LOCATION	Turn onto Ski Hill Road from Main Street (the second stoplight). The Inn is 2-1/2 blocks up on the left.
OPEN	All year.
DESCRIPTION	A 1994 three-story Bavarian mountain chalet with wooden architecture and eclectic furnishings.
NO. OF ROOMS	Eight rooms with private bathrooms. Carl recommends the Britannia Suite.
RATES	Rates are seasonal. During the High Season (December through March) rates are $135-145 for a single or double with private bathroom and $160-180 for a suite. During Low Season (April through November) rates are $115 for a single or double with private bathroom and $145 for a suite. There is a minimum stay during Christmas and on weekends during the low season. Ask about cancellation policy.
CREDIT CARDS	American Express, Diners Club, Discovery, MasterCard, Visa
BREAKFAST	Full breakfast, served in the dining room, includes three courses: fresh orange juice with hot or cold cereal; daily hot entree; and a dessert course of creme bulee, pecan mousse, fruit salad.

AMENITIES	Private decks, fireplaces in suites and sitting areas, afternoon hors d'oeuvres, coffee and tea always available on sideboard, concierge service, historic gold mine adjacent, meeting room, and handicapped accessible.
RESTRICTIONS	No smoking, no pets, children over 11 are welcome.
REVIEWED	TV series "Romantic Inns of America," *New York Newsday* ("Ten Favorite Rocky Mountain B&Bs"), *Denver Post*, *America's Wonderful Little Hotels & Inns, Bed & Breakfasts and Country Inns, Bed & Breakfast Coucher-Dejeuner*
MEMBER	Professional Association of Innkeepers International, Breckenridge Bed & Breakfast Association, Bed & Breakfast Inns of Colorado, Colorado Hotel and Lodging Association.
RATED	AAA 3 Diamonds

LITTLE MOUNTAIN LODGE

98 Sunbeam Drive, PO Box 2479, Breckenridge, CO 80424   970-453-1969
Lynn Esmond, Resident Owner   800-468-7707
FAX 970-453-1919

KUDOS/COMMENTS	"Outstanding, beautiful log house." ... "Romantic, very charming; Lynn is very friendly and helpful." (1997)

MUGGINS GULCH INN

4023 Tiger Road, PO Box 3756, Breckenridge, CO 80424   970-453-7414
Beth Anne & Tom Hossley, Resident Innkeepers   800-275-8304
970-453-2711

KUDOS/COMMENTS	"Hard to get to but worth it." ... "My favorite. Owners built a fabulous log and beam. His antiques fill the great rooom, her art is everywhere." (1996) "Incredible views and wildlife; Good people." (1997)

RIDGE STREET INN

212 North Ridge Street, PO Box 2854,   970-453-4680
Breckenridge, CO 80424
Carol Brownson, Resident Owner

LOCATION	Downtown Breckenridge, one block east of Main Street.
OPEN	All year.

Ridge Street Inn, Breckenridge

DESCRIPTION	An 1890 two-story Victorian inn on the Colorado Historic Register, with antiques and country French furnishings
NO. OF ROOMS	Four rooms with private bathrooms and two rooms share one bathroom. The best room: Parlor Suite.
RATES	High season, December through April and July through September, rates are $70-115 for a single or double with a private bathroom and $65-90 for a single or double with a shared bathroom. Off season rates are $60-70 for a single or double with a private bathroom and $55 for a single or double with a shared bathroom. There is a minimum stay during the winter and a reservation/cancellation policy.
CREDIT CARDS	MasterCard, Visa
BREAKFAST	Full breakfast, served in the breakfast room/kitchen, includes waffles or scrambled eggs, cereals, coffee cake and beverages.
AMENITIES	TV in rooms, phone in living room, fireplace, guide service for hiking and biking.
RESTRICTIONS	No smoking, no pets, children over six are welcome. There are two Springer Spaniels called Tilly and Simon.
MEMBER	Bed & Breakfast Innkeepers of Colorado, Summit County Bed & Breakfast Association

Swan Mountain Inn, Breckenridge

SWAN MOUNTAIN INN

16172 Highway 9, Breckenridge, CO 80424   970-453-7903
PO Box 2900, Dillon, CO 80435   800-578-3687
Steve Gessner, Resident Owner

LOCATION	From Denver, take I-70 west approximately 70 miles to exit 203 at Frisco; take Route 9 South about four miles. The Inn is halfway between Frisco and Breckenridge at the corner of Highway 9 and Swan Mountain Road.
OPEN	All year.
DESCRIPTION	A 1986 three-story log home with cathedral and vaulted ceilings, a fireside bar and candlelit dining room; furnished with antiques, Waverly fabrics and light cedar walls.
NO. OF ROOMS	Three rooms with private bathrooms and one room shares one bathroom. The best room is the Blue River Hideaway.
RATES	The inn has three rate schedules. High season is Christmas and March with rates of $100-135 for a single or double with private bathroom, $60 for a single or double with shared bathroom and $220 for the suite. Low season is July 1st to September 15th and January 3rd to April 15th with rates of $75-100 for a single or double with private bathroom, $50 for a single or double with shared bathroom and $165 for the suite. There is a minimum stay on weekends, Christmas and March. Cancellations must be made at least two weeks prior to stay to receive full refund (less 10 percent service charge).

CREDIT CARDS	Discover, MasterCard, Visa
BREAKFAST	Full gourmet breakfast, served in the dining room, includes choice of entree, orange juice, coffee or tea, granola, fresh breads and pasties. Lunch and dinner are available in summer and winter.
AMENITIES	Outdoor hot tub, TV/VCR, two fireplaces, two decks and large front porch, afternoon tea time, weddings and private parties, croquet in the summer, bath amenities, robes, handicapped access on lower level.
RESTRICTIONS	No smoking, no pets.
REVIEWED	*Rocky Mountain News, Westword*
MEMBER	Bed & Breakfast Innkeepers of Colorado, Summit County Bed & Breakfast Association
AWARDS	Voted "Best New Restaurant" in 1992 and "Best Brunch" in 1993 and 1994 by the local paper, the Summit Daily News.

SWISS INN BED & BREAKFAST

205 South French Street, PO Box 556,　　　　970-453-6489
Breckenridge, CO 80424　　　　FAX 970-453-1842
Lynn & Carl Cavalluzzi, Resident Owners

THE WALKER HOUSE

211 East Lincoln Street, PO Box 509,　　　　970-453-2426
Breckenridge, CO 80424　　　　800-365-6365
Sue Ellen Strong, Resident Owner　　　　FAX 970-468-6222
Polish spoken.

LOCATION	Going south, turn left at the corner of Main Street and Lincoln (opposite the ski area), proceed two blocks, turn right on French, first driveway on right.
OPEN	November 1 to May 30
DESCRIPTION	An 1875 three-story log Victorian with original Victorian furnishings.
NO. OF ROOMS	One room with a private bathroom and one room shares one bathroom. Check out the Boudoir Suite.
RATES	Regular rates are $89 for a single or double with shared bathroom and $118 for the suite. Christmas rates are 10% more. There is a two-day minimum stay and a cancellation policy.
CREDIT CARDS	No

The Walker House, Breckenridge

BREAKFAST	Full breakfast, served in the dining room, includes informal vegetarian style with eggs and milk. Dinner and special meals are available.
AMENITIES	Very quiet and private, snacks, tea and coffee anytime.
RESTRICTIONS	No smoking, no pets, no noise ("We don't serve alcohol"), children over 16 are welcome.
REVIEWED	*Feather Beds & Flap Jacks*
MEMBER	Breckenridge Bed & Breakfast Association

THE WELLINGTON INN

200 North Main Street, PO Box 5890,
Breckenridge, CO 80424
Hollie & Bill VanderHoeven, Resident Owners

970-453-9464
800-655-7557

BRIGHTON

A suburban community just north of Denver metroplex. Don't overlook Barr Lake State Park, a water fowl habitat and hatching area for Bald Eagles with excellent facilities for fishing, and X-C skiing.

COUNTRY GARDENS BED & BREAKFAST

1619 East 136th Avenue, Brighton, CO 80601   *303-451-1724*
Arlie & Donna Munsie, Resident Owners   *800-475-1724*

LOCATION	Thirteen miles north of Denver, one mile east of I-25. From I-25 take exit 223 east to Washington Street (3rd light), turn north to 136th Avenue, then right 1-1/2 blocks.
OPEN	All year, closed December 15 through January 2.
DESCRIPTION	A 1979 two-story Country Victorian with covered porch on three sides, located on four acres with gardens, waterfall and pond.
NO. OF ROOMS	Four rooms with private bathrooms. The owners recommend the Turret Suite.
RATES	Year-round rates are $60-70 for a single with bath, $70-80 for a double with bath and $115 for a suite. There is a reservation/cancellation policy.
CREDIT CARDS	American Express, MasterCard, Visa
BREAKFAST	Full "hearty" breakfast, served in the dining room or the sunroom, includes egg and meat dishes, waffles, pancakes, homemade breads and fresh fruit in season.
AMENITIES	Gardens with walking paths and sitting areas, walking and riding trails adjacent to property, gazebo, hot tub, weddings and receptions available. Queen-sized beds, flowers and mints in the rooms and beautiful views of the Front Range including Long's Peak. Common room with cable TV and piano, complimentary refreshments and off-street parking for RVs.
RESTRICTIONS	No smoking, no pets (resident Cocker Spaniel named Reggie and two cats, Brie and Casey, all of whom are outside pets), children over 12 are welcome.
KUDOS/COMMENTS	"A quiet country experience with the warmest innkeepers ever! The food and friendliness keep us going back." (1996)

BROOMFIELD

Halfway between Boulder and Denver, this small but growing city on the east side of Highway 36 is handy to the best of both, and all things west.

BROOMFIELD GUEST HOUSE

9009 West Jeffco Airport Avenue, Broomfield, CO 80021   303-469-3900
Betty Aldrick, Manager   800-233-5633
                                                   FAX 303-438-1457

LOCATION	Three quarters of a mile south of the Broomfield exit off Highway 36 at the Jeffco Airport.
OPEN	All year.
DESCRIPTION	A 1988 two-story traditional building with Thomasville furnishings, a courtyard and private entrances.
NO. OF ROOMS	Sixteen rooms with private bathrooms. The owner suggests the Kittredge Jacuzzi Suite.
RATES	Year-round rates are $90-150. Cancellation requires two days' notice.
CREDIT CARDS	American Express, Diners Club, MasterCard, Visa
BREAKFAST	Continental Plus is served in the dining room. Catering is available for eight or more.
AMENITIES	Phone, TV, complimentary sodas and snacks in the rooms, refrigerator, all rooms air conditioned, microwave and fireplace in each room, Jacuzzis in three rooms, handicapped access, conference facilities.
RESTRICTIONS	No smoking, no pets. Children of all ages are welcome.

BUENA VISTA

This "Beautiful View" overwhelms, ringed by a bounty of 14ers in the soaring Sawatch and Collegiate Ranges. Must-do's: rafting on the Arkansas River, Gold Rush Days and Burro Jamboree (the Tripple Crown of pack-burro racing), Gem and Mineral Show and Folklife Festival, all in July and August, or the Octoberfest and Moonlight Madness. From Denver, 117 miles southwest via Highway 285.

THE ADOBE INN

303 North Highway 24, Buena Vista, CO 81211   719-395-6340
Paul, Majorie and Michael Knox, Resident Owners

LOCATION	Two blocks north of stoplight at Highway 24 and Sterling Avenue.
OPEN	All year.
DESCRIPTION	A 1982 southwestern adobe hacienda with Mexican restaurant.
NO. OF ROOMS	Five rooms with private baths. The Knox's favorite room is the Indian Room.
RATES	Seasonal rates are $69-89 for a single or double from May through October and $59-79 for a single or double from November through April. There is no minimum stay and cancellation requires seven days.
CREDIT CARDS	MasterCard, Visa
BREAKFAST	Full breakfast is served in the dining room and includes eggs, meat, croissants, fruit and drinks.
AMENITIES	Cable TV in all rooms, two-person Jacuzzi, solarium with piano, fireplace and library.
RESTRICTIONS	No smoking, no pets
REVIEWED	*The Colorado Guide, Recommended Country Inns of the Rocky Mountain Region, America's Wonderful Little Hotels & Inns*
MEMBER	Bed & Breakfast Innkeepers of Colorado
RATED	AAA 3 Diamonds

BLUE SKY INN

719 Arizona Street, Buena Vista, CO 81211   719-395-8862
Butch & Marge Henley, Resident Owners   800-654-6297

LOCATION	Turn right at the one traffic light from Highway 24 to East Main, take a right on Court Street, go 1/4 mile to the B&B.
OPEN	All year.
DESCRIPTION	A 1960 contemporary mountain home, furnished with antiques, on 25 acres along the Arkansas River and Cottonwood Creek.
NO. OF ROOMS	One room with private bathroom and three rooms share one bathroom. The best room is the Master Bedroom.
RATES	Summer rates are $70 for the room with private bathroom and $60 for a room with shared bath. Winter rates are $10 less. There is no minimum stay and a three-day cancellation policy.
CREDIT CARDS	MasterCard, Visa
BREAKFAST	Full country breakfast is served in the sun porch or on the patios.
AMENITIES	Hot tub on the Arkansas river, outdoor dining, beautiful professional landscaping, fishing on the Arkansas River, hiking trails.
RESTRICTIONS	No smoking, no pets, children are welcome.
REVIEWED	*The Colorado Guide*

BUTTERFIELDS' BED & BREAKFAST

15860 Fairway Drive, Buena Vista, CO 81211   719-395-9146
Kathy & Jim Butterfield, Resident Owners

MEISTER HOUSE BED & BREAKFAST

414 East Main Street, Buena Vista, CO 81211   719-395-9220
Barbara & Frank Hofmeister, Resident Owners   800-882-1821
                                                        FAX 719-395-9128

LOCATION	Downtown Buena Vista.
OPEN	All year.
DESCRIPTION	An 1879 renovated two-story Victorian stucco and brick hotel with western Victorian furnishings, listed on the Colorado Historic Register.

NO. OF ROOMS	Five rooms with private bathrooms and two rooms share one bathroom.
RATES	Year-round rates are $65 for a single with shared bathroom, $85-105 for a double with private bathroom and $90 for a suite. There is no minimum stay and a 10-day cancellation policy.
CREDIT CARDS	Discover, MasterCard, Visa
BREAKFAST	Full breakfast is served in the dining room or courtyard.
AMENITIES	Sauna, a sink in each room, robes, afternoon treats, library, "great views and wonderful courtyard."
RESTRICTIONS	No smoking, no pets, children over eight are welcome. The resident Miniature Dachshund is called Bruno.

THE MOUNTAIN SHACK BED & BREAKFAST

15120 CR 306, Buena Vista, CO 81211   719-395-6745
Jon & Ruth Johnson, Resident Innkeepers

THE POTTER'S HOUSE BED & BREAKFAST

28490 Chaffee County Road 313, Buena Vista, CO 81211   719-395-6458
Veryl Rember, Resident Owner

LOCATION	One mile south of town.
OPEN	May 1 through October 15.
DESCRIPTION	A 1986 adobe home with antique furnishings.
NO. OF ROOMS	One room with private bathroom and two rooms share one bathroom.
RATES	Seasonal rates are $70 for a single or double with private bathroom and $65 for a single or double with shared bathroom. There is a reservation/cancellation policy.
CREDIT CARDS	MasterCard, Visa
BREAKFAST	Full breakfast is served in the dining room or garden patios. Sack lunches are available.
AMENITIES	Fireplace in one room, complimentary refreshments.
RESTRICTIONS	No smoking, no pets (resident dog), children over 12 are welcome.

TROUT CITY INN

PO Box 431, Buena Vista, CO 81211   719-395-8433
Juel & Irene Kjeldsen, Resident Owners

LOCATION	On Trout Creek Pass, five miles east of Johnson Village (two miles south of Buena Vista) at Highways 24 and 285 and McGee Gulch Road.
OPEN	June 15 through September 15.
DESCRIPTION	A 1987 reconstruction of an historic railroad depot in the San Isabel National Forest with Victorian furnishings. Also a breeding and training farm for registered horses.
NO. OF ROOMS	Four rooms with private bathrooms, two rooms in depot, one suite in Pullman Car, one suite in Drover's Caboose. Choose the private Pullman Car.
RATES	Seasonal rates are $50-70 for a single or double with a private bathroom. There is no minimum stay and cancellation requires 72 hours' notice.
CREDIT CARDS	MasterCard, Visa
BREAKFAST	Full breakfast, served in the dining room, includes egg entree, meats, fresh-baked breads or muffins, biscuits and gravy, a dozen homemade preserves and a number of house specialties.
AMENITIES	Fishing, gold pannning, handcar rides, railroad museum, Victorian saloon game room, VCR library.
RESTRICTIONS	No smoking indoors, no pets, children over 10 are welcome—all ages welcome in the caboose.
REVIEWED	*America's Wonderful Little Hotels & Inns, Recommended Country Inns of the Rocky Mountain Region, Best Places to Stay in the Rocky Mountains, Great Affordable B&B Getaways*
MEMBER	Bed & Breakfast Innkeepers of Colorado.

CAÑON CITY

LEMON DROP INN

1131 Harrison Avenue, Cañon City, CO 81212   719-269-8387
Linda Smith, Resident Owner

CARBONDALE

An independent and spirited community at the base of towering Mt. Sopris, and if you liked the 60s, you'll love it here. Other good reasons: Gold Medal fishing in the Roaring Fork and Crystal Rivers; polo at the Roaring Fork Polo Club; the exceptional Mountain Fair in July and the summer-long Performance in the Park Series, and a feasting on spuds on Potato Day in October. And, of course, skiing at the Spring Gulch X-C Center and neighboring big resorts. Cyclists alert: absolutely do not ride the 30-mile stretch of Highway 82 between Carbondale and Aspen — life is short enough as it is.

AMBIANCE INN BED & BREAKFAST

66 North Second Street, Carbondale, CO 81623   970-963-3597
Norma & Robert Morris, Resident Owners   800-350-1515

LOCATION	At Main Street turn left, go to 2nd, turn left, second house on the right.
OPEN	All year.
DESCRIPTION	A 1975 two-story contemporary Manor House.
NO. OF ROOMS	Four rooms with private bathrooms. Norma suggests the Aspen Suite.
RATES	Year-round rates are $50-100 for a single or double with a private bathroom, the entire B&B rents for $290. There is no minimum stay and cancellation requires 30 days' notice...too long...TI
CREDIT CARDS	MasterCard, Visa
BREAKFAST	Full breakfast, served in the dining room, includes fresh ground coffee, juices, fruit bowl, homemade breads and muffins, special egg dish or waffles or French toast, with bacon or sausage. Lunch and "picnic to go" are available.
AMENITIES	Library, afternoon tea and coffee, TV, radio, phone, robes and sitting room.
RESTRICTIONS	No smoking, no pets. Children over seven are welcome.
REVIEWED	*The Colorado Guide, Denver Post, Rocky Mountain News*
MEMBER	Bed & Breakfast Innkeepers of Colorado, Colorado Hotel and Lodging Association.

Aunt Grace's Bed & Breakfast

0045 Willow Lane, Carbondale, CO 81623   970-963-8293
"Aunt" Grace Baker & Mary Haggart, Resident Owners

LOCATION	From Carbondale, take Main Street east until it crosses the tracks out of town, go past the cattle and horse pastures 1/4 mile and you'll see our sign...a giant headboard.
OPEN	All year.
DESCRIPTION	A 1978 ranch house with comfortable brick and wood interior that is inviting and open. Large king and queen rooms with views of the mountains and horse pastures.
NO. OF ROOMS	Two rooms with private bathrooms and two rooms share one bathroom. Ma & Pa's room is the most private and Aunt Bea's room is the most romantic.
RATES	High season rate, July and August, is $75 for a single or double with a private bathroom and $65 for a single or double with a shared bathroom. The rest of the year a single or double with a private bathroom is $55-65 and a single or double with a shared bathroom is $45-55. There is a two-day minimum stay during high season and cancellation requires 14 days' notice.
CREDIT CARDS	No
BREAKFAST	Full breakfast is served in the dining room or or the deck with china and crystal and includes such things as omelets, sausage, home fries, farm-fresh eggs, juice, coffee and tea. Special lowfat and diabetic meals are available.
AMENITIES	Horse boarding, popcorn in the evenings, coffee and tea and cocoa at all times, game cabinet, VCR and movies, information on local attractions, candy and local paper in the rooms, and a fireplace in the common room.
RESTRICTIONS	No smoking in room ("We have a smoking area"), no pets. There are three resident mini long-haired Dachshunds, Gretta, Lucy and Sassy, who are quiet and love to adopt our guests, plus two Quarter horses. All well-behaved children are welcome.

Landmark Bed & Breakfast

689 Main, Carbondale, CO 81623   970-963-1850
FAX 970-963-8993

Mt. Sopris Inn, Carbondale

MT. SOPRIS INN

0165 Mt. Sopris Ranch Road, Carbondale, CO 81623 970-963-2209
Barbara Fasching, Resident Owner 800-437-8675
FAX 970-963-8975

LOCATION	Three miles southwest of the intersection of Highways 82 and 133.
OPEN	May 28 through October 15. Call for the rest of the year.
DESCRIPTION	A 1993 two-story log country inn on 14 acres along the Crystal River with country furnishings.
NO. OF ROOMS	Fourteen rooms with private bathrooms. Choose room #1.
RATES	Year-round rates are $85-175 for a single or double with private bathroom. There is a two-night minimum stay during summer weekends and cancellation requires seven days' notice plus a $25 fee.
CREDIT CARDS	MasterCard, Visa
BREAKFAST	Full breakfast, served in the dining room, includes meat plus entree, rolls and bread, fruit and beverages. Advance notice is required for other meals.
AMENITIES	TV and telephones in rooms, grand piano in Great Room, seven fireplaces, pool table, swimming pool, four Jacuzzis, handicapped access, conference facilities with room for eighteen.
RESTRICTIONS	No smoking, no pets. Wildlife and llamas on the property.
MEMBER	Bed & Breakfast Innkeepers of Colorado, Professional Association of Innkeepers International.

ROARING FORK RIVER BED & BREAKFAST

16613 Highway 82, Carbondale, CO 81623   970-963-8853
Lou & Diana Moore, Resident Owners   800-328-9337
                                            FAX 970-963-8853

VAN HORN HOUSE AT LIONS RIDGE

0318 Lions Ridge Road, Carbondale, CO 81623   970-963-3605
John & Susan Laatsch, Resident Owners   888-453-0395
                                            FAX 970-963-1681

LOCATION	From Carbondale go 3.5 miles to Catherine Store (just beyond mile marker 15), turn left at the intersection, turn right at the first street, the B&B is the first house on the right at the top of the hill.
OPEN	All year.
DESCRIPTION	A 1980 three-story European cottage with antiques and country furnishings.
NO. OF ROOMS	Two rooms with private bathrooms and two rooms share one bathroom. Susan recommends the Minnie Maud.
RATES	Year-round rates, except for December 15 through January 10, are $60 for a single with private bathroom, $70 for a double with private bathroom, $50 for a single with shared bathroom and $60 for a double with shared bathroom. There is a two-night minimum stay over the last weekend of July and cancellation requires 10 days' notice.
CREDIT CARDS	MasterCard, Visa
BREAKFAST	Full breakfast, served in the dining room, includes entree, meat, muffins, fruit and beverages.
AMENITIES	Homebaked cookies and TV in the lounge, complimentary beverages, robes, fresh flowers, hot tub under the stars, and special amenities on request.
RESTRICTIONS	No smoking, no pets. Children over eight are welcome. The resident cats are called Sophie and Mex.
REVIEWED	*Recommended Country Inns (Rocky Mountain Region)*
MEMBER	Bed & Breakfast Innkeepers of Colorado

CASCADE
(COLORADO SPRINGS)

A small residential mountain community in the Ute Pass area, and access point to Pikes Peak Highway toll road. Wind up to the 14,100 foot summit or opt for Santa's Village and theme park at the North Pole. About 15 miles west of downtown Colorado Springs on Highway 24.

BLACK BEAR INN OF PIKES PEAK

5250 Pikes Peak Highway, Cascade, CO 80809   719-684-0151
Christi & Kevin Heidenreich, Resident Owners   FAX 719-684-0151

LOCATION	Ten miles west of I-25 and Highway 24 west. Follow the signs to Pikes Peak Highway. Go five miles west of Manitou Springs on Highway 24 to just above the North Pole and before the toll gate to Pikes Peak.
OPEN	All year.
DESCRIPTION	A 1994 two-story New England farmhouse with mountain views and comfortable furnishings.
NO. OF ROOMS	Nine rooms with private bathrooms. Pick room #8.
RATES	Year-round rates for a single or double with a private bathroom are $70-95, and the entire inn rents for $660. There is no minimum stay and cancellation requires five days' notice.
CREDIT CARDS	Discover, MasterCard, Visa
BREAKFAST	Full breakfast is served in the dining room and includes Florintene and Scotch eggs, fruit platters, fresh pastries, cinnamon rolls, muffins, cereal and yogurt.
AMENITIES	Hot tub in the woods, hiking trails from the inn, wine and beer, cookies, large deck, great views from all rooms.
RESTRICTIONS	No smoking, no pets.
REVIEWED	Opened in 1995.
MEMBER	Colorado Bed & Breakfast Association
RATED	AAA 3 Diamonds

EASTHOLME IN THE ROCKIES

4445 Haggerman Street, Cascade, CO 80809   800-672-9901
Terry Thompson & family, resident owners

LOCATION	From I-25 in Colorado Springs take exit #141 to Highway 24 west for eleven miles. Exit to the right at the Cascade exit, drive 1-1/2 blocks, turn right on Topeka, go one block and turn right on Haggerman.

Eastholme in the Rockies, Cascade

OPEN	All year.
DESCRIPTION	A restored 1885 three-story Victorian with front porch and balcony, listed on the Colorado Historic Register .
NO. OF ROOMS	Four rooms with private bathrooms and two rooms share one bathroom. Pick the Marriott Suite.
RATES	Year-round rates for a single or double with a private bathroom are $87-99, $69 for a single or double with a shared bathroom, $99 for a suite, $135 for a cottage, and $784 for the entire B&B. There is no minimum stay and cancellation requires seven days' notice less 10% of the deposit.
CREDIT CARDS	American Express, Discover, MasterCard, Visa
BREAKFAST	Full gourmet breakfast, served in the dining room, includes fresh-from-the-oven breads, pastries and main courses like frittatas with fruit juice, coffee and tea.
AMENITIES	Guest parlor with fireplace, library, piano, TV/VCR, guest kitchen, 40-foot balcony and hiking trails nearby.
RESTRICTIONS	No smoking, "pets in crates allowed but must accompany guests when they are out." The resident dogs are Chessie and Ebony and the Cat is called Owen...do they have crates?...TI
REVIEWED	*Recommended Country Inns of the Rocky Mountain Region*
MEMBER	Bed & Breakfast Innkeepers of Colorado
AWARDS	1989 Preservation Excellence Award by Colorado Preservation, Inc., Ute Pass Landmark designated by 1976 Bicentennial Committee
KUDOS/COMMENTS	"A wonderful tribute to western hospitality!" ... "Terry is making the place look like new." (1996)

CEDAREDGE

Known as the southern gateway to the Grand Mesa, this is slightly off the beaten path and worth it. The Apple Festival in October is a major event. From Grand Junction, six miles southeast at the southern terminus of Scenic Highway 65.

CEDARS' EDGE LLAMAS BED & BREAKFAST

2169 Highway 65, Cedaredge, CO 81413   970-856-6836
Ray & Gail Record, Resident Owners

LOCATION	Five miles north of Cedaredge on Highway 65.
OPEN	All year.
DESCRIPTION	A 1990 two-story contemporary cedar country inn and cottage with country furnishings and working llama farm.
NO. OF ROOMS	Four rooms with private bathrooms. Try the Hummingbird Suite.
RATES	Year-round rates are $50-75 for a double with private bathroom, $75 for the suite and $295 for the entire B&B. There is a minimum stay during July 4th and Labor Day weekends and a two-week cancellation policy.
CREDIT CARDS	MasterCard, Visa
BREAKFAST	Full "hearty country fare" is served in the dining room, guestrooms or on decks. Entrees may be whole-wheat blueberry pancakes, sausage casserole, mushroom scramble, French toast, served with hashbrowns, bacon or sausage, fresh fruit and beverages.
AMENITIES	Llamas, llamas, llamas, "all the llama petting you can stand," private decks. "Plus, llamas!"
RESTRICTIONS	No smoking, no pets, children are welcome. There is an outdoor Golden Retriever named Woody (Sir Woodward of Cedars' Edge).
REVIEWED	*Recommended Country Inns of the Rocky Mountain Region, Frommer's Colorado, The Non-Smokers Guide to Bed & Breakfasts*
MEMBER	Bed & Breakfast Innkeepers of Colorado

EAGLE'S NEST HUNTING LODGE

2450 Highway 65, Cedaredge, CO 81413   970-856-3521
Ron Moore, Resident Owner

CENTRAL CITY

This small Victorian mining town and National Historic District is known for its Summer Opera and Jazz Festival from July through August; and now casinos offer gambling. Thirty miles west of Denver of Denver on Highway 119.

→ HIGH STREET INN

215 West High Street, Central City, CO 80427   303-582-0622
Patrick & Selina Hughes, Resident Owners

LOCATION	In Central City go right on County Road (next to St. James Church), first left onto West High Street, seventh house from that corner.
OPEN	All year.
DESCRIPTION	An 1890 Victorian with full front porch and comfortable furnishings.
NO. OF ROOMS	One room with private bathroom and two rooms share two baths. Owners like the Stained Glass Room.
RATES	Summer rates are $85 for a double with a private bathroom, $65 for a single with shared bath and $75 for a double with shared bath. Winter rates are $10-20 cheaper. There is no minimum stay and cancellation policy is 72 hours.
CREDIT CARDS	Discover, MasterCard, Visa
BREAKFAST	Full breakfast, served in the dining room, includes ham and cheese omelet, meats, hash browns, homemade bread and biscuits, fruit, coffee, tea and juice.
AMENITIES	Fresh flowers in each room, terry robes, turndown service, carafe of ice water, chocolates, cookies, fruit and beverages always available, TV in all rooms, free parking, walking distance to casinos and opera.
RESTRICTIONS	No pets (resident dog is Toby), supervised children are welcome, smoking allowed on porch and in front room.

THE PRIMROSE INN

310 East First High Street, Central City, CO 80427   303-582-5808
Janice Ward, Resident Owner

LOCATION	Two blocks northeast of the central business district.
OPEN	All year.

DESCRIPTION	An 1864 two-story Victorian with Victorian furnishings.
NO. OF ROOMS	Three rooms share one bathroom. Choose the upstairs front room.
RATES	Year-round rates are $75 for a single or double with shared bathroom and $150 for a three room suite. There is no minimum stay and cancellation requires seven days' notice.
CREDIT CARDS	MasterCard, Visa
BREAKFAST	Continental breakfast is served in the dining room or kitchen.
AMENITIES	Oversized towels, robes, TV in den, piano in parlor, lawn chairs in the garden and off-street parking.
RESTRICTIONS	Smoking restricted to the kitchen, no pets.

WINFIELD SCOTT GUEST QUARTERS

210 Hooper Street, Central City, CO 80427 303-582-3433
Patty & Scott Webb, Resident Owners FAX 303-582-3434

LOCATION	At the traffic light (there is only one) turn left and follow Spring Street up hill past two parking lots and three houses on the right. You then come to an open lot, at the end of the lot is Hooper Street, turn right and go up hill.
OPEN	All year.
DESCRIPTION	A 1991 Victorian architecture and southwestern interior decor with one- and two-bedroom condo-like suites, all on one acre of beautiful grounds.
NO. OF ROOMS	Two suites. The Webbs' favorite room is the Matchless Suite.
RATES	Year-round rates are $84 for the one-bedroom suite and $159 for the two-bedroom suite. Reservations are required and there is a seven-day cancellation policy.
CREDIT CARDS	Discover, MasterCard, Visa
BREAKFAST	Continental Plus is served in the guestrooms and includes baked goods, fresh fruit salad, hot and cold cereals and coffee, tea and hot chocolate.
AMENITIES	On quiet grounds with an excellent view. TV, VCR, fireplaces, kitchens and phones are in the suites. Deck with BBQ grill, FAX and copier are available.
RESTRICTIONS	No smoking, no pets, children over two are welcome. Please inquire about children under two. The resident English Setter is Winnie.
REVIEWED	*The Colorado Guide, Best Places to Stay in the Rockies*
MEMBER	Bed & Breakfast Innkeepers of Colorado

CHIPITA PARK
(COLORADO SPRINGS)

One of a cluster of small mountain towns in the Ute Pass area, at the edge of Pike National Forest. Handy to the entrance of Pikes Peak Highway, about 15 miles west of Colorado Springs on Highway 24.

TOP OF TIMPA

5620 Timpa Road, Chipita Park, CO 80809   719-684-2296
Dick & Elizabeth Dolbee, Resident Owners

LOCATION	Between Cascade and Green Montain Falls, take Highway 24 west to Pikes Peak/Cascade exit, northwest on Chipita Park Road, then south on Timpa Road all the way to the top.
OPEN	All year.
DESCRIPTION	A 1957 mountain compound with eclectic furnishings.
NO. OF ROOMS	Three suites with private bathrooms plus a cottage with private bathrooms.
RATES	Year-round rates are $70-75 for a single or double with private bathroom. There is a reservation/cancellation policy.
CREDIT CARDS	No
BREAKFAST	Full breakfast is served in the dining room.
AMENITIES	Eight-person hot tub; robes and cable TV in every room; radio, phone, refrigerator in room; one suite and cottage have fireplaces; complimentary evening snacks; picnic, laundry, and meeting facilities; corral can accommodate two horses.
RESTRICTIONS	No smoking, no pets.

CIMARRON

Located just west of Curecanti National Recreation Area and 20 miles east of Montrose on Highway 50.

THE INN AT ARROWHEAD

21401 Alpine Plateau Road, Cimarron, CO 81220   970-249-5634
Mike Thompson, Resident Manager   800-654-3048
Some Spanish   FAX 970-249-2802

LOCATION	From Highway 50, turn south on Alpine Plateau Forest Access Road and travel 5.5 miles to the inn.
OPEN	All year.
DESCRIPTION	A 1989 two-story contemporary ranch-style inn with country and ranch furnishings.
NO. OF ROOMS	Twelve rooms with private bathrooms. The best room is the Honeymoon Suite.
RATES	Year-round rates are $85 for a single with a private bathroom and $95-125 for a double with a private bathroom. There is no minimum stay and cancellation requires seven days' notice.
CREDIT CARDS	American Express, Discover, MasterCard, Visa
BREAKFAST	Full "hearty!" breakfast served in the dining room. Lunch, dinner and special meals are also available.
AMENITIES	Hot tub on deck, fireplaces in all rooms, horseback riding, snowmobiling, mountain biking, cross-country skiing, hiking, fishing, meeting facilities. Common area with TV/VCR, fireplace and bar/lounge,
RESTRICTIONS	No smoking except in designated areas, no pets. Children are welcome, "but we request that their parents supervise them"...a truly novel concept...CH
RATED	AAA 3 Diamonds

COALMONT

A little hideaway 45 miles northeast of Steamboat Springs and south of Walden. The southern jumping off place for Delany Butte Lakes (BIg Fish!), north Platte and North Forks Rivers and various creeks.

SHAMROCK RANCH

4363 County Road 11, Coalmont, CO 80430   970-723-8413
Bruce & Cindy Wilson, Resident Owners   FAX 970-723-8413

LOCATION	Highway 14 north from Highway 40, 16 miles to County Road 28, right on County Road 28. Go one mile and take a right fork onto a gravel road. The sign for the ranch is 4.5 miles on the left.
OPEN	Memorial Day through September 30.
DESCRIPTION	A 1934 rustic lodge inn with cabins on 400 acres. Western furnishings.
NO. OF ROOMS	Two rooms with private bathrooms and two rooms share one bathroom. Try the Corner Room.
RATES	Seasonal rates are $80 for a single or double with a private bathroom and $250 for a cabin. There is no minimum stay and there is a reservation/cancellation policy.
CREDIT CARDS	Visa
BREAKFAST	Full breakfast is served in the dining room with a variety of egg dishes, meats and baked goods. Dinner is also included in the rates.
AMENITIES	Private trophy trout fishing on property, hot tub, beverages and hors d'oeuvres, large rock fireplace, wet bar, refigerator, managerie of domestic pets, horseback riding.
RESTRICTIONS	No pets. Are you ready for this? Brenda and Peaches are the dogs; Muffy, Oreo and Frisky are the cats; Big Jake, Sunny and Nelson are the horses; and Folger is the rabbit. There is also a pig, lambs and chickens..."They all think they are dogs, i.e., they follow you around and like to be petted." I am not making any of this up...TI
MEMBER	Professional Association of Innkeepers International, Colorado Hotel and Lodging Association.

COLORADO SPRINGS

Purple mountain majesties start here at the base of Pikes Peak. The state's second largest city is a major tourist, sports, military and industrial center. Things not to miss: the Olympic Training Center, U.S. Air Force Academy, and the Cheyenne Mountain Zoo. Major summer events: Race-car drivers take to the clouds in the grueling Pikes Peak Hill Climb in July; Pikes Peak or Bust Rodeo in August; Hot Air Balloon Classic in September and competitive track cycling events at the 7-11 Velodrome. Handy to the Larkspur Renaissance Festival in June-July. From Denver, 65 miles south on I-25.

ALPINE CHALET COUNTRY INN B&B

11685 Howells Road, Colorado Springs, CO 80908   *719-495-9266*
Joseph & Eveline Kelly, Resident Owners   *FAX 719-495-3182*

KUDOS/COMMENTS   "Everything was lovely and perfect; and the breakfasts...ahhh, the breakfasts, outstanding!" (1996)

AWARENEST VICTORIAN B&B

1218 West Pikes Peak Avenue, Colorado Springs, CO 80904 719-630-8241
Rex & Karla Hefferan, Resident Owners

KUDOS/COMMENTS   "The perfect spot for a secluded getaway. Only one room but Karla dotes on her guests." ... "Charming, comfortable parlor and beautiful dining room with stained glass." (1996)

BLACK FOREST BED & BREAKFAST

11170 Black Forest Road, Colorado Springs, CO 80908   719-495-4208
Robert & Susan Putnam, Resident Owners   800-809-9901
"Survival" Spanish spoken.   FAX 719-495-0688

LOCATION	From I-25 take Woodman exit 149 east six miles to Black Forest Road, turn left and go three miles north to Baptist church, 1/4 mile further north look for an orange mailbox and turn left there, go up the drive for another 1/4 mile.
OPEN	All year.
DESCRIPTION	A 1984 two-story Log Gambrel on 20 acres of pines. The furnishings are rustic and country with homemade accessories.
NO. OF ROOMS	Four rooms with private bathrooms. Susan suggests The Haven.
RATES	Year-round rates are $75-100 for a single or double with a private bathroom and $125-150 for a suite or guesthouse. Cancellation requires seven days' notice.
CREDIT CARDS	American Express, Discover, MasterCard, Visa
BREAKFAST	Continental Plus is served in the guestrooms.
AMENITIES	Greenhouse with indoor lap pool, sauna and fireplaces, tub for two, kitchens, TV/VCR, telephone, and wheelchair accessible.
RESTRICTIONS	No smoking, no pets. The resident dog is a Goldie called Honey and the cat goes by Little Orphan Andy.
MEMBER	Bed & Breakfast Innkeepers of Colorado

CHEYENNE CAÑON INN

2030 West Cheyenne Road, Colorado Springs, CO 80906   719-633-1348
John, Barbara & Josh Starr, Resident Owners   800-633-0625
French spoken.

LOCATION	From I-25, take exit 141 and go west on Highway 24 about one mile to 21st Street. Left on 21st to Cheyenne Boulevard, right on Cheyenne to last house. The driveway to parking is 140 yards beyond the inn.
OPEN	All year.
DESCRIPTION	A 1921 two-story Mission-style mansion with arts & crafts and eclectic furnishings. The inn has 13,000 square feet and each room is decorated from a different region of the world.
NO. OF ROOMS	Eight rooms with private bathrooms. Your hosts recommend the Le Petit Chateau.

Cheyenne Cañon Inn, Colorado Springs

RATES	Year-round rates are $65-175 for a single or double with a private bathroom, a suite is $110-175 and the guesthouse is $150-175. A multi-night stay is required on holidays and many Saturdays. Cancellation requires five days' notice.
CREDIT CARDS	American Express, Discover, MasterCard, Visa
BREAKFAST	Full breakfast is served in the dining room. The menu changes daily and includes omelets, specialty quiches, malted waffles, baked fruit, orange cream French toast and crepes. Gourmet dinners are available by special arrangements
AMENITIES	Private hot tub (by reservation), Jacuzzis, antique soaking tubs, complimentary refreshments, bottomless cookie jar, well-stocked library, in-room phone, cable TV and modem jacks, historic tour and hiking.
RESTRICTIONS	No smoking, no pets, children over 12 are welcome. The resident cat, a native of Switzerland, goes by Pommes Frites and is not allowed in the B&B.
REVIEWED	*Recommended Country Inns, American Historic Inns, America's Great Little Hotels and Guesthouses*
MEMBER	Bed & Breakfast Innkeepers of Colorado, American Bed & Breakfast Association
RATED	ABBA AAA+
KUDOS/COMMENTS	"Most striking location, great house with important history and unique decor" ... "Spectacular mansion with 'theme' rooms." ... "Very spacious, well appointed rooms. Great location." (1996) "Unbelievable, breathtaking location; huge rooms, historic setting; A real gem." (1997)

Dogs' Best Friend Bed & Breakfast

7305 Maine Lane, Colorado Springs, CO 80922   719-495-2983
Bill Fuqua, Resident Owner
Dog spoken.

LOCATION	From I-25, go east on Woodman Road for approximately six miles and turn south onto Maine Lane, go one block to the B&B on left.
OPEN	All year.
DESCRIPTION	A 1990 country inn dog house with a "clean & comfortable" interior.
NO. OF ROOMS	Forty units with private baths, heating and air conditioning
RATES	Year-round rates are $9-11 for a single with private bath. There is a three-day cancellation policy.
CREDIT CARDS	No
BREAKFAST	Full lamb and rice breakfast served.
AMENITIES	Large open outside play areas for social gatherings, organized sports. Private in-home lessons, pre-puppy consultations.
RESTRICTIONS	No smoking, proof of current innoculations must be on file.
REVIEWED	*The Best Dog B&Bs in the World, Dog B&Bs USA and Canada.*
RATED	AAA 3 bowls

The Hearthstone Inn

506 North Cascade Avenue, Colorado Springs, CO 80903   719-473-4413
Dot Williams and Ruth Williams, Owners   800-521-1885
                                                    FAX 719-473-1322

LOCATION	On the corner of Cascade and St. Vrain, four blocks from downtown.
OPEN	All year.
DESCRIPTION	Two three-story 1885/1900 Victorian inns on both the National and State Historic Registers. Victorian furnishings.
NO. OF ROOMS	Twenty-three rooms with private bathrooms and two rooms share one bathroom. The best room is called Fireside.
RATES	Year-round rates are $68-138 for a single with private bathroom, $78-148 for a double with private bathroom, $62-68 for a single or double with shared bathroom and $135-148 for a suite. There is a two-night minimum stay on Memorial Day, Labor Day and college graduation. There is a reservation/cancellation policy.

CREDIT CARDS	American Express, MasterCard, Visa
BREAKFAST	Full breakfast, served in the dining room, includes a unique egg entree, homemade bread, fresh fruit and beverages. Luncheons prepared for groups with reservations.
AMENITIES	Some rooms have fireplaces and private porches. Early traveler breakfast, conference space for 48, one room is wheelchair accessible.
RESTRICTIONS	No smoking, no pets. Watch out for the local resident squirrel, Jaws.
REVIEWED	*Country Inns & Backroads, Recommended Country Inns of the Rocky Mountain Region,*
MEMBER	Independent Innkeepers Association, Professional Association of Innkeepers International, Distinctive Inns of Colorado, Association of Historic Hotels-West, Colorado Hotel and Lodging Association
RATED	AAA 3 Diamonds, Mobil 3 Stars
KUDOS/COMMENTS	"Dot and Ruth have been in business for 20 years and have perfected the 'art' of innkeeping better than anyone else I know." ... "Wonderful antiques, located on one of the most beautiful streets in Colorado Springs." ... "Delightful food." ... "The Hearthstone Inn was the inspiration for the decor, hospitality, etc. of our inn." ... "Great breakfasts and impeccable housekeeping." (1997)

HOLDEN HOUSE 1902 BED & BREAKFAST INN

1102 West Pikes Peak Avenue, Colorado Springs, CO 80904   719-471-3980
Sallie & Welling Clark, Resident Owners

LOCATION	One mile west of downtown. From I-25 take exit 141 (Highway 24) go west, then right on 8th Street, left on West Colorado, right on 11th and down one block.
OPEN	All year.
DESCRIPTION	A 1902 two-story Victorian Colonial Revival and carriage house with antique and heirloom furnishings.
NO. OF ROOMS	Five suites with private bathrooms. Sallie suggests the Independence Suite.
RATES	Year-round rates are $105-120 for a single or double with private bathroom and $105-115 for a suite. There is a minimum stay of two to three nights on holidays, weekends, special events and during high season from May through October. Cancellation requires eight days' notice and 30 days' for holidays and special events and a $15 fee.
CREDIT CARDS	American Express, Carte Blanche, Diners Club, Discover, MasterCard, Visa

Holden House 1902 Bed & Breakfast Inn, Colorado Springs

BREAKFAST	Full breakfast, served in the dining room, includes fresh fruit with yogurt sauce, fresh-baked muffins (blueberry/corn, oatmeal/raspberry), main entree such as southwestern eggs fiesta, ruffled crepes Isabel, juice and coffee or tea. Romance package available for selected suites includes breakfast in bed.
AMENITIES	Honeymoon suites with fireplaces and tubs for two, telephones, TV in the parlor, guest refrigerator, 24-hour coffee/tea service, fresh-baked cookies, turndown service, FAX and copier available, air conditioning in summer and one suite with limited handicapped access.
RESTRICTIONS	No smoking, no pets. The inn is "unsuitable for children." The two resident cats, Muffin and Mingtoy, "have been featured in *Cats* magazine."
REVIEWED	*America's Wonderful Little Hotels & Inns, Recommended Country Inns of the Rocky Mountain Region, Best Places to Stay in the West, The Colorado Guide, Romantic Inns of the Rocky Mountains, Fodor's, Frommer's Denver, Boulder & Colorado Springs*
MEMBER	Bed & Breakfast Innkeepers of Colorado, Professional Association of Innkeepers International, Colorado Hotel and Lodging Association.
RATED	AAA 3 Diamonds, Mobil 3 Stars
AWARDS	*Country Inns* magazine, 1993 Best Inn Buys
KUDOS/COMMENTS	"They have the best bed & breakfast inn in the entire state." (1994)

Hughes Hacienda B&B

12060 Calle Corvo, Colorado Springs, CO 80926   719-576-2060
Wayne Hughes, Resident Owner

KUDOS/COMMENTS   "A unique one-bedroom B&B in a truly spectacular spot,
                  exceptional host and food." ... "Great breakfast spot." (1996)

Our Hearts Inn Old Colorado City

2215 West Colorado Avenue, Colorado Springs, CO 80904   719-473-8684
Andy & Pat Fejedelem, Resident Owners   800-533-7095

LOCATION	Highway 24 to 21st Street, go north three blocks to Colorado Avenue and turn left or west.
OPEN	All year.
DESCRIPTION	An 1895 two-story Victorian with hand-stenciled interior, curved vaulted ceilings and antique furnishings.
NO. OF ROOMS	Four rooms with private bathrooms. "Hearts Out West" is the owner's favorite. It's a cottage.
RATES	Year-round rates are $80-110 for a single or double with private bathroom. The cottage is $110. Off season (winter) rates are discounted 10%. Seniors receive a year-round 10% discount.
CREDIT CARDS	American Express, Diners Club, Discover, MasterCard, Visa
BREAKFAST	Full breakfast, served in the dining room, includes entree, sweet muffins, home-baked bread and beverages.
AMENITIES	Flowers, robes, cookies always available, Jacuzzi and fireplace in cottage, two units are air conditioned.
RESTRICTIONS	No smoking, no pets.
MEMBER	Bed & Breakfast Innkeepers of Colorado
KUDOS/COMMENTS	"Quaint country decor, homey, hand stenciling adds a personal touch." (1996) "Beautiful French garden, friendly atmosphere, good breakfast." (1997)

THE PAINTED LADY BED & BREAKFAST INN

1318 West Colorado Avenue, Colorado Springs, CO 80904   719-473-3165
Valerie & Zan Maslowski, Resident Owners   *800-370-3165*
Limited Spanish spoken.   *FAX 719-635-1396*

LOCATION	From Highway 24 westbound take the first right on 8th Street, turn left on West Colorado Avenue and go five blocks. The inn is on the north side of the street.
OPEN	All year.
DESCRIPTION	An 1894 three-story gingerbread Victorian with renovated Victorian furnishings and wraparound porch.
NO. OF ROOMS	Two guestrooms and two suites with private bathrooms. The best room: Laura Belle suite.
RATES	Year-round rates are $75-125 for a single or double with private bathroom. There is a minimum stay during holidays, special events and summer. There is an eight-day cancellation policy, increased to 30 days during holidays and special events.
CREDIT CARDS	American Express, Discover, MasterCard, Visa
BREAKFAST	Full breakfast, served in the dining room, includes hot entree, muffins or breads, fruit and beverages.
AMENITIES	Private outdoor hot tub and deck, coffee and tea service all day long, cookies and other snacks in the parlor, cool drinks in the summer.
RESTRICTIONS	No smoking, no pets, children over four are welcome. Zandra the cat is "as much a partner in the innkeeping business as the owner...a true silent partner."
MEMBER	Bed & Breakfast Innkeepers of Colorado

ROOM AT THE INN BED & BREAKFAST

618 North Nevada Avenue, Colorado Springs, CO 80903   719-442-1896
Jan & Chick McCormick, Resident Owners   *800-579-4621*
*   FAX 719-442-6802*

LOCATION	Half mile north of downtown and 1/2 mile east and south of the Uintah Street exit (#143) off I-25.
OPEN	All year.
DESCRIPTION	An 1896 three-story Queen Anne with a wraparound porch and cottage in back. The furnishings are turn-of-the-century antiques.
NO. OF ROOMS	Seven rooms with private bathrooms. The owners recommend the Banker's Room.

Room at the Inn Bed & Breakfast, Colorado Springs

RATES	High season, May through September, rates are $85-125 for a single or double with a private bathroom. Off season, October through April, rates are $70-115 for a single or double with a private bathroom. There is a minimum stay during high season and cancellation requires 14 days' notice.
CREDIT CARDS	American Express, Diners Club, Discover, MasterCard, Visa
BREAKFAST	Full breakfast, served in the dining room or on the veranda during the summer, includes fresh-squeezed orange juice, fresh fruit (often baked or broiled), muffins, bread, hot entree and homemade granola.
AMENITIES	Hot tub on the deck, air conditioning, fresh-cut flowers, robes, afternoon tea, baked goodies, chocolate coins, designer linens, romance packages, FAX, handicapped accessible room.
RESTRICTIONS	No smoking, no pets, children over 12 are welcome.
REVIEWED	*Recommended Country Inns of the Rocky Mountain Region*
MEMBER	Bed & Breakfast Innkeepers of Colorado, Professional Association of Innkeepers International, American Bed & Breakfast Association, Colorado Hotel and Lodging Association
RATED	Mobil 3 Stars
KUDOS/COMMENTS	"Wonderful Victorian, great antiques, great location; Romantic." (1997)

TWILIGHT CANYON INN

2275 Twilight Canyon Road, Colorado Springs, CO 80926   719-576-7707
                                                           800-355-7707

KUDOS/COMMENTS   "A showplace." ... "Outstanding furnishings and grounds,
                 innkeepers are very personable and very attentive to detail." ...
                 "Great location." ... "The most elegant B&B in Colorado Springs.
                 Excellent hosts." (1996)

VALLEY VIEW HOMESTAY BED & BREAKFAST

2839 Valley Hi Avenue, Colorado Springs, CO 80910   719-635-2859
Norm & Norma Merritt, Resident Innkeepers   FAX 719-635-2859

LOCATION   From Interstate 25 (exit 138), turn left onto Circle Drive and drive
                  northeast to Airport Road, turn right (east) for a short block to
                  Valley Hi Avenue and take a right.

OPEN   April 15 through November 15.

DESCRIPTION   A 1960s ranch-style home with contemporary furnishings.

NO. OF ROOMS   One room with a private bathroom and two rooms share one
                  bathroom. The King Suite is the best room.

RATES   Seasonal rates are $85 for a single or double with private bathroom
                  and $65-75 for a single or double with a shared bathroom. There is
                  a bunkhouse for kids (four bunks renting for $20 each). There is a
                  cancellation policy.

CREDIT CARDS   No

BREAKFAST   Full "western gourmet" breakfast is served in the dining room "to
                  meet your schedule."

AMENITIES   Balcony overlooking the 9th green of the golf course, croquet,
                  swing set and toy room for children, wine and hors d'oeuvres on
                  arrival.

RESTRICTIONS   No smoking, no pets. Children of all ages are welcome.

WEDGEWOOD COTTAGE BED & BREAKFAST INN

1111 West Pikes Peak Avenue, Colorado Springs, CO 80904   719-636-1829
Shannon & Karen Jones, Resident Owners

LOCATION	Take Highway 24 westbound, exit at 8th Street, turn left on West Colorado Avenue, go 2-1/2 blocks to 11th Street, turn right, continue down one block, turn left at West Pikes Peak Avenue.
OPEN	All year.
DESCRIPTION	An 1899 Victorian cottage with antique furnishings.
NO. OF ROOMS	One two-room luxury suite with private bathroom.
RATES	Year-round rates are $110.00 for a single or a double. There is a minimum stay on weekends and May through September.
CREDIT CARDS	MasterCard, Visa
BREAKFAST	Full breakfast, served in the guestroom, includes a "gourmet main course," fresh fruit, muffins and beverages.
AMENITIES	Fireplaces, Jacuzzi tub for two, cable TV, self-serve coffee and tea, stereo and refrigerator in room.
RESTRICTIONS	No smoking, no pets, no children.
KUDOS/COMMENTS	"Very homey; Great food!" (1996)

COMO

Railroad buffs will love this place, a partial ghost town of the 1870s railraod era. Much of its colorful past can still be sampled at the Old Como Eatery, Como Mercantile and restored Como Depot. And a rare, historic roundhouse still stands here. In the South Park Valley, 75 miles southwest of Denver and 25 miles northeast of Fairplay on Highway 285.

COMO DEPOT

PO Box 110, Como, CO 80432   *719-836-2594*
Keith & Jo Hodges, Resident Owners

LOCATION	Nine miles north of Fairplay, 1/4 mile west of Highway 285.
OPEN	March through December
DESCRIPTION	A restored 1898 railroad depot with restaurant and eclectic furnishings. On the National Historic Register.
NO. OF ROOMS	Four rooms share one bathroom.
RATES	Seasonal rates are $25 for a single with shared bathroom and $45 for a double with shared bathroom.
CREDIT CARDS	No
BREAKFAST	Full breakfast is served in the dining room. Other meals available in the restaurant.
AMENITIES	One room with fireplace, clawfoot bathtub in bathroom.
RESTRICTIONS	No pets.
REVIEWED	*The Colorado Guide*

CORTEZ

Just to the west of Mesa Verde National Park, the heart of the Anasazi ruins.
From Durango, 45 miles west on Highway 160.

A BED & BREAKFAST ON MAPLE STREET

102 South Maple Street, Cortez, CO 81321 970-565-3906
Roy & Nonnie Fahsholtz, Resident Owners 800-665-3906

LOCATION	Take Highway 160 (main street) into downtown Cortez, turn south on South Maple and go one block.
OPEN	All year.
DESCRIPTION	A two-story log and rock home on a large fenced yard with country furnishings.
NO. OF ROOMS	Four rooms with private bathrooms.
RATES	Year-round rates for a single or double with a private bathroom are $59-79. There is no minimum stay and cancellation requires seven days' notice.
CREDIT CARDS	MasterCard, Visa
BREAKFAST	Full breakfast is served in the dining room and includes fresh fruit, blueberry upside-down pancakes with almond and whip topping, hot maple syrup, bacon, cold cereal, yogurt, juice, coffee and hot tea. Sack lunches are available.
AMENITIES	Gazebo-enclosed hot tub, evening refreshments, homemade cookies, games to play, air conditioning, rose garden and piano.
RESTRICTIONS	No smoking, no pets.
MEMBER	Professional Association of Innkeepers International, Bed & Breakfast Innkeepers of Colorado
KUDOS/COMMENTS	"Very comfortable, excellent hosts." (1996)

GRIZZLY ROADHOUSE BED & BREAKFAST

3450 Highway 160, Cortez, CO 81321 970-565-7738
Michelle Boyer, Resident Owner 800-330-7286

KUDOS/COMMENTS	"Great food! Tops in cleanliness." (1996)

KELLEY PLACE

14663 County Road G, Cortez, CO 81321 970-565-3125
Rodney & Kristie Carriker, Resident Owners 800-745-4885

CRAWFORD

BECKER RANCH BED & BREAKFAST

3798 Highway 92, Crawford, CO 81415   970-921-6877
JoAnne Becker, Resident Owner

BLACK CANYON RANCH

B-76 Road, Crawford, CO 81415   970-921-4252
Dennis Grieve, Resident Owner

SLEEPING INDIAN MOUNTAIN LODGE

80082 Highway 92, Crawford, CO 81415   970-921-7378
Joanna Rodden, Resident Owner

VAN ENGEN HOUSE BED & BREAKFAST

345 Cedar Avenue, Crawford, CO 81415   970-921-6177
Grace Nugent, Resident Owner   FAX 970-921-6177

CREEDE

An 1892 mining boom built this town from scratch. The last mine closure was in
1985. Events of note include the "Taste of Creede" over Memorial Day weekend,
the Creede Repetory Theater, "Days of '92" celebration over July 4th weekend.
Check out the underground mining museum and underground firestation.

CREEDE HOTEL

120 North Main Street, Creede, CO 81130   719-658-2608
Cathy & Rich Ormsby, Resident Owners   FAX 719-658-2608
Some Spanish spoken.

LOCATION   Take Highway 149 to Creede (22 miles north of South Fork). Jog
                  left (west) to Main Street. The hotel is ½ mile up on the right next
                  to the Creede Repertory theater.

Creede Hotel, Creede

OPEN	March through November, limited rooms available December through April.
DESCRIPTION	An 1892 two-story mining-town hotel with "old hotel" furnishings and a full service restaurant.
NO. OF ROOMS	Seven rooms with private bathrooms. The best room is #4, "unless you don't mind the noise of Main Street, then choose #3."
RATES	High season (Memorial Day through September) rates are $59-79 for a single or double with private bathroom. Low season rates are $35-69 for a single or double with private bathroom. There is no minimum stay and cancellation requires seven days' notice plus $15 charge.
CREDIT CARDS	American Express, Discover, MasterCard, Visa
BREAKFAST	Full breakfast, served in the dining room, varies depending on whether hotel restaurant is serving breakfast. If it is open, choose anything off the menu, like salsa eggs, hot grains and fruit, scones and beverages. Lunch, dinner and special meals are also available.
AMENITIES	Cross-country ski guides, great restaurant, "unspoiled" mining town, room for small meetings, some rooms handicapped accessible, bike boarding.
RESTRICTIONS	No smoking inside, no pets during high season, children of all ages are welcome. The resident Siamese cat is called Beer Can. The Golden is called Bear.
REVIEWED	*The Colorado Guide, Recommended Country Inns, Colorado Restaurants and Recipes, Non-Smokers Guide to American & Canadian Bed & Breakfasts.*

THE OLD FIREHOUSE NO. 1

Creede Avenue, Creede, CO 81130   719-658-0212
R. Katherine Brennand, Resident Owner
Spanish and French spoken.

LOCATION	Across from the Creede Repertory Theatre on Main Street. "Since Main Street is only two blocks long, it is very easy to find anything in Creede."
OPEN	All year.
DESCRIPTION	An 1892 two-story renovated western Victorian firehouse with Victorian furnishings and a main floor ice-cream parlor and restaurant.
NO. OF ROOMS	Four rooms with private baths. Katherine Brennand recommends room #5...which confused us a tad bit, but she'll explain when you get there...TI
RATES	Summer rates are $65-70 for a single or double with a private bathroom and $125 for the two bedroom suite. Winter rates are $10 less. There is no minimum stay and cancellation requires seven days' notice.
CREDIT CARDS	Discover, MasterCard, Visa
BREAKFAST	Continental breakfast is served in the dining room.
AMENITIES	Ice-cream parlor, gift shop, library and games for children.
RESTRICTIONS	No smoking except on the outside balcony, no pets. Children are welcome.

CRESTED BUTTE

Crested Butte features historic Elk Avenue with original buildings dating to 1860, Wildflower Festival, Mountain Biking Festival, Aerial Weekend, Arts Festival.

THE CLAIM JUMPER B&B & CATERING CO.

704 Whiterock Avenue, PO Box 1181,   970-349-6471
Crested Butte, CO 81224
Jerry & Robbie Bigelow, Resident Owners

LOCATION	As you enter town, a carved wooden sign says, "Welcome to Crested Butte." Turn right at the sign and go two blocks, we are on the right across from the town park.
OPEN	All year.
DESCRIPTION	This rebuilt historic log home is on the National and Colorado Historic Registers and features six theme rooms, each with its own unique collection of antiques, heirlooms and treasures.
NO. OF ROOMS	Six rooms with private baths.
RATES	High season rates (November 15 to April 15 and June 15 to October 15) are $89-129. Off season rates are $69-89 for a double. There is a minimum stay during high season and cancellation requires 30 days' notice.
CREDIT CARDS	Discover, MasterCard, Visa
BREAKFAST	Hearty gourmet breakfast, served in the dining room, includes homemade buckwheat waffles, sausages, breads, fruits, stuffed pastries with eggs and feta. Special meals are available.
AMENITIES	European sauna with pine water, antique game room, book and classic movie library and glassed-in hot tub, TV/VCR in rooms, telephone, and special location wedding ceremonies performed by Reverend Jerry Bigelow.
RESTRICTIONS	No smoking, Children over the age of 12 are welcome. Otis, the resident Newfoundland, is large and loveable and may join guests on outdoor activities.
REVIEWED	*America's Small Inns, The Colorado Guide*
MEMBER	Bed & Breakfast Innkeepers of Colorado
KUDOS/COMMENTS	"More 'stuff' than the Smithsonian."... "An incredible experience! Very warm welcome and service"... "Jerry does a great narrative breakfast." ... "The decorations are really fun." ... "Words can't describe it." (1996)

CRISTIANA GUESTHAUS BED & BREAKFAST

621 Maroon Avenue, PO Box 427, Crested Butte, CO 81224   970-349-5326
Rosie & Martin Catmur, Resident Owners   800-824-7899
Some Spanish spoken.   FAX 970-349-1962

LOCATION	Half block east of Highway 135, one block north of Elk Avenue.
OPEN	Open all year except for mid-April to mid-May and late-October to mid-November.
DESCRIPTION	A 1962 two-story alpine lodge with country furnishings.
NO. OF ROOMS	Twenty-one rooms with private bathrooms. Ask for room 16.
RATES	Winter season rates, November through April, are $67-89 for a single or double with a private bathroom. Off season rates, May through October, are $56-66 for a single or double with a private bathroom. There is a minimum stay for some holidays and weekends and special events. Cancellation in the winter requires 45 days' notice; in summer, by noon of the day of arrival.
CREDIT CARDS	American Express, Discover, MasterCard, Visa
BREAKFAST	Continental Plus, served fireside in the lobby, includes granola, fresh fruit, varying selection of fresh-baked pastries, choice of juices, teas, coffee, hot chocolate and spiced cider.
AMENITIES	Individually decorated rooms, comforters or quilts on the beds, outdoor hot tub, sauna, sundeck, TV and fireplace in lounge, and hot drinks available throughout the day.
RESTRICTIONS	No smoking, no pets. The resident cat is called Piglet.
REVIEWED	*The Colorado Guide, Colorado Handbook, Skiing America*

CRYSTAL INN BED & BREAKFAST

624 Gothic Avenue, PO Box 125, Crested Butte, CO 81224   970-349-1338
Dennis & Charlene Goree, Resident Owners   800-390-1338
FAX 970-349-1942

LOCATION	Go two blocks from the only four-way stop sign in town at the intersection of Elk and Gothic, turn right and go one-half block down Gothic Avenue.
OPEN	All year.
DESCRIPTION	A 1992 two-and-one-half-story cedar mountain home with mill work and country Victorian interior decor.
NO. OF ROOMS	Five rooms have private bathrooms.
RATES	Ski season rates are $79-99 for a single or double with private bathroom. Off season rates are $69-85 for a single or double with a private bath. The entire B&B can be reserved for $350-500. There is a minimum stay during holidays and some weekends and 30-day cancellation policy during ski season, 14 days in the summer.
CREDIT CARDS	American Express, Discover, MasterCard, Visa
BREAKFAST	Full breakfast, served in the dining room, includes fruit, juices, fresh breads, cereals, a meat dish and special entree of the day.
AMENITIES	Fresh-cut flowers, indoor hot tub, balconies and decks, magestic views, guest icebox, bar, cookies, apres ski, pinball game and two fireplaces.
RESTRICTIONS	No smoking, no pets
REVIEWED	*The Rocky Mountain News* travel section
MEMBER	Bed & Breakfast Innkeepers of Colorado, Crested Butte Bed & Breakfast Association.

Elizabeth Anne B&B

703 Maroon Avenue, PO Box 1051,   970-349-0147
Crested Butte, CO 81224   888-745-4620
Carl & Judy Jones, Resident Owners

LOCATION	As you enter town, take first right on 7th Avenue, drive to the intersection of 7th & Maroon. The inn is on the northeast corner.
OPEN	Open late-May through mid-October and mid-November through mid-April.
DESCRIPTION	A 1992 two-story Victorian with period furniture, wallpaper and accessories.
NO. OF ROOMS	Four rooms with private bathrooms. The T&K room is the best.
RATES	Winter rates, mid-November to mid-April, are $75-99 for a single or double with private bathroom. Summer rates, mid-May through mid-October, are $65-79 for a single or double with a private bathroom. There is a $15 per person additional charge for up to six people in the large room. There is a two-day minimum on weekends. 100% refund requires 30 days' notice, 21 days' gets you 75%, etc....dumb policy...TI
CREDIT CARDS	American Express, MasterCard, Visa
BREAKFAST	Full breakfast, served in the dining room, includes buttermilk waffles, stuffed French toast, blueberry pancakes, coffee, fruit juice and other offerings.
AMENITIES	TV in rooms, indoor hot tub, refreshments each afternoon, refrigerator, washer, dryer, ski and bike storage, and telephone in parlor.
RESTRICTIONS	No smoking, no pets, children are welcome in the T&K room only. The resident Australian Shepherd is called Jake.
REVIEWED	*Non-Smokers Guide to Bed & Breakfasts, America's Wonderful Little Hotels & Inns, Access Western US Ski Country*
MEMBER	Bed & Breakfast Innkeepers of Colorado

THE ELK MOUNTAIN LODGE

129 Gothic Avenue, PO Box 148, Crested Butte, CO 81224   970-349-7533
Jacob Hedberg, Resident Owner   800-374-6521
Swedish spoken.   FAX 970-349-5114

LOCATION	The corner of Second Street and Gothic Avenue, two blocks north of the Old Town Hall.
OPEN	All year.
DESCRIPTION	A 1919 three-story Victorian lodge (originally a miners' lodge) with traditional furnishings.
NO. OF ROOMS	Nineteen rooms with private bathrooms. Jocob thinks you will really like rooms 4 or 20.
RATES	Winter rates are $88-108 for a single or double with private bath and summer rates are $69-89 for a single or double with private bath. There is a minimum stay during winter and summer holidays and cancellation requires 30 days in winter and seven days in summer.
CREDIT CARDS	American Express, Discover, MasterCard, Visa
BREAKFAST	Full breakfast, served in dining room, features a home-cooked buffet with many southern and Swedish specialties.
AMENITIES	Telephones, cable TV, hot tub room, rustic bar and library for guests.
RESTRICTIONS	No smoking, no pets, children over 12 are welcome. The resident dog is a Border Collie.

The Gothic Inn, Crested Butte

THE GOTHIC INN

18 Gothic Avenue, PO Box 1488, Crested Butte, CO 81224   970-349-7215
Sonja Ruta, Resident Owner   FAX 970-349-7215
Czech-German spoken.

LOCATION	Four-tenths-of-a-mile from Elk Street ("main street") in the town of Crested Butte.
OPEN	From November 18 to April 10 and June 10 to September 27.
DESCRIPTION	A 1980 two-story mountain wood structure with European decoration, hand-painted furniture, and cathedral ceiling.
NO. OF ROOMS	Three rooms with private bathrooms and two rooms with shared bathroom. Sonja Ruta recommends the Mon Cheri suite.
RATES	Winter rates are $97-110 for a single or double with a private bathroom, $75-87 for a single or double with a shared bathroom, and $160 for a suite. Summer rates are $87-90 for a single or double with a private bathroom, $65-77 for a single or double with a shared bathroom, and $120 for a suite. In the winter there is a three-night minimum stay and cancellation requires 21 days' notice, in the summer there is no minimum stay and cancellation requires seven days' notice.
CREDIT CARDS	MasterCard, Visa
BREAKFAST	Full breakfast, served in the dining room or in the suite, changes daily but includes entree (such as Florentine quiche), desert, juice, coffee and tea.
AMENITIES	Large, open patio in summer with garden furniture and flowers, chocolate on arrival, glassed-in veranda with panoramic view and spa.
RESTRICTIONS	No smoking, no pets, children over the age of 13 are welcome.
MEMBER	Crested Butte Bed & Breakfast Association, Crested Butte Mountain Association

INN AT CRESTED BUTTE

510 White Rock Avenue, PO Box 2619,   970-349-1225
Crested Butte, CO 81224   800-949-4828
M. Claybaugh, Resident Owner   FAX 970-349-1825

THE LAST RESORT

213 Third Street, PO Box 722, Crested Butte, CO 81224   970-349-0445
Rita Wengrin, Resident Owner   800-349-0445
French and Spanish spoken.

LOCATION	Entering Crested Butte, turn left onto Elk Avenue (main street), take a right at Third Street, the road dead ends at the inn.
OPEN	All year.
DESCRIPTION	Begun in 1887 and finished in 1991, a two-story contemporary log cabin with dark woods and overstuffed furniture.
NO. OF ROOMS	Seven rooms with private bathrooms. The best room is the Miner's Cabin.
RATES	High season (every month except May, June and October) rates are $85-95 for a single or double with private bathroom. Low season (May, June and October) rates are $50-70 for a single or double with a private bathroom. There is no minimum stay and a 30-day cancellation policy.
CREDIT CARDS	MasterCard, Visa
BREAKFAST	"Hearty, all-you-can-eat" breakfast is served "any time you want it" in the dining room.
AMENITIES	Steam room, two solariums, private Jacuzzis in rooms, coffee delivered to rooms in the morning, robes, limited access to kitchen, guided cross-country and hiking at no cost.
RESTRICTIONS	No smoking, no pets, children over 12 are welcome.
MEMBER	Crested Butte Bed & Breakfast Association
KUDOS/COMMENTS	"Great location and warm, casual atmosphere." (1996)

PURPLE MOUNTAIN

714 Gothic Avenue, PO Box 547, Crested Butte, CO 81224   970-349-5888
Paul & Marilyn Caldwell, Resident Owners   800-286-3574
                                                            970-349-7194

LOCATION	In the town of Crested Butte, two blocks north and 1.5 blocks east of the 4-way stop.
OPEN	All year.
DESCRIPTION	A 1927 two-story renovated miners' lodge with French country furnishings.
NO. OF ROOMS	Five rooms with private bathrooms.
RATES	Year-round rates for queen with a private bathroom are $88 and a double with a shared bathroom is $62-81. Weekends and holidays are about 10% higher. There is a minimum stay on holidays and cancellation requires 30 days' notice...dumb policy...TI, and a $15 fee.
CREDIT CARDS	Discover, MasterCard, Visa
BREAKFAST	Full gourmet breakfast, served in the dining room, includes fruit, homemade breads, meats, egg dishes, waffles and pancakes. "Nothing ordinary to be found."...how about ordinary coffee, black, no cream, no designer flavors, just plain old black coffee...rant, rant, rant...TI
AMENITIES	Thick robes, foot warmers, down comforters, sun room with a hot tub, fresh flowers in season, stone fireplace, apres ski is served year-round with hot appetizers daily.
RESTRICTIONS	No smoking, no pets.
MEMBER	Crested Butte Bed & Breakfast Association

CRESTONE

The Sangre de Cristo range towers over this tiny hamlet at the base of Crestone Peak and Crestone Needle. Technical climbers love this place and spelunkers will want to explore the seven limestone caves in Marble Mountain. From Alamosa, 40 miles north on Highway 17, turn east on County Road T for 12 miles.

SACRED EARTH BED & BREAKFAST

10 Baca Grant Way, PO Box 178, Crestone, CO 81131   719-256-4010
Patricia Pieropan, Resident Owner

LOCATION	Crestone is between Alamosa and Salida in southern Colorado. From Highway 17, turn onto Baca Grant Way in Moffat. Crestone is 15 miles from the Highway.
OPEN	All year.
DESCRIPTION	A 1976 three-story mountain host home with Egyptian, angel and country theme rooms.
NO. OF ROOMS	Three rooms share two bathrooms. Owner recommends the Egyptian Room.
RATES	Year-round rates are $30-40 for a single or double with a shared bathroom and continental breakfast. Rates with full breakfast are $5-10 more. The two first-floor rooms with kitchen rent for $90. There is no minimum stay and cancellation requires 48 hours' notice.
CREDIT CARDS	American Express, MasterCard, Visa
BREAKFAST	Continental breakfast is served in the kitchen and includes bagels, English muffins, bread or corn muffins and beverages.
AMENITIES	Private entrance, full kitchen.
RESTRICTIONS	No smoking, no pets, the resident cat is called Black Velvet.

SLICE OF HEAVEN BED & BREAKFAST

Carefree Way, PO Box 185, Crestone, CO 81131   719-256-4150
Lea Black, Resident Manager

CRIPPLE CREEK

It ain't what it used to be (or maybe it is). An historic Gold Rush boomtown is now booming with casinos. From Colorado Springs 40 miles west on Highway 24.

CHERUB HOUSE BED & BREAKFAST

415 Main, Cripple Creek, CO 80813   719-689-0526
Eyvonne, Resident Owner   800-679-7366

THE COZY CABIN

232 Thurlow, Cripple Creek, CO 80813   719-689-3351
Rita Mason, Resident Manager

LOCATION	Six blocks from downtown Cripple Creek.
OPEN	All year.
DESCRIPTION	Two log cabins, one built in 1930 (The Cozy Cabin) and the other in 1995 (The Cowboy Cabin), both with "wild west" decor.
NO. OF ROOMS	Two cabins with kitchens and private bathrooms.
RATES	Based on season, holidays, number of guests and duration of stay.
CREDIT CARDS	No
BREAKFAST	Both cabins have kitchens and cupboards stocked with breakfast goodies.
AMENITIES	Complimentary fruit and snacks, The Cozy Cabin has a fireplace, both cabins have phones, TVs and VCRs...to reinforce that authentic "wild west" feel...CH, irons and ironing boards.
RESTRICTIONS	None. Children are welcome.

GREYHOUND RANCH BED & BREAKFAST

401 South 2nd, Cripple Creek, CO 80813   719-689-2599
Barbara Wray, Resident Owner

Iron Gate Inn

204 North 2nd Street, Cripple Creek, CO 80813   719-689-3384
Arlia McManis, Innkeeper   800-315-3384

The Last Dollar Inn

315 East Carr, Cripple Creek, CO 80813   719-689-9113
Rick & Janice Wood, Resident Owners

Sarahouse at Cripple Creek

216 West Masonic Avenue, Cripple Creek, CO 80813   719-689-3384
Arlia McManis, Innkeeper   800-315-3384

Thurlow House Bed & Breakfast

319 Thurlow Avenue, Cripple Creek, CO 80813   719-689-3074
John & Jenny Lord, Resident Owners

Victorian Lady Bed & Breakfast

127 West Carr, Cripple Creek, CO 80813   719-689-2143
Jack & Lorene Weikert, Resident Managers

DEL NORTE

An agricultural treasure on the Rio Grande River, at the western edge of the San Luis Valley and bounded by the La Garita Mountains. Visit the Museum and Cultural Center for interesting exhibits and lectures, and don't miss a visit to the Monte Vista Wildlife Refuge and Crane Festival in mid-March. August offers up Mountainman Rendevous, Covered Wagon Days and Heritage Fair. From Alamosa, 31 miles west on Highways 285 and 160.

WILD IRIS INN AT LA GARITA CREEK RANCH

38145 Road E-39, Del Norte, CO 81132　　　　　　*719-754-2533*
Jeff & Liz Wilkin, Resident Owners　　　　　　*FAX 719-754-2533*

LOCATION
From Del Norte, take Highway 112 northeast for three miles to La Garita turnoff, then left for seven miles, then turn left at the ranch sign and go one mile.

OPEN
All year.

DESCRIPTION
A 1970s two-story contemporary log inn with a mixture of southwestern and country furnishings, on 155 acres along La Garita Creek.

NO. OF ROOMS
Six rooms with private bathrooms and eight rooms share five-and-a-half bathrooms. Try the Deluxe Cabin or the Family Cabin.

RATES
Year-round rates are $66 for a single with private bathroom, $76 for a double with private bathroom, $46 for a single with shared bathroom, $56 for a double with shared bathroom, $107 for a cabin and $849 for the entire B&B. There is a two-day minimum stay (cabins only) and cancellation requires 30 days' notice.

CREDIT CARDS
Discover, MasterCard, Visa

BREAKFAST
Full "delicious and healthy" breakfast, served in the dining room, includes huevos rancheros (a specialty), homemade muffins, rolls and beverages. Lunch, dinner and special meals available.

AMENITIES
Outdoor hot tub by the creek, tennis court, sauna, pool, volleyball, horseshoes, weekend wine and cheese welcome hour, fresh flowers, reading and TV rooms, piano and bar, moss-rock fireplace, secluded, facilities for retreats, family reunions, weddings.

RESTRICTIONS
No smoking in rooms, no pets. There are two ranch dogs (Grits and Dot), two cats named Bridget and Gidget and ducks and geese that are named (ready for this?), Henry, Iris, Duck, Daffy and Chuckles. "The ducks will eat out of your hand."

KUDOS/COMMENTS
"Wonderful location, lots of potential, a few minor things missing, but overall pleasant." (1995)

DELTA

An agricultural center for all the local orchards and ranchs. From Grand Junction, 61 miles southeast on Highway 50.

ESCALANTE RANCH BED & BREAKFAST

701 650 Road, Delta, CO 81416
Dick Miller, Resident Owner
Spanish spoken.

970-874-4121
800-426-2191
FAX 970-426-0366

LOCATION	Approximately 14 miles northwest of Delta. From Highway 50, turn south at Road 650 and go 3 miles to Escalante Canyon.
OPEN	All year.
DESCRIPTION	A working cattle ranch on 100,000 acres. The main ranch house is on the Gunnison River with contemporary western furnishings.
NO. OF ROOMS	Two rooms share one bathroom and there is a three bedroom suite. Remote cabins are also available. The best room is the Grand Mesa.
RATES	Year-round rates are $48 per person. There is no minimum stay and a reservation/cancellation policy.
CREDIT CARDS	MasterCard, Visa
BREAKFAST	Full breakfast is served in the dining room.
AMENITIES	Common room with TV/VCR, complete kitchen.
RESTRICTIONS	None. This is a working ranch with livestock and all sorts of wildlife including deer, bear, mountain lion and elk.
REVIEWED	Several books have been written about the ranch including "Red Hole in Time" and "Trails and Trials."
MEMBER	Colorado Hotel and Lodging Association

FAIRLAMB HOUSE BED & BREAKFAST

700 Leon Street, Delta, CO 81416
John Taylor & Elizabeth Thompson, Resident Owners

970-874-5158

DENVER

Colorado's capitol and mile high city with the flatlands to the east and mountains to the west is a major cosmopolitan, cultural, manufacturing, financial and transportation center (with the world's most unneed new airport). Outstanding oasis: City Park includes the terrific Denver Zoo, Gates Planetarium, and Museum of Natural History. And we have the Broncos and the Rockies.

CAPITOL HILL MANSION

1207 Pennsylvania, Denver, CO 80203
Kathy Robbins, Resident Owner
French spoken.

303-839-5221
800-839-9329
FAX 303-839-9046

LOCATION	Two blocks south of the State Capitol and two blocks east.
OPEN	All year.
DESCRIPTION	An 1891 three-story Victorian in the Richardsonian Romanesque style with hierlooms and contemporary furnishings, listed on the National Historic Register .
NO. OF ROOMS	Eight rooms with private bathrooms. Try the Gold Banner.
RATES	Year-round rates are $80-155 for a single with private bathroom, $90-165 for a double with private bathroom. There is no minimum stay and there is a three-day cancellation policy.
CREDIT CARDS	American Express, Discover, MasterCard, Visa
BREAKFAST	Full breakfast is served in the dining room or can be taken to the guest rooms.
AMENITIES	Some rooms with fireplaces, whirlpools and private balconies, other amenities include refrigerators, coffeemakers, hair dryers, cable TV, clock radios, private phones, complimentary beverages, air conditioning, off-street parking, original regional art.
RESTRICTIONS	No smoking, no pets.
RATED	AAA 3 Diamonds
AWARDS	American Bed & Breakfast Association's "Highest Award"

Castle Marne — A Luxury Urban Inn, Denver

CASTLE MARNE — A LUXURY URBAN INN

1572 Race Street, Denver, CO 80206   303-331-0621
Diane & Jim Peiker, Resident Owners   800-926-2763
Hungarian spoken.   303-331-0623

LOCATION	From the State Capitol go east 20 blocks on Colfax to Race Street. Turn right at Race Street and go one block north to Race and 16th Avenue.
OPEN	All year.
DESCRIPTION	An 1889 three-story Richardsonian Romanesque with Victorian furnishings. The Inn is on the National and State Historical Registers and is "the finest example of the work of America's most eclectic architect, William Lang."
NO. OF ROOMS	Nine rooms with private bathrooms. Pick the Presidential Suite...if Bubba isn't in town...TI
RATES	Year-round rates are $85-165 for a double with a private bathroom and $200 for a suite. There is no minimum stay. Reservations are recommended and cancellation requires 48 hours' notice.
CREDIT CARDS	American Express, Diners Club, Discover, MasterCard, Visa
BREAKFAST	Full breakfast, served in the dining room, includes homemade breads and muffins, juice, at least five different kinds of fruit, a hot entree that changes daily, "Marne blend" coffee and a variety of teas.

AMENITIES	Fresh flowers in the rooms in season, robes in some rooms, Jacuzzis in two rooms, hot tubs on private balconies of three rooms, telephones in all rooms, afternoon tea served daily in the parlor, game room with pool table and darts, guest office with computer and meeting facilities for up to 12, free parking.
RESTRICTIONS	No smoking, no pets, children over 10 are welcome.
REVIEWED	*Frommer's Denver, Boulder and Colorado Springs, The Colorado Guide*
MEMBER	Independent Innkeepers of America, Carter Collection of Inns, Distinctive Inns of Colorado, American Historic Hotels of the West, Bed & Breakfast Innkeepers of Colorado.
RATED	AAA 3 Diamonds, ABBA 3 Crowns, Mobil 3 Stars
AWARDS	*Country Inns* magazine, One of the Top 12 Inns in the US, 1994; Colorado State Historical Society, Stephen H. Hart Preservation Award
KUDOS/COMMENTS	"Elegant rooms, elegant breakfast, and friendly down-to-Earth innkeepers." ... "Castle Marne and the Peiker's are 11.5 on a scale of one to ten."... "Castle Marne is so exquisite you feel like a princess in a beautiful castle." (1994) "An impressive stone mansion in the Denver historical district near parks and museums." (1996)

The Christmas Tree Inn, Englewood

THE CHRISTMAS TREE INN

3530 West Edgemoore Place, Englewood, CO 80110   303-795-3333
Hal & Kathy Trout, Resident Owners

LOCATION	From Highway 285 go south on Sheridan Boulevard to west Quincy to Lowell and south one block.
OPEN	All year.
DESCRIPTION	A 1972 bi-level frame host home surrounded by a forest of pine trees.
NO. OF ROOMS	Two rooms share two bathrooms.
RATES	Year-round rates are $45 for a single with shared bathroom and $55 for a double with a shared bathroom. There is a reservation/cancellation policy.
CREDIT CARDS	No
BREAKFAST	Full breakfast is served in the country kitchen or sun porch.
AMENITIES	Robes, TV, library, wood-burning stove and complimentary refreshments.
RESTRICTIONS	No pets, no children, smoking allowed in certain areas. There are two resident Cockers, Daphne and Cornelious, and two "just cats" named Minerva and Remington.

FRANKLIN HOUSE B&B

1620 Franklin Street, Denver, CO 80218   303-331-9106
George & Sharon Bauer, Resident Owners   FAX 303-320-6555
German, Spanish and some French spoken.

LOCATION	One-and-a-half miles east of Denver and two blocks south of St. Joseph's Hospital.
OPEN	All year, closed Christmas.
DESCRIPTION	An 1890 three-story brick Queen Anne with antique furnishings and front porch.
NO. OF ROOMS	One with private bathroom, seven rooms share three bathrooms. The Bauer's favorite room is the Franklin Room.
RATES	Year-round rates of $40 for a single with bathroom and $45 for a double with bathroom. A single with shared bathroom is $25 and a double with shared bathroom is $30. There is no minimum stay, but there is a reservation/cancellation policy.
CREDIT CARDS	Discover, MasterCard, Visa
BREAKFAST	Full breakfast, served in the dining room, includes quiche, breads, pastry, fruit, juices, tea and coffee.
AMENITIES	Lounge with TV, books, brochures and restaurant menus, pay phone in the lobby. Back yard patio with umbrella tables.
RESTRICTIONS	No pets, children over 10 are welcome. There are three resident cats, Spiffer, S. Klause and Checkers...is there a speech that goes along with Checkers?...TI
KUDOS/COMMENTS	"Sharon and George Bauer were most gracious and hospitable and provided excellent service at all times. George was an excellent breakfast host, learning quickly what I enjoyed for breakfast and providing it." (1996)

HAUS BERLIN

1651 Emerson Street, Denver, CO 80218   303-837-9527
Christiana & Dennis Brown, Resident Owners   800-659-0253
German spoken.   FAX 303-837-9527

LOCATION	Nine blocks east of Broadway (downtown) on 17th Avenue and Emerson Street.
OPEN	All year.
DESCRIPTION	An 1892 three-story Victorian townhouse with mix of upscale European furnishings and antiques, listed on the National Historic Register.
NO. OF ROOMS	Four rooms with private bathrooms. The owners recommend #4, the third floor suite.
RATES	Year-round rates are $85-130 for a double with private bathroom. Cancellation requires seven days' notice.
CREDIT CARDS	American Express, Discover, MasterCard, Visa
BREAKFAST	Full breakfast is served in the dining room, suite or on the courtyard and includes fresh-squeezed orange juice, fruit plate and a choice of entrees such as wild mushroom quiche or German pancakes, plus fresh rolls, homemade scones and tarts, cold meats and cheeses.
AMENITIES	Flowers, TV, phones, FAX, complimentary beverages, air conditioning, ceiling fans, courtyard and fine cotton linens.
RESTRICTIONS	No smoking, no pets, no children. The resident cat is named Ophelia.
REVIEWED	*America's Wonderful Little Hotels & Inns, Recommended Country Inns of the Rocky Mountain Region, Non-Smokers Guide to Bed & Breakfasts, American Cities Bed & Breakfast Guide, Recommended Country Inns of the Rocky Mountain Region*
MEMBER	Bed & Breakfast Innkeepers of Colorado

HOLIDAY CHALET, A VICTORIAN HOTEL

1820 East Colfax Avenue, Denver, CO 80218   303-321-9975
Margot Hartmann, Resident Owner   800-626-4497
Some Spanish and German spoken.   FAX 303-377-6556

LOCATION	On the corner of Colfax Avenue and High Street, 18 blocks east of the State Capitol and two blocks from Cheesman Park.
OPEN	All year.
DESCRIPTION	A restored 1896 Queen-Anne brownstone, owned and operated by the same family for three generations, decorated with Victorian furnishing and family hierlooms.
NO. OF ROOMS	Ten suites/rooms have private bathrooms and kitchens.
RATES	Year-round rates are $54-82.50 for a single with private bathroom and $59-87.50 for a double with private bathroom. There is no minimum stay and cancellation requires 48 hours' notice.
CREDIT CARDS	American Express, Diners Club, Discover, MasterCard, Visa
BREAKFAST	Continental breakfast is served in the music room or brought in baskets to the guest rooms.
AMENITIES	TV, radio, grand piano and upright piano, phone, flowers or plants, courtyard with flowers, grills in the summer and small meeting space available with catered meals.
RESTRICTIONS	No smoking. The resident Schnauzer goes by Dixie.
REVIEWED	*The Colorado Guide*
MEMBER	Colorado Hotel and Lodging Association, Professional Association of Innkeepers International.
RATED	AAA 3 Diamonds

THE LUMBER BARON INN

2555 West 37th Avenue, Denver, CO 80211   303-477-8205
Maureen & Walter Keller, Resident Owners   800-697-6552

KUDOS/COMMENTS	"A magnificent restoration of a great old mansion. Immense third floor ballrooms and outside garden/yard for weddings and special events. The wallpapered ceilings and walls are unbelievable. Walter and Maureen are very nice people." (1997)

Merritt House Bed & Breakfast Inn, Denver

MERRITT HOUSE BED & BREAKFAST INN

941 East 17th Avenue, Denver, CO 80218   *303-861-5230*
Mary & Tom Touris, Resident Owners   *FAX 303-861-9009*

LOCATION	Downtown, eight blocks from the State Capitol.
OPEN	All year.
DESCRIPTION	An 1889 three-story Victorian on the National Historic Register.
NO. OF ROOMS	Ten rooms with private bathrooms.
RATES	Year-round rates are $85-95 for a single or double with a private bathroom and $100-115 for a single or double with a Jacuzzi.
CREDIT CARDS	American Express, Discover, MasterCard, Visa
BREAKFAST	Full breakfast is served in the dining room. Lunch, dinner available on request.
AMENITIES	Cable TV, honor bars, radio and phone in room, free parking available.
RESTRICTIONS	Smoking limited, no pets, children over 12 are welcome.
REVIEWED	1988 Colorado Preservation Award.

Queen Anne Bed & Breakfast Inn, Denver

QUEEN ANNE BED & BREAKFAST INN

2147-51 Tremont Place, Denver, CO 80205   303-296-6666
Tom King and Chris King, Resident Owners   800-432-4667
Some Spanish and French spoken.   FAX 303-296-2151

LOCATION	In downtown Denver on the east side. From I-25 take the Colfax exit east to Logan, turn left to 20th, then left to Tremont Place.
OPEN	All year.
DESCRIPTION	Two side-by-side 1879-1886 Queen Anne Victorians are furnished with comfortable, antique period pieces. Both buildings are listed on the National and State Historic Registers.
NO. OF ROOMS	Fourteen rooms with private baths. Tom King favors the Rooftop with its private deck and two person tub.
RATES	High season, May through October, rates for a single or double with a private bathroom are $85-145, suites are $145-165. Off season, November through April, rates are $10 less. There is no minimum stay except for some holiday weekends and cancellation requires 72 hours' notice.
CREDIT CARDS	American Express, Diners Club, Discover, Eurocard, MasterCard, Visa
BREAKFAST	A full breakfast is served from 7:15 to 9:30 a.m. in the dining room or in guest rooms and includes various hot entrees, all natural granola, croissants, fresh fruit, special coffee blends, breads and muffins.

AMENITIES	Fresh flowers, chamber music, special tubs in some rooms, free on- and off-site parking, air conditioning in the summer, Colorado wine and hors d'oeuvres 6:00 to 7:30 p.m., meeting room for up to 15, outdoor reception for up to 75, cable TV in some rooms, dedicated outgoing phone lines for modems, and concierge.
RESTRICTIONS	No smoking, no pets. Children over the age of 12 are welcome.
REVIEWED	"In all regional and national books that include Colorado"
MEMBER	Distinctive Inns of Colorado, Professional Association of Innkeepers International, National Tourist Home Association, Colorado Hotel & Motel Association
RATED	AAA 3 Diamonds, ABBA Excellent, Mobil 3 Stars
AWARDS	Since 1987, 32 awards for excellence.
KUDOS/COMMENTS	"Very accommodating innkeepers and staff, delightful social hour, wonderful breakfasts, everything business travelers could need at their fingertips." (1996)

VICTORIA OAKS INN

1575 Race Street, Denver, CO 80206　　　　　303-355-1818
Clyde & Ric Stephens, Resident Owners　　　　800-662-6257

LOCATION	One mile east of downtown Denver, just north of Colfax in Historic Capitol Hill District.
OPEN	All year.
DESCRIPTION	An 1897 three-story Denver Square with antique furnishings, hanging staircase, plaster decorated ceilings and leaded glass windows.
NO. OF ROOMS	Seven rooms with private bathrooms and two rooms share one bathroom.
RATES	Year-round rates are $75 for a single with private bathroom, $85 for a double with private bathroom, $50 for a single with shared bathroom and $60 for a double with shared bathroom. There is a seven-day cancellation policy.
CREDIT CARDS	American Express, Diners Club, Discover, MasterCard, Visa
BREAKFAST	Continental Plus is served in the dining room.
AMENITIES	Telephones/radios/TV in the rooms, two rooms with fireplaces, refreshments in the afternoon, concierge, meeting and special occasion facilities, kitchen and laundry privileges.
RESTRICTIONS	No pets, no children.
REVIEWED	*The Colorado Guide, Frommer's Denver, Boulder and Colorado Springs.*
RATED	Mobil 2 Stars

DILLON
(SUMMIT COUNTY)

A bustling year-round vacation destination on the shores of Lake Dillon Reservoir. This is a summer mecca for fishing and sailboats that try to stay upright in the wind that can come from anywhere. August is especially for Dillonfest and the Sailing Regatta; and nearby Montezuma Downs Horse Race (to see is to believe). From Denver, 70 miles west on I-70.

ANNABELLE'S B&B

276 Snowberry Way, Dillon, CO 80435   970-468-8667
Ann & Tim Mealey, Resident Owners   FAX 970-468-2476
French spoken.

LOCATION	From I-70 take the Dillon/Silverthorn exit and go toward Dillon. Turn right at Swan Mountain Road, second left on Cove Boulevard, first left on Summit Road; after the second stop sign turn left on Idylwild; at the top of the hill, turn left on Snowberry Lane.
OPEN	All year.
DESCRIPTION	A 1987 four-story contemporary mountain host home with eclectic country furnishings.
NO. OF ROOMS	One room with private bathroom and two rooms and a kitchen share one bathroom. Ann says pick Coyote.
RATES	Winter rates, November to April, are $80-90 for a single or double with a private bathroom, $60-80 for a single or double with a shared bathroom and $110 for a suite. The entire B&B rents for $180. Off season, April through November, rates are $10 less except for the entire B&B, which rents for $160. There is no minimum stay and cancellation requires 14 days' notice for a full refund.
CREDIT CARDS	MasterCard, Visa
BREAKFAST	Full breakfast is catered to individual guest's needs and may include Belgian waffles with strawberries, decadent French toast, cheese blintzes, quiches, cheese strata served with homemade breads, fresh fruit and cappuccino. Sack lunches are made upon request.
AMENITIES	Hot tub, swimming and sauna facility nearby, babysitting, daily maid service, TV/VCR in each room, bathrobes and phone in room, wine and snacks.
RESTRICTIONS	No smoking, sometimes we take small pets. Children of any age are welcome, encouraged even. The resident pets are a cat called Orangey and a Golden Retriever mix called Elmo.
MEMBER	Summit County Bed & Breakfast Association

GORE RANGE BED & BREAKFAST

396 Tanglewood Lane, Dillon, CO 80498   970-468-5786
Jim & Edna Parham, Resident Owners

LOCATION	Two blocks north of I-70 exit on Ptarmigan Mountain.
OPEN	All year.
DESCRIPTION	A 1973 contemporary two-story cedar with contemporary furnishings.
NO. OF ROOMS	One room with private bathroom and two rooms share a bathroom.
RATES	Year-round rates are $40-70 for a single or double with private bathroom, $35-70 for a single or double with shared bathroom. There is a reservation/cancellation policy.
CREDIT CARDS	No
BREAKFAST	Full breakfast is served in the dining room.
AMENITIES	TV, radio, phone in the rooms, TV/VCR and fireplace in the living room, complimentary refreshments, refrigerator and laundry facilities.
RESTRICTIONS	No smoking, no pets, no children.
MEMBER	Summit County Bed & Breakfast Association
KUDOS/COMMENTS	"Great food!" (1996)

GRANNY'S B&B

5435 Montezuma Road, Dillon, CO 80435   970-468-9297
Donna Hellyer, Resident Owner

LOCATION	Six miles and "100 years from the Keystone Resort."
OPEN	All year except for Christmas Day.
DESCRIPTION	A log home with antique mining and cabin era furnishings. A high-mountain hide-a-way surrounded by grand mountain peaks, towering pines, and postcard views of historic Montezuma.
NO. OF ROOMS	Three rooms share one bathroom. Donna Hellyer calls her best room "Columbine."
RATES	Year-round rates are $50 for a single with shared bath and $70 for a double with shared bath. The cancellation policy is 20 days for a full refund and 72 hours for a 50% refund.
CREDIT CARDS	MasterCard, Visa

BREAKFAST	Full breakfast is served in the dining room and includes sausage, ham, hash browns, sourdough pancakes, eggs, fruit, juices and coffee.
AMENITIES	Apres ski or hot soup and Granny's sourdough. Dinner sleigh rides in the winter available at extra charge.
RESTRICTIONS	No smoking, no pets (resident outside dogs and cats, horses and burro), no children...Granny!...TI
MEMBER	Summit County Bed & Breakfast Association
KUDOS/COMMENTS	"Old mining atmosphere and mountain setting, small town, antiques, sleigh rides, excellent food, full breakfast and other meals." (1996)

HOME & HEARTH

PO Box 891, Dillon, CO 80435
Bruce & Trudy Robinson, Resident Owners

970-468-5541
800-753-4386
FAX 970-262-6242

LOCATION	Take exit 205, first exit after the Eisenhower Tunnel, turn right to Wendy's, Rainbow Drive is a block away. Turn right and travel another 1.5 miles. Call for directions.
OPEN	All year.
DESCRIPTION	A 1973 mountain home filled with antiques and a huge fireplace.
NO. OF ROOMS	Five rooms share three baths. Trudy recommends the Raggedy Ann Room.
RATES	High season rates are $30-35 for a single sharing a bath and $75 for a double sharing a bath. Low season rates are $25-30 for a single sharing a bath and $55 for a double sharing a bath. Cancellation requires 10 days' notice.
CREDIT CARDS	No
BREAKFAST	Full breakfast, served in the dining room, includes sausage or bacon, an egg dish, homemade bread, pancakes or French toast.
AMENITIES	Hot tub on the deck, evening hors d'oeuvres and a large seminar room available in the summer.
RESTRICTIONS	Smoking is restricted and previous arrangements need to be made for pets. The resident Lab is Charlie.
MEMBER	Summit County Bed & Breakfast Association

Paradox Lodge, Dillon

PARADOX LODGE

5040 Montezuma Road, Dillon, CO 80435   970-468-9445
George & Connie O'Bleness, Resident Owners   FAX 970-262-6466

LOCATION	From Highway 6 exit on Montezuma Road, 4.8 miles east of Keystone Resort.
OPEN	All year.
DESCRIPTION	A 1987 two-story country lodge and cabins on 24 acres with antique furnishings.
NO. OF ROOMS	Three cabins with private bathrooms and four rooms share two bathrooms. Choose cabin #2 or Lucky Dick.
RATES	There are six seasons and three rate levels at the Paradox Lodge. A single or double with a private bathroom in the cabins is $80-120 and a single or double with a shared bathroom is $55-90. There is a three-night minimum stay over the Christmas holidays, ask about a cancellation policy.
CREDIT CARDS	American Express, Diners Club, Discover, MasterCard, Visa
BREAKFAST	Continental Plus includes "always homemade" cinnamon rolls and breads, fruit, hot and cold cereals, coffee, tea, hot chocolate, spiced cider and orange juice.
AMENITIES	Outside cedar-wood-fired hot tub, cross-country skiing, hiking and biking from the lodge.
RESTRICTIONS	Smoking in the cabins only.
REVIEWED	*The Colorado Guide*
MEMBER	Summit County Bed & Breakfast Association

PINEY ACRES INN

864 Anemone Trail, Dillon, CO 80435
Judith McVeigh, Resident Owner

970-468-6206
800-746-3969
FAX 970-468-6723

LOCATION	Seventy miles west of Denver off I-70. Take the Dillon/Silverthorne exit and turn left, go 0.5 mile and turn right on Anemone Trail.
OPEN	All year.
DESCRIPTION	A 1963 two-story log-trimmed mountain inn, remodeled in 1995, with hardwood floors and mountain and traditional decor.
NO. OF ROOMS	Ten rooms with private bathrooms. Judith recommends the Memories room.
RATES	Prime season and holiday rates are $125-155 for a single or double with private bath and $1165 for the entire B&B. Regular season rates are $110-140 for a single or double with private bath and $1037 for the entire B&B. Low season rates are $95-125 for a single or double with a private bath and $857 for the entire B&B. A minimum stay may be required. Ask about cancellation policy.
CREDIT CARDS	American Express, Discover, MasterCard, Visa
BREAKFAST	Full breakfast is served in the dining room and includes homemade muffins and breads, fresh fruit, a special hot entree and beverages.
AMENITIES	Private and communal decks, Colorado newspapers with coffee or tea in the mornings, rooms with tubs for two, robes, sun porch, books for trade, outdoor hot tub, two great rooms, grand piano with pianist, TV and VCR for communal use, complimentary Colorado beer or wine plus hors d'oeuvres in the evening, evening turndown of beds, mints on pillows, concierge service, hot and cold drinks.
RESTRICTIONS	No smoking, no pets, children over 12 are welcome. The resident Scot-Terrier is Razz-ma-tazz.
REVIEWED	*Yellow Brick Road*
MEMBER	Professional Association of Innkeepers International, Bed & Breakfast Innkeepers of Colorado
KUDOS/COMMENTS	"New construction, well appointed." ... "Live piano music a nice touch." (1996)

SNOWBERRYHILL BED & BREAKFAST

236 Snowberry Way, Dillon, CO 80435   970-468-8010
George & Kristi Blincoe, Resident Owners

LOCATION	Between Dillon and Keystone, off Swan Mountain Road.
OPEN	All year.
DESCRIPTION	A 1984 three-story contemporary mountain host home with eclectic furnishings.
NO. OF ROOMS	One suite with a private bathroom.
RATES	Seasonal, November through March, rates are $105 for a single or double with private bathroom. Off season rates are $75 for a single or double with private bathroom. There is no minimum stay and cancellation requires 14 days notice.
CREDIT CARDS	MasterCard, Visa
BREAKFAST	Full breakfast, served in the dining room, may include Belgian waffles with strawberries, quiches, souffles, stuffed French toast, served with fresh-baked breads, fresh fruit and beverages.
AMENITIES	Daily maid service, full kitchen in suite, robes, TV/VCR, phone, ski locker, laundry facilities, crib and baby equipment.
RESTRICTIONS	No smoking, no pets.
MEMBER	Bed & Breakfast Innkeepers of Colorado, Summit County Bed & Breakfast Association

DIVIDE
(COLORADO SPRINGS)

This small mountain community is the Ute Pass area is the main access route to Cripple Creek and the splendid Mueller State Park and handy to Penitente Canyon for world-class rock climbing. On the high road to Florissant Fossil Beds National Monument, 30 miles west of Colorado Springs and seven miles west of Woodland Park on Highway 24.

MOUNTAIN MAN BED & BREAKFAST

603 Kutsu Ridge Road, Divide, CO 80814   719-687-2796
Dean & Jeanne Wilson, Resident Owners   888-687-2796

SILVER WOOD BED & BREAKFAST AT DIVIDE

463 County Road 512, Divide, CO 80814   719-687-6784
Larry & Bess Oliver, Resident Owners
Texan spoken.

LOCATION	Drive north from the only traffic signal in Divide. Half-a-mile north of the signal, take the left fork and follow the paved road for 3.5 miles. The B&B is on the right, 1/4 mile past the Golden Bell Camp sign.
OPEN	All year.
DESCRIPTION	A 1990 contemporary two-story home in the mountains with eclectic furnishings, outstanding views and abundant hiking trails.
NO. OF ROOMS	Two rooms with private bathrooms. The best room is the Southwest.
RATES	Year-round rates for a single or double with a private bathroom are $65-85, extra twin beds are $15 each. There is no minimum stay.
CREDIT CARDS	Discover, MasterCard, Visa
BREAKFAST	Full breakfast, served in the dining room, includes juice, homemade breads, seasonal fresh fruit and various quiches, French toast or gourmet sausage with gravy and angel biscuits...Okay, sausage & biscuits are one of the four main food groups, like pizza & beer, but "gourmet" sausage & biscuits? We'll need a field report here...AS
AMENITIES	TV in rooms, queen beds and private decks with complimentary coffee, tea, soft drinks and homebaked goods.
RESTRICTIONS	No smoking, no pets, the resident cats, Lucy and Frisco, are the "comfort assurance engineers." Children are welcome.
MEMBER	Bed & Breakfast Innkeepers of Colorado

DOLORES

In the southwestern Four Corners area, this little hamlet on the beautiful Dolores River sits at the edge of McPhee Reservoir and the San Juan National Forest. Good reasons to be here: Mesa Verde National Park is only 20 miles southeast of town and heading north on Scenic Highway 145 gets you to Telluride. From Cortez, 11 miles northeast on Highways 145 and 160.

LAUGHING COYOTE LODGE

At Groundhog Lake, PO Box 21, Dolores, CO 81323   970-882-7321
Kevin & Paulette Barlow, Resident Owners   800-373-7321

LEBANON SCHOOLHOUSE BED & BREAKFAST

24925 County Road T, Dolores, CO 81323   970-882-4461
Bob & Penny Richardson, Resident Owners   800-349-9829

MOUNTAIN VIEW BED & BREAKFAST

28050 County Road P, Dolores, CO 81323   970-822-7861
Brenda & Cecil Dunn, Resident Owners   800-228-4592

LOCATION	From Cortez go 4.3 miles north toward Dolores on Highway 145. Turn right on Road P and travel one mile. Road P then curves left, but you take the gravel road to the right. The inn is the second house.
OPEN	All year.
DESCRIPTION	A 1984 two-story ranch with southwestern furnishings, wraparound porches and decks on 22 acres.
NO. OF ROOMS	Eight rooms with private bathrooms. The Sunroom might be the best room in the house.
RATES	Year-round rates are $44 for a single with a private bathroom, $54 for a double with a private bathroom, $64 for a suite with a private bathroom and $10 for each additional person. Cancellation requires seven days' notice.
CREDIT CARDS	MasterCard, Visa
BREAKFAST	Full breakfast, served in the dining room, enclosed porch or the deck, includes hot entrees such as bacon & eggs, sausage, breakfast casserole and beverages.

AMENITIES	Guest TV room and kitchen, hot tub, evening refreshments.
RESTRICTIONS	No smoking, no pets and no alcohol. There are two resident Arabians called Moriah and Misty, but they are not for guest use.
MEMBER	Colorado Hotel and Lodging Association

PRIEST GULCH LODGE BED & BREAKFAST

27646 Highway 145, Dolores, CO 81323   970-562-3810
Margaret Allsup, Resident Owner

RIO GRANDE SOUTHERN HOTEL

---

101 South 5th Street, PO Box 516, Dolores, CO 81323   970-882-7527
Fred & Cathy Green, Resident Owners   800-258-0434

LOCATION	On Town Square.
OPEN	All year.
DESCRIPTION	An 1893 railroad hotel with Victorian furnishings. On the National Historic Register.
NO. OF ROOMS	Three rooms with private bathrooms, four rooms share two bathrooms.
RATES	Year-round rates are $54-60 for a single or double with a private bathroom and $35-49 for a single or double with a shared bathroom. There is a reservation/cancellation policy.
CREDIT CARDS	Discover, MasterCard, Visa
BREAKFAST	Full breakfast is served in the dining room. Lunch and dinner are available in the restaurant.
RESTRICTIONS	No smoking, no pets. Children of all ages are welcome.
REVIEWED	*Hidden Secrets of the Southwest*

DURANGO

Awesome is an understatement. This southwestern gateway to one of the state's most scenic areas is surrounded by the San Juan Mountains, and the Animas River runs right through town. For rafting and kayaking, choose from the Upper Animas —dangerous and rugged — or Lower Animas — exciting but not terrifying. Or traverse 90 miles of spactacular scenery on the Historic Durango & Silverton Narrow Guage Railroad; Ski Purgatory; soak it up at Trimble Hot Springs; and be around for Snowdown, the zany, five-day winter festival in January; Iron Horse Bicycle Classic in May, and one of the country's biggest Western Arts, Film and Cowboy Poetry Gathering in September. Best of all, the month-long events around Aspen Colorfest, September and October. Bonus: it's only 36 miles west of Mesa Verde National Park and the cliff dwellings. From Denver, 330 scenic miles via Highways 285 and 160.

APPLE ORCHARD INN

7758 County Road 203, Durango, CO 81301   970-247-0751
Celeste & John Gardiner, Resident Owners   800-426-0751
Portuguese and Italian spoken.   FAX 970-385-6976

LOCATION	Six miles north of Durango on Highway 550, turn west on Trimble Lane, turn north on County Road 203, drive 1.4 miles, the inn is on the right.
OPEN	All year.
DESCRIPTION	A 1993 two-story farmhouse inn and six cottages with country furnishings and a wraparound porch located on a 4.5-acre apple orchard with views of the mountains.
NO. OF ROOMS	Four rooms with private bathrooms. Six cottages with private bathrooms, three with fireplaces. Pick the Cortland Cottage.
RATES	High season, June through September, rates for a single or a double with a private bathroom are $95-150, the entire house rents for $410 and the house and cottages for $1,150. Off season rates are $70-135, the entire house rents for $370, and the house and cottages for $1,000. There is no minimum stay and cancellation requires 14 days' notice and a $20 fee.
CREDIT CARDS	Discover, MasterCard, Visa
BREAKFAST	Full breakfast is served in the dining room or on the patio in the summer and includes something fresh out of the oven such as sauteed apples or peaches in a peach and cinnamon-butter sauce, omelets, light quiches, roasted potatoes or sourdough pancakes, waffles or French toast made from homebaked sourdough walnut bread. Dinner and special vegetarian meals are available by reservation.

Apple Orchard Inn, Durango

AMENITIES	Fresh flowers in room, robes in some rooms, wine, hors d'oeuvres, bottomless cookie jar, dining room handicapped accessible, featherbeds throughout, TV and fireplace in common room, three cottages are wheelchair accessible, hot tub in the garden, and apples to take home in the fall.
RESTRICTIONS	No smoking, no pets, children over eight are welcome. The resident Golden Retriever is called Woody and the 15 year-old cat is Newman, who is allegedly bi-lingual "having lived with us in Brazil."
REVIEWED	*America's Wonderful Little Hotels & Inns*
MEMBER	Bed & Breakfast Innkeepers of Colorado, National Bed & Breakfast Association
RATED	AAA 3 Diamonds
KUDOS/COMMENTS	"Owners have incredible enthusiasm and a beautiful home"... "Excellent cook, wonderful gourmet breakfasts"... "Warm and open common area."... "Beautiful landscaping." ..."Country setting but convenient to the city."... "The cottages are adorable." (1996)

BLUE LAKE RANCH

16000 Highway 140, Durango, CO 81326   *970-385-4537*
David & Shirley Alford, Resident Owners   *888-258-3525*
German and French spoken.   *FAX 970-385-4088*

LOCATION	From Highway 160 at Hesperus go south 6.5 miles on Highway 140, driveway on the right.
OPEN	All year.
DESCRIPTION	Country estate with Victorian architecture and "eclectic (fabulous, not cute)" interiors overlooking the private Blue Lake and mountains. Nationally publicized gardens.
NO. OF ROOMS	Nine rooms, suites or cabins all have private baths. David recommends the garden room but thinks the best accomodations are at the cabin on the lake.
RATES	Summer rates, May 1 through October 31, are $60-245 for a single or double with a private bathroom. Winter rates, November through April, are $45-190 for a single or double with a private bathroom. There is a two-night minimum stay and cancellation requires 30 days' notice and a $30 handling fee.
CREDIT CARDS	No
BREAKFAST	Full European buffet is served in the dining room.
AMENITIES	Magnificent gardens, flowers, robes, telephones, TVs, peace, quiet, fishing, cross-country skiing and afternoon tea.
RESTRICTIONS	No smoking, no pets, (there is a resident cat called Fuzzy and a small flock of peacocks). Children are welcome at the innkeeper's discretion.
REVIEWED	*The Colorado Guide*
MEMBER	Bed & Breakfast Innkeepers of Colorado, Professional Association of Innkeepers International, Distinctive Inns of Colorado
RATED	AAA 3 Diamonds
AWARDS	*Country Inns* magazine, Top 12 Inns, 1992.
KUDOS/COMMENTS	"A delightful country inn with acres of rolling hills and ponds." ... "Famous for fabulous mountain gardens! An exceptional retreat." .... "Interesting owner, nice facilities for the price." ... "Fabulous views of the the LaPlata Mountains. The gardens are large and well-kept and the owners are very personable." ... "Great in every way." (1996).

Country Sunshine Bed & Breakfast, Durango

COUNTRY SUNSHINE BED & BREAKFAST

35130 Highway 550 North, Durango, CO 81301   970-247-2853
Beanie & Gary Archie, Resident Owners   800-383-2853
          FAX 970-247-1203

LOCATION	Twelve miles north of Durango on Highway 550. At mile marker 35 there is a large redwood mailbox with '35130' on the front and signs on the east side of the highway.
OPEN	All year.
DESCRIPTION	A 1979 two-story ranch-style country inn with wraparound decks and rustic furnishings.
NO. OF ROOMS	Six rooms with private bathrooms. The owners recommend the Rose Room.
RATES	Summer (May 15 to October 15), Christmas season and spring break, the rates are $85 for a single or double with a private bathroom. Off season rates are $70. During the holidays guests are requested to stay two nights and there is a 15-day cancellation policy.
CREDIT CARDS	American Express, Diners Club, Discover, MasterCard, Visa
BREAKFAST	Full breakfast is served in the dining room.
AMENITIES	Large outdoor spa, complimentary beer and wine, extensive library and bicycles for use. Common area with TV/VCR.
RESTRICTIONS	No smoking, no pets, children over five are welcome. There is a resident dog and cat.
MEMBER	Bed & Breakfast Innkeepers of Colorado
KUDOS/COMMENTS	"Very friendly atmosphere, filled with country charm." ... "Very comfortable home, charming innkeepers." (1997)

THE EDGEMONT RANCH

158 The Silver Queen South, Durango, CO 81301   970-247-2713
Gregory Cano, Resident Manager   800-748-2502
                                                      FAX 970-382-0373

LOCATION	Take County Road 240 (Florida Road) 6.5 miles. The ranch is on the right side of the road and back about 1/4 mile, office on the left.
OPEN	All year.
DESCRIPTION	A 1985 farmhouse and ranchhouse with Victorian furnishings on 1,400 acres.
NO. OF ROOMS	Three rooms share one-and-a-half baths, two rooms have private bathrooms and one executive suite has its own kitchen. The master suite is the best.
RATES	The rate schedule is elaborate. Please call about rates.
CREDIT CARDS	American Express, MasterCard, Visa
BREAKFAST	Continental Plus is delivered to each room.
AMENITIES	Fly fishing, hot tub, tennis courts, playground, hiking and cross-country trails.
RESTRICTIONS	No smoking, no pets. Children of all ages are welcome.
MEMBER	Durango Hotel and Motel Association, Colorado Hotel and Lodging Association

GABLE HOUSE

805 East 5th Avenue, Durango, CO 81301   970-247-4982
Heather Bryson, Resident Owner   FAX 970-247-1454
Spanish spoken.

LOCATION	Three blocks north and five blocks east of the Narrow Gauge Railroad station.
OPEN	All year.
DESCRIPTION	An 1892 four-story Queen Anne Victorian with antiques and Oriental furnishings, and a fine art collection. The B&B is on both the State and National Historic Registers.
NO. OF ROOMS	Three rooms share two bathrooms. The owner suggest the room with the private balcony.
RATES	Year-round rates for a single or double with a shared bathroom are $75-100. There is no minimum stay and a two-week cancellation policy.

Leland House B&B Suites / Rochester Hotel, Durango

CREDIT CARDS	MasterCard, Visa
BREAKFAST	Full hot breakfast is served in the dining room on fine china with silver.
AMENITIES	Robes, fresh flowers, libations offered upon arrival, picnics in the private yard.
RESTRICTIONS	Smoking on porch and balconies only, no pets, children over 12 are welcome.
REVIEWED	*Non-Smokers Guide to Bed & Breakfasts, Dallas Morning News* Travel section
MEMBER	Bed & Breakfast Innkeepers of Colorado

LELAND HOUSE B&B SUITES / ROCHESTER HOTEL

721 East Second Avenue, Durango, CO 81301 970-385-1920
Kirk & Diane Komick, Resident Owners 800-664-1920
FAX 970-385-1967

LOCATION	Turn east off Highway 550 onto College Drive, cross over Main, turn left onto Second Avenue. Located between Seventh and Eighth streets.
OPEN	All year.

DESCRIPTION	Historic inns built in 1892 and 1927 with "Brick Craftsman" architecture and "Western Victorian" decor.
NO. OF ROOMS	Twenty-six rooms with private bathrooms. The owners' favorite is the "Support Your Local Gunfighter" room in the Rochester.
RATES	Year-round rates are $95-185 for a single or double with private bath and $135-185 for a suite. Two-night minimum stay at Christmas. Cancellation requires 14 days' notice, 30 days for holidays.
CREDIT CARDS	American Express, Discover, MasterCard, Visa
BREAKFAST	Full breakfast, served in lobby and courtyard of the Rochester, includes coffee, juices, fruit plate, baked goods, homemade granola and daily hot entree. Boxed lunches available.
AMENITIES	Courtyard, robes, social hour with tea and fresh-baked cookies, meeting rooms, handicapped accessible room.
RESTRICTIONS	No smoking, no pets.
REVIEWED	*Recommended Country Inns (Rocky Mountain Region).*
MEMBER	American Bed & Breakfast Association, Bed & Breakfast Inns of Colorado, Professional Association of Innkeepers International, Distinctive Inns of Colorado
RATED	AAA 3 Diamonds, Mobil 2 Stars
AWARDS	1995 Durango Historic Preservation Board Special Recognition; 1994 Durango Park & Forestry Board Award for Landscaping; September 1995 Conde Nast Traveler's Flagship Hotel of Colorado.
KUDOS/COMMENTS	"Perfect location for exploring the heart of Durango, very comfortably furnished, excellent breakfast." (1997)

LIGHTNER CREEK INN

999 County Road 207, Durango, CO 81301   970-259-1226
Julie & Richard Houston, Resident Owners   800-268-9804
                                        FAX 970-259-0732

LOCATION	From Highway 160, three miles west of Durango, take County Road 207 for 1.1 mile.
OPEN	All year.
DESCRIPTION	A 1903 renovated Cape Cod located on 20 acres, furnished with Victorian antiques.
NO. OF ROOMS	Six rooms with private bathrooms and two rooms share one bathroom. The best room is the Karen Olivia room.

Lightner Creek Inn, Durango

RATES	High season, May through October, rates are $85-150. Off season rates are about 10% less. There is no minimum stay. There is a two-week cancellation policy and a $20 handling charge.
CREDIT CARDS	Discover, MasterCard, Visa
BREAKFAST	Full breakfast is served in the dining room.
AMENITIES	Gazebo, stream and pond on 20 acres, common room with baby grand piano, sunroom, afternoon tea and goodies, handicapped access, small meeting facilities, seasonal trout fishing.
RESTRICTIONS	No smoking, no pets, children over 10 are welcome. Miss Whitney Houston is the resident Goldie and the two cats go by Miss Freckles and Lucy Ducy. George, Daisy, Ruth and Ethel are the resident ducks.
MEMBER	Professional Association of Innkeepers International, Bed & Breakfast Innkeepers of Colorado, Distinctive Inns of Colorado
RATED	AAA 3 Diamonds, Mobil 3 Star
KUDOS/COMMENTS	"Best decorated B&B I've ever seen; Great hosts." ... "A dream come true. A perfect country getaway in a picture-perfect setting. We couldn't ask for nicer hosts." ... "Beautifully decorated, located only three miles from town but with a country atmosphere." ... "Breakfast was fantastic." (1997)

LOGWOOD / THE VERHEYDEN INN

35060 Highway 550 North, Durango, CO 81301
Debby & Greg Verheyden, Resident Owners

970-259-4396
800-369-4082
FAX 970-259-7812

LOCATION	From Durango go north 8.5 miles, take a right at the Timberline Academy exit and an immediate right again onto Logwoods Drive.
OPEN	All year.
DESCRIPTION	A three-story log inn with a two-story river-rock fireplace and country western decor, on 15 acres along the Animas River.
NO. OF ROOMS	Six rooms with private bathrooms. The Mesa Verde room has views of the river and valley.
RATES	High season rates (May through October) are $65-80 for a single with bath and $75-125 for a double with bath. Winter rates are $55-65 for a single and $65-125 for a double. There is a minimum stay on weekends and holidays and $20 fee for cancellation. Check-in is from 4-6 p.m., none accepted after 8 p.m.
CREDIT CARDS	MasterCard, Visa
BREAKFAST	Full breakfast is served in the dining room. Special meals include Christmas night, New Year's Eve and Thanksgiving Day.
AMENITIES	Tickets to hot springs, "award winning" desserts served in the evenings, fresh flowers. Meeting facility available from October to April (except holidays).
RESTRICTIONS	No smoking, no pets (resident cats Aspen and Pepper), children over eight are welcome.
REVIEWED	*Durango Magazine*
MEMBER	Bed & Breakfast Innkeepers of Colorado, National Bed & Breakfast Association, American Bed & Breakfast Association
RATED	AAA 3 Diamonds
KUDOS/COMMENTS	"Debby and Greg made my stay very special, a great place to come home to." (1994)

Logwood / The Verheyden Inn, Durango

RIVER HOUSE BED & BREAKFAST

495 Animas View Drive, Durango, CO 81301   970-247-4775
Kate & Lars Enggren, Crystal Carroll, Resident Owners   800-254-4775
Some Spanish spoken.   FAX 970-259-1465

LOCATION	Head north on Highway 550 and turn right on Animas View Drive (last right before heading out of town), go 1/2 mile north, the B&B is on the left side.
OPEN	All year.
DESCRIPTION	A 1960 southwest-style ranch with southwestern and antique furnishings.
NO. OF ROOMS	Seven rooms with private bathrooms. Try the Rio Grande or Gunnison rooms.
RATES	Year-round rates are $70-90 for one person with a private bathroom and $75-100 for two people with a private bathroom, $170 for a suite, $170 for the honeymoon guesthouse, and $800 for the entire B&B. There is no minimum stay and cancellation requires 14 days' notice.
CREDIT CARDS	American Express, Discover, MasterCard, Visa
BREAKFAST	Full "healthy gourmet, sometimes decadent" breakfast is served buffet style in the atrium. Lunch is also available and special diets can be accommodated.
AMENITIES	Hot tub, atrium with waterfall and skylights, game room with pool table, large-screen TV, big brass fireplace, library, massage and hypnotherapy available, large backyard with reading areas and chess table, customized Jeep tours are available. The entire house can be rented for wedding parties or reunions.
RESTRICTIONS	No smoking, no pets. Saygee is the resident pooch and Molly is the outside cat.
MEMBER	Bed & Breakfast Innkeepers of Colorado, Professional Association of Innkeepers International
RATED	ABBA 3 Crowns
KUDOS/COMMENTS	"Soothing, delightful stay, pleasant innkeepers." ... "Warm and homey, a good place for kids also." (1997)

SCRUBBY OAKS BED & BREAKFAST INN

PO Box 1047, Durango, CO 81302   970-247-2176
Mary Ann Craig, Resident Owner

LOCATION	From the intersection of 3rd Avenue and Florida Road, take Florida 2.7 miles, the inn is on the left side.
OPEN	End of April until the end of October.
DESCRIPTION	A 1959 ranch house with comfortable country antiques located on 10 acres overlooking the Animas Valley and the surrounding mountains.
NO. OF ROOMS	Three rooms with private bathrooms and four rooms share two bathrooms.
RATES	Year-round rates are $60 for a single with a private bathroom, $75 for a double with a private bathroom, $50 for a single with a shared bathroom and $65 for a double with a shared bathroom.
CREDIT CARDS	No
BREAKFAST	Full breakfast, served in the country kitchen, includes 12 menu items plus beverages.
AMENITIES	Three large common areas, fresh flowers in the rooms during the summer, sauna, TV/VCR, gardens, patios, pool table and snacks in the afternoon.
RESTRICTIONS	No smoking, no pets. The resident Old English Sheepdog sometimes responds to Archie...sort of like our editor, Carl...TI
REVIEWED	*Non-Smokers Guide to Bed & Breakfasts, Journey to the High Southwest*
MEMBER	Bed & Breakfast Innkeepers of Colorado, Colorado Hotel and Lodging Association
AWARDS	"Beautiful location; run by a seasoned innkeeper who knows the area." (1996)

VAGABOND INN BED & BREAKFAST

2180 Main Avenue, Durango, CO 81301   970-259-5901
Omnia Elhakim & Rashwan Ibrahim, Resident Owners   800-259-5977
Spanish and Arabic spoken.   FAX 970-247-5345

LOCATION	On the corner of 22nd and Main on the east side of the road.
OPEN	All year.
DESCRIPTION	A 1981 two-story "turn-of-the-century roadhouse" inn with provincial furnishings.
NO. OF ROOMS	Eight rooms with private bathrooms. The best room is the Bridal Suite.
RATES	High season, June through September and holidays, rates are $88 for a single with private bathroom, $99 for a double with private bathroom and $138 for the Bridal Suite. Off season rates are $43-50 for a single with private bathroom, $59-66 for a double with private bathroom and $115 for the Bridal Suite. There is no minimum stay and cancellation requires 24 hours' notice, three days' for holidays.
CREDIT CARDS	American Express, Diners Club, Discover, MasterCard, Visa
BREAKFAST	Continental Plus is served in the dining room.
AMENITIES	Telephone, cable TV, hot tub, pool and spa, guest laundry, living room with fireplace.
RESTRICTIONS	No pets.
MEMBER	Professional Association of Innkeepers International

WATERFALL BED & BREAKFAST

4138 County Road 203, Durango, CO 81301   970-259-4771
Joan & Hall Sippy, Resident Owners

EATON

A pleasant suburb of Greeley, eight miles north on Highway 85, just four miles south of Scenic Highway 14 on the way to Pawnee National Grasslands.

THE VICTORIAN VERANDA BED & BREAKFAST

515 Cheyenne Avenue, Eaton, CO 80615　　　　　　*970-454-3890*
Richard & Nadine White, Resident Owners

LOCATION	At Eaton's only stoplight go west three blocks and north 5-1/2 blocks. The B&B is on the east side of the road.
OPEN	All year.
DESCRIPTION	An 1894 two-story Queen Anne with a wraparound porch, two crystal chandeliers, an ornate staircase, a baby grand piano and a grandfather clock.
NO. OF ROOMS	One room with a private bathroom and two rooms share a bathroom. Pick the room with the private whirlpool bath on the east.
RATES	Year-round rates are $45-60. There is a reservation/cancellation policy
CREDIT CARDS	No
BREAKFAST	Full breakfast, served in the dining room, includes bacon, eggs, pancakes and beverages.
AMENITIES	Bicycles built for two, Nadine is happy to share her knowledge of local activities.
RESTRICTIONS	No smoking except on the veranda or balcony, no pets, and children of all ages are welcome.
REVIEWED	*Non-Smokers Guide to Bed & Breakfasts*
MEMBER	Bed & Breakfast Innkeepers of Colorado
KUDOS/COMMENTS	"Lovely, very welcoming atmosphere; Quiet and restful." ... "Full of wonderful antiques." ... "Very gracious innkeepers." (1994) "Warm and friendly hosts and lovely atmosphere." ... "Four beautiful Victorian rooms, gracious hosts." (1997)

EDWARDS

THE LAZY RANCH

0057 Lake Creek Road, Edwards, CO 81632   970-926-3876
Buddy & Linda Calhoun, Resident Owners   800-655-9343
                                           FAX 970-926-3876

KUDOS/COMMENTS   "A wonderful little place with great hosts. Working ranch that's
been in the same family for over 100 years." (1996)

EMPIRE

A small mountain community in a star-shaped valley on the high road to Winter
Park and all its year-round offerings. At the foot of Berthoud Pass on Highway 40,
west of Denver.

MAD CREEK BED & BREAKFAST

167 Park Avenue (US 40), Empire, CO 80438   303-569-2003
Myrna and Tonya Payne, Resident Owners
Some Spanish spoken.

LOCATION	Exit 232 from I-70 and go two miles to Empire where the B&B is on the north side of Park Avenue going west.
OPEN	All year.
DESCRIPTION	An 1875 two-story Victorian cottage offering both rustic atmosphere and mountain charm, country antiques, relics of the mining and skiing past.
NO. OF ROOMS	One room with a private bathroom, two rooms share one bathroom. Best room is the one with the private bath.
RATES	Year-round rates for a single or double with a private bathroom are $65-75, a single or double with a shared bathroom is $45-55. There is a 15% discount for renting the entire B&B. There is no minimum stay. Ask about a cancellation policy.
CREDIT CARDS	MasterCard, Visa
BREAKFAST	Full breakfast, served in the dining room, includes homemade granola (Mad Creek Crunch), blueberry waffles, fresh fruit, orange juice, yogurt, gourmet coffee and tea.
AMENITIES	Outdoor hot tub, robes, ceiling fans, TV/VCR and movie selection, library of books and maps for Colorado adventures, use of cross-country skis and snowshoes.

RESTRICTIONS
No smoking, no pets and children over 10 are welcome. The resident Samoyed is called Sequoya.

REVIEWED
Inn for the Night, Great Affordable Bed & Breakfast Getaways

KUDOS/COMMENTS
"Charming."... "Wonderful owners." (1996)

THE PECK HOUSE

83 Sunny Avenue, Empire, CO 80438   303-569-9870
Gary & Sally St. Clair, Resident Owners   FAX 303-569-2743
French, Spanish spoken.

LOCATION	Take exit 232 from I-70 and travel two miles on Highway 40 to Empire. We are a block or so up the hill.
OPEN	All year.
DESCRIPTION	The oldest hotel in Colorado, an 1860-1862 two-story stagecoach stop and restaurant with antiques.
NO. OF ROOMS	Nine rooms with private bathrooms and two rooms share one bathroom. Check out the Bridal Suite.
RATES	Year-round rates are $80 for a double with bath, $45 for a double with shared bath and $100 for a suite. The rates are $5 higher December 23 through January 1, and $10 higher on Valentine's Day. Cancellation requires 48 hours' notice with special requirements for holidays, August and September.
CREDIT CARDS	Just about anything
BREAKFAST	Continental breakfast is served in the dining room. Dinner is available in the restaurant and lunch is served in the summer only.
AMENITIES	Bar, five-star gourmet restaurant, hot tub.
RESTRICTIONS	No pets. Resident pets include Benjamin and Topper (cats), Boo and Red (horses), Daisy & Grover (donkeys), and Henry the chicken.
REVIEWED	*Best Places to Stay in the Rocky Mountain Region, The Colorado Guide, The Official Guide to American Historic Inns, Recommended Country Inns of the Rocky Mountain Region, Restaurants from 101 Colorado Small Towns*
RATED	AAA 3 Diamonds for the restaurant.
AWARDS	Uncle Ben's Inc., Finalist for the 10 Best Country Inns of the Year award; Colorado Department of Agriculture, 1993 Winner of the Governor's Award for the Best All-Colorado Meal.

ESTES PARK

The eastern entrance to Rocky Mountain National Park and all its splendid beauty, majestic Longs Peak and the Continental Divide. In June, shop for llamas, sheep angora rabbits and goats (or just their products) at the Wool Market; Rooftop Rodeo and Western Week in July is a major event as are the Rocky Mountain Folk Festival in August and the Long's Peak Scottish-Irish Festival in September. Fall is spactacular — besides the aspen, look for elk everywhere, and listen to their bugling. They like to congregate on the golf course. From Denver, 65 miles northwest via I-25 and Highway 36.

ALPENAIRE INN AND RESTAURANT

---

215 Virginia Drive, PO Box 1594, Estes Park, CO 80517   970-586-6607
Tres & Tracy Riordan, Resident Managers   800-668-0301
Some Spanish spoken.   FAX 970-586-6607

LOCATION	Head north for 1-1/2 blocks at the second stoplight on Elkhorn Avenue (Estes Park's "main street").
OPEN	All year.
DESCRIPTION	A 1909 2-1/2-story post-Victorian inn with antique interior decor, plus cabins.
NO. OF ROOMS	Four rooms with private bathrooms and two rooms share one bathroom. Try the Log Cottage on the hilltop.
RATES	Year-round rates are $95-135 for a single or double with private bathroom, $75 for a single or double with a shared bathroom, $135 for a suite, $115 for a guesthouse, and $1,089 for the entire B&B for two nights. There is a two-night minimum stay all year. Cancellation requires three days' notice, 30 days' notice if renting the entire inn.
CREDIT CARDS	American Express, Discover, MasterCard, Visa
BREAKFAST	Full breakfast, served in the dining room and guestrooms, includes three courses: fresh fruit, grain and accompaniments, entree and baked goods. A basket with lighter fare may be delivered to rooms on request. Lunch and dinner are available. Special meals for private parties and weddings are available upon request. Guests with special dietary needs are provided for.
AMENITIES	Gourmet restaurant, baked goodies and free drinks at check-in, help with planning National Park and area itineraries, sunny rooms look across downtown to lake and mountains.
RESTRICTIONS	No smoking, no pets, no children
MEMBER	Professional Association Innkeepers International, American Bed & Breakfast Association, Colorado Hotel & Motel Association

---

The Anniversary Inn B&B, Estes Park

THE ANNIVERSARY INN B&B

1060 Mary's Lake Road, Moraine Route,   970-586-6200
Estes Park, CO 80517
Norma & Harry Menke, Resident Owners
Some German spoken.

LOCATION	On Route 36, one-and-a-half miles west of town. Turn left at the stop light on Mary's Lake Road. The driveway is 0.1 mile on the left.
OPEN	All year except for Thanksgiving and Christmas.
DESCRIPTION	An 1890 two-story mountain log inn furnished with country antiques on two acres.
NO. OF ROOMS	The main house has three rooms with private baths. The cottage has a private bath, fireplace and whirlpool tub for two. The Sweetheart's Cottage is the most popular room.
RATES	Year-round rates are $90-140 for a double with a private bathroom. A two-night minimum stay preferred. There is a cancellation policy.
CREDIT CARDS	MasterCard, Visa
BREAKFAST	Full breakfast, served on wraparound glassed-in porch, includes hot entree, fresh-baked goods and fresh fruit.
AMENITIES	Robes in rooms, evening hors d'oeuvres, beverages, custom toiletries, fresh cookies, turndown service, extra pillows & blankets in rooms, moss-rock fireplace in living room, library with books and games, TV/VCR, refrigerator use and whirlpool-for-two in three rooms.

RESTRICTIONS	No smoking, no pets, children over 14 are welcome.
REVIEWED	*America's Wonderful Little Hotels & Inns, Best Places to Stay in the Rocky Mountain Region, Recommended Country Inns, The Birder's Guide to Bed & Breakfasts, The Official Guide to American Historic Inns: Bed & Breakfasts and Country Inns, Recommended Romantic Inns.*
MEMBER	Bed & Breakfast Innkeepers of Colorado, Professional Association of Innkeepers International
KUDOS/COMMENTS	"A beautiful old log home."... "Honeymoon cottage is great as well." ... "Eating on porch with beautiful views is a special delight."... "Quiet getaway." ... "Super-quiet setting and gorgeous decor." (1996)

THE BALDPATE INN

4900 South Highway 7, PO Box 4445,   970-586-6151
Estes Park, CO 80517
Mike & Lois Smith, Resident Owners

LOCATION	At the junction of Highway 36 and County Highway 7, turn south and go seven miles to the Lily Lake Area of Rocky Mountain National Park. Turn left at the sign.
OPEN	Memorial Day weekend to September 30.

The Baldpate Inn, Estes Park

DESCRIPTION	A 1917 two-story Adirondack log inn and three cabins with log and lace interior decor, listed on the National and State Historic Registers.
NO. OF ROOMS	Two rooms have private bathrooms and 10 rooms share five bathrooms. Room #4 is the largest and has the best view, #21 has a great view and private bath.
RATES	Seasonal rates (May through September) are $90 for a double with a private bathroom, $125 for a cabin and $75 for a double with a shared bathroom. The main lodge may be reserved for $1,000. The lodge has no minimum stay, the cabins requre a two-night minimum stay. Cancellation requires seven days' notice.
CREDIT CARDS	Discover, MasterCard, Visa
BREAKFAST	Full three-course breakfast is served in the dining room, includes fresh fruit and muffins, a quiche entree and cinnamon roll for dessert. Lunch and dinner are also available.
AMENITIES	Native-stone fireplaces in lodge and cabins, historic key and photo collections, front porch, homemade quilts in rooms, and evening snacks in the lobby.
RESTRICTIONS	No smoking, no pets. Duke is the resident German Shepherd.
REVIEWED	*Country Living's "Inns Across America," Frommer's Colorado*
MEMBER	Bed & Breakfast Innkeepers of Colorado

BARBARA'S BED & BREAKFAST

255 Cyteworth, PO Box 540, Estes Park, CO 80517   970-586-5871
Barbara Felte, Resident Owner   800-597-7903

LOCATION	Half-mile south of the park on main street. Turn left from Elkhorn Avenue onto East Riverside Drive. Go about three blocks then turn left on to Cyteworth and follow the paved road up the hill. The B&B is the fifth house on the left.
OPEN	All year.
DESCRIPTION	A 1950 two-story western wood-frame home with knotty pine paneling, hardwood floors and moss-rock fireplace.
NO. OF ROOMS	Two rooms with private bathrooms and two rooms share one bathroom. Pick Arlene's Room.
RATES	Year-round rates for a single or double with a private bathroom are $100-115, a single or double with a shared bathroom is $85 and the entire B&B rents for $350. There is no minimum stay and ask about the cancellation policy.
CREDIT CARDS	American Express, Discover, MasterCard, Visa
BREAKFAST	Full country breakfast is served family style in the dining room and includes homemade breads, eggs, meats and fruits.

AMENITIES	Robes in the rooms, antiques and crafts shop, sodas in the refrigerator, cookies and treats around the house, coffees, teas and hot chocolate at all times.
RESTRICTIONS	No smoking, no pets, children over five are welcome.
MEMBER	Bed & Breakfast Innkeepers of Colorado

BIG HORN GUEST HOUSE

PO Box 4486, Estes Park, CO 80517   970-586-4175
Calla Ferrari Hack, Resident Owner

BLACK DOG INN BED & BREAKFAST

650 South St. Vrain Avenue, PO Box 4659,   970-586-0374
Estes Park, CO 80517
Pete & Jane Princehorn, Resident Owners

LOCATION	On Highway 7 one-half mile south of the Holiday Inn between Graves and Morgan Streets on the east side of the road. Look for oval sign and rail fence in front of inn.
OPEN	All year except for Thanksgiving Day, Christmas Eve and Day.
DESCRIPTION	A 1910 mountain inn with hardwood floors, knotty pine walls, antique furnishings and original art on an acre surrounded by old aspen. Owners live in a cabin behind the B&B.
NO. OF ROOMS	Four rooms with private bathrooms. Try the Sundance Mountain room.
RATES	High season (May 1 through October 1, plus holidays and weekends) rates are $70-140 for a single or double with a private bathroom and $125-140 for suites. There is a minimum stay during the high season and on weekends and holidays. Cancellation requires 15 days' notice.
CREDIT CARDS	MasterCard, Visa
BREAKFAST	Full breakfast, served in the dining room, includes Featherbed Eggs, German Puff Pancakes, Eggs Ole, stuffed French toast with fruit sauce, homebaked breads, muffins, scones, potatoes Colorado, cereal and beverages. Special meals, including those for guests with special dietary needs, are available by prior arrangement.
AMENITIES	In-room fireplaces, fireplace in the living room, Jacuzzi for two, TV/VCR and videos, full cookie jar, snacks and beverages available, footpath connects with river walk, outdoor seating, trail maps, bicycles, day packs, water bottles, binoculars and guest parking.

RESTRICTIONS	No smoking, no pets, no cooking, children over 12 are welcome.
REVIEWED	*Recommended Country Inns of the Rocky Mountain Region, The Birder's Guide to Bed & Breakfasts (United States & Canada).*
MEMBER	Bed & Breakfast Innkeepers of Colorado, Colorado Hotel and Lodging Association, Professional Association of Innkeepers International
KUDOS/COMMENTS	"Make yourself at home because you are home. I didn't want to leave. I never do. Jane and Pete make you feel like a family visiting." ... "Lovely antiques and decorations, very nice folks." (1997)

EAGLE CLIFF HOUSE

2383 Highway 66, PO Box 4312, Estes Park, CO 80517   970-586-5425
Nancy & Mike Conrin, Resident Owners   800-414-0922

LOCATION	Two miles west of the center of Estes Park. Follow signs for Highway 36, which connects with Highway 66, 3/4 mile before YMCA.
OPEN	All year.
DESCRIPTION	Mountain home with guest cottage nestled in the Ponderosa Pines at the base of Eagle Cliff Mountain within walking distance to Rocky Mountian National Park.
NO. OF ROOMS	Main house: Two rooms with private baths; cottage with private bathroom and kitchenette. The cottage comes highly recommended.
RATES	Year-round rates are $80 for a double or single with bath and $115 for the cottage. There is a two-day minimum stay at the cottage on weekends and cancellation requires three weeks' notice.
CREDIT CARDS	MasterCard, Visa for reservations only.
BREAKFAST	Full breakfast includes whole grain pancakes and homemade granola.
AMENITIES	Flowers for birthdays and anniversaries, TV and extensive movie collection, snacks are always available. The Conrins are hiking and backpacking consultants and offer trailhead pickup or delivery.
RESTRICTIONS	None, children are welcome.
MEMBER	Bed & Breakfast Innkeepers of Colorado, Colorado Hotel and Lodging Association
KUDOS/COMMENTS	"Lovely cozy home, exceptional hosts, breakfasts are superb! Excellent decor." (1996)

ESTES PARK BED & BREAKFAST

141 Courtney Lane, PO Box 482, Estes Park, CO 80517   970-586-7781
Orie Vaye & Dick Williams, Resident Owners   800-492-3425
                                                   FAX 970-586-7782

FRICKEY MCSHANE'S BED & BREAKFAST

1731 Avalon Drive, Estes Park, CO 80517   970-586-0872
Norm & Sharon Frickey, Resident Owners

GLENN'S MOUNTAIN VISTA ACRE

PO Box 5219, Estes Park, CO 80517   970-586-3547

HEARTHSIDE INN BED & BREAKFAST

271 Big Horn Drive, PO Box 442, Estes Park, CO 80517   970-586-3100
Mary Alice Zoeter, Resident Owner

LOCATION	Take Highway 34 into downtown, turn north on Big Horn Drive. The inn is at the top of the hill on the left.
OPEN	All year.
DESCRIPTION	A 1928 two-story European chalet with French country furnishings.
NO. OF ROOMS	Three rooms with private bathrooms. Try the Monet Room.
RATES	Year-round rates are $110-140 for a single or double with a private bathroom and $380 for the entire B&B. There is a two-night minimum stay and a three-night minimum stay on holidays. Cancellation requires 14 days' notice.
CREDIT CARDS	MasterCard, Visa
BREAKFAST	Full breakfast, served in the dining room, includes fruits, juices, pastries and hot entrees. Lunch, dinner and special meals are available upon request and at additional cost.
AMENITIES	Fireplaces and whirlpools in the rooms, robes, turndown and chambermaid service, club room with TV, phone, wood-burning stove, books, games, complimentary refreshments and homemade treats.
RESTRICTIONS	No smoking, no pets, children over 15 are welcome.
KUDOS/COMMENTS	"Wonderful, friendly atmosphere." ... "Good views of mountains, especially Long's Peak." (1997)

HENDERSON HOUSE BED & BREAKFAST

5455 Highway 36, PO Box 3134, Estes Park, CO 80517   970-586-4639
Carl & Vicki Henderson, Resident Owners

LOCATION	Five miles east of Estes Park on Highway 36.
OPEN	June 15 to October 31.
DESCRIPTION	A 1988 three-story Cape Cod Victorian "homestay country inn" with Victorian-country furnishings, on 11 acres.
NO. OF ROOMS	Five rooms with private bathrooms. The King and Queen suite is the most popular.
RATES	Seasonal rates are $105-155 for a double occupancy with private bathroom. There is a minimum stay on July 4th and Labor Day. Cancellation requires seven days' notice and a $15 fee.
CREDIT CARDS	MasterCard, Visa
BREAKFAST	Full breakfast is served in the dining room, gazebo or on the deck.
AMENITIES	Gazebo, king-sized beds, two rooms have whirlpool tubs, fresh flowers, robes, central TV room with phone, fruit and cheese baskets, local dinner reservations.
RESTRICTIONS	No smoking, no pets, no children, married couples only...so don't forget to pack the marriage license...CH. The resident dogs are called Tyson and Benny.
KUDOS/COMMENTS	"Carl and Vicki Henderson were wonderful! The rooms were beautiful and clean (very clean!)." ... "Breakfast included fruit and a main course, Carl is a wonderful cook and Vicki is the perfect hostess. We'll go again." (1994) "The Hendersons are delightful and their home is beautiful and spacious." ... "Superb meals and wonderful snacks." ... "We loved every room." (1997)

HOLLYHOCK COTTAGE BED & BREAKFAST

5475 North St. Vrain, Highway 36,   *970-586-0785*
PO Box 3092, Estes Park, CO 80517
Virginia Denton, Resident Owner

THE QUILT HOUSE BED & BREAKFAST

310 Riverside Drive, PO Box 339, Estes Park, CO 80517   970-586-0427
Hans & Miriam Graetzer, Resident Owners
German spoken.

LOCATION	From Elkhorn Avenue (the main street through town), turn south at the traffic light to Riverside Drive. Continue about one mile on Riverside Drive past a Pizza Hut to a large brown house on the left.
OPEN	All year.
DESCRIPTION	A 1924 two-story mountain host home decorated with quilts.
NO. OF ROOMS	Three rooms with private bathrooms and separate guest cabin.
RATES	Year-round rates for a single or double with a private bathroom are $30-50. The guesthouse with a kitchenette rents for $60 and the entire B&B rents for $210 for up to eight people. There is no minimum stay and cancellation requires five days' notice.
CREDIT CARDS	No
BREAKFAST	Full breakfast is served in the dining room and includes juice, hot dish, fruit plate, homemade bread or muffins, choice of coffee, tea, hot chocolate and friendly conversation....coffee...TI
AMENITIES	Guest lounge, games, books, snack area, homemade quilts on the beds, guest house is wheelchair accessible, file of restaurant menus, hiking trail guidebook available.
RESTRICTIONS	No smoking, no pets, children over 10 are welcome.

ROMANTIC RIVERSONG INN

1765 Lower Broadview Road, PO Box 1910,   *970-586-4666*
Estes Park, CO 80517
Gary & Sue Mansfield, Resident Owners
Some Spanish spoken.

LOCATION	Take Highway 36 from Denver. Proceed through Estes Park to Moraine Avenue, at the stop light at Mary's Lake Road turn left, go one block and cross bridge, then make an immediate right and proceed to the end.
OPEN	All year.
DESCRIPTION	Early 1920s Craftsman duplexes, carriage house and lodge with country/Victorian furnishings, along the Big Thompson River with hiking trails and wildlife on the property.
NO. OF ROOMS	Nine rooms with private bathrooms. Try MeadowBright with the waterfall shower.

Romantic RiverSong Inn, Estes Park

RATES	Year-round rates are $125-250 for a single or double with a private bathroom. There is a minimum stay of two nights and cancellation requires 15 days' notice and a $25 fee, 30 days' for holidays.
CREDIT CARDS	MasterCard, Visa
BREAKFAST	Full breakfast is served in the dining room. The Inn has its own chef. Dinner is available by reservation.
AMENITIES	Robes, gazebo and pond, Jacuzzis for two, fresh flowers, afternoon tea, on-site weddings for elopers! Three rooms are wheelchair accessible.
RESTRICTIONS	No smoking, no pets (resident wildlife), children over 12 are welcome.
REVIEWED	*America's Romantic Inns, Birder's Guide to Bed & Breakfast Inns, The Colorado Guide, Country Inns and Back Roads, Non-Smokers Guide to Bed & Breakfasts, Recommended Country Inns of the Rocky Mountain Region, Special Places*
MEMBER	Independent Innkeepers Association, Distinctive Inns of Colorado, Professional Association of Innkeepers International
RATED	AAA 3 Diamonds, Mobil 3 Stars
KUDOS/COMMENTS	"Definitely a place for couples to make memories." ... "Beautiful rooms with unique furnishings. Peaceful setting for a great getaway." (1997)

EVERGREEN

A foothills commuter and trust-funder community, with a couple decent restaurants, a little lake and the peace and quiet of the mountains 28 miles west of Denver taking I-70 and then Highway 74.

HIGHLAND HAVEN CREEKSIDE INN

4395 Independence Trail, Evergreen, CO 80439   303-674-3577
Thomas Statzell and Gail Riley, Resident Owners   800-459-2406
FAX 303-674-9088

LOCATION	From I-70, take the Evergreen Parkway exit and go about seven miles past lake and on through mainstreet Evergreen. At the east end of town, turn right at blue lodging sign, the inn is visable on the creek.
OPEN	All year.
DESCRIPTION	A 1960 two-story wood-sided lodge on Bear Creek furnished with contemporary and French country pieces.
NO. OF ROOMS	Four rooms, five suites, and seven cottages with private bathrooms.
RATES	Year-round rates for a single or double with a private bathroom are $65-160 and suites are $110-160. There is a minimum stay on holidays and cancellation requires 10 days, 30 days for the holidays and 24 hours for business travelers...good idea...TI
CREDIT CARDS	American Express, Discover, MasterCard, Visa
BREAKFAST	"Enhanced" Continental is served in the dining room and includes home-baked items, fresh fruit, bagel bar with flavored cream cheeses, gourmet coffees and teas.
AMENITIES	Bottled water by bedside, custom chocolates, flowers, romantic poems on bed to celebrate weddings and anniversaries, Jacuzzi tub, gardens for picnics and celebrations, catered small meetings on log "pioneer porch."
RESTRICTIONS	No smoking, no pets. The Border Collie is Queenie and the Poodle is Misha.
MEMBER	Bed & Breakfast Innkeepers of Colorado
RATED	AAA 3 Diamonds, Mobil 3 Stars

Highland Haven Creekside Inn, Evergreen

FAIRPLAY

THE BEAR'S DEN

PO Box 1326, Fairplay, CO 80440
Thelma Milburn, Innkeeper

719-836-0921

HAND HOTEL BED & BREAKFAST

531 Front Street, Fairplay, CO 80440
Pat Pocious, Resident Owner

719-836-3595

FLORENCE

THE WILSON HOUSE BED & BREAKFAST

104 Lock, Florence, CO 81226
Earline Wilson, Resident Innkeeper

719-784-3650

FLORISSANT

PINECREST LODGE

178 Palmer Drive, Florissant, CO 80816
Cavin & Larry Harper, Resident Owners

719-687-3425
FAX 719-687-3496

FORT COLLINS

A medium-sized city with its roots in farming and ranching, the presence of Colorado State University gives it a "college town" flavor. The newly restored Old Town is a definite must to explore; there's art, theater and music at the Lincoln Center; and the Anheuser-Busch Clydesdales and Visitors Center is a kick, as are the New West Fest in August and the Balloon Festival in September. But the main attraction of the area are natural: Wild and Scenic Cache la Poudre (Poo der) River and Canyon, Lory State Park and Horsetooth Reservoir. From Denver, 60 miles north on I-25.

BENNET HOUSE BED & BREAKFAST

314 East Mulberry Street, Fort Collins, CO 80524   970-482-0025
C. L. Goodwin, Resident Innkeeper

THE EDWARDS HOUSE BED & BREAKFAST

402 Mountain Avenue, Fort Collins, CO 80521   970-493-9191
Gregory Belcher & Leslie Vogt, Resident Owners   800-281-9190
Spanish, French and German spoken.   FAX 970-484-0706

LOCATION	Three blocks west of College Avenue.
OPEN	All year.
DESCRIPTION	A neo-classical Denver Four Square with Victorian furnishings.
NO. OF ROOMS	Five rooms with private bathrooms and one room shares one bathroom. The owners recommend the Montezuma Fuller Suite.
RATES	Year-round rates are $99 for a single or double with a private bathroom, $79 for a single or double with a shared bathroom and $125-135 for a suite. There is no minimum stay and cancellation requires two weeks' notice.
CREDIT CARDS	American Express, Discover, MasterCard, Visa
BREAKFAST	Full breakfast, served in the dining room, includes special daily entree, seasonal fruits, homemade baked goods and beverages. Special meals are available on request.
AMENITIES	Fresh flowers, robes, private phones, TV/VCRs, evening hors d'oeuvres, use of library, parlor, exercise room, FAX, copy machines, computer ports, telephones and large conference room for meetings and special events.
RESTRICTIONS	No smoking, no pets, children over 10 years of age are welcome.
MEMBER	Bed & Breakfast Innkeepers of Colorado, Professional Association of Innkeepers International
KUDOS/COMMENTS	"Wonderful variety of rooms, beautifully furnished and decorated." ... "Warm reception and great breakfast." (1997)

Elizabeth Street Guest House B&B, Fort Collins

ELIZABETH STREET GUEST HOUSE B&B

202 East Elizabeth Street, Fort Collins, CO 80524 970-493-2337
John & Sheryl Clark, Resident Owners FAX 970-493-6662

LOCATION	In the Historic District, one block east of Colorado State University campus on the northeast corner of Elizabeth and Remington.
OPEN	All year.
DESCRIPTION	A restored 1905 two-story American "Four Square" brick home with oak woodwork, turn-of-the-century antiques and folk art.
NO. OF ROOMS	One room with private bathroom and two rooms share one bathroom. The Clark's favorite room is the Alaska.
RATES	Year-round rates are $65-95 for a single or double with a private bathroom and a single or double with a shared bathrom are $45-70. Minimum stay on CSU weekends, e.g., graduation. Cancellation requires one week's notice.
CREDIT CARDS	American Express, MasterCard, Visa
BREAKFAST	Full breakfast, served in the dining room, includes tea and coffee, juice, three kinds of cereal, fruit, homemade muffins and breads, eggs and specialty dishes.

AMENITIES	Robes and turndown service, TV in parlor, tea and coffee always available, books and games, guest refrigerator, airport shuttle, ironing board and iron.
RESTRICTIONS	No smoking, no pets. Louie, the resident Blue Heeler, plays Frisbee and loves to go on walks with guests and show off his food dispenser...just like the editor of this book...TI. Children over 10 years of age are welcome.
REVIEWED	*Recommended Country Inns of the Rocky Mountain Region, Best Places to Stay in the Rockies*
MEMBER	Tourist House Association

Mariposa on Spring Creek

706 East Stuart, Fort Collins, CO 80525   970-495-9604
Michele Kyle, Resident Owner   800-495-9604

The West Mulberry Street Bed & Breakfast Inn

616 West Mulberry Street, Fort Collins, CO 80521   970-221-1917
Michael & Rebecca Martin, Resident Owners   FAX 970-490-2810

LOCATION	Two blocks north of Colorado State University.
OPEN	All year.
DESCRIPTION	A 1905 two-story Four Square with quartersawn oak floors, beveled and stained-glass windows and turn-of-the-century furnishings.
NO. OF ROOMS	Four rooms with private bathrooms, plus a two room business suite. Rebecca recommends the West Garden Room.
RATES	Year-round rates (including tax) are $56-99 for a single or double with private bathroom. The business suite rents for $150. There is a minimum stay on some weekends and holidays and a seven-day cancellation policy, 30 days during special events.
CREDIT CARDS	American Express, Diners Club, Discover, MasterCard, Visa
BREAKFAST	Full breakfast, served in the dining room, includes quiche, omelets, waffles, crepes, homemade baked goods and beverages.

The West Mulberry Street Bed & Breakfast Inn, Fort Collins

AMENITIES   Fresh flowers, evening snack, bicycles, robes, TV room, down
                   comforters and historical reading material on the area.

RESTRICTIONS   No smoking, no pets, children over 12 are welcome.

MEMBER   Bed & Breakfast Innkeepers of Colorado

KUDOS/COMMENTS   "The B&B makes you feel very comfortable and the rooms are
                   beautiful." ... "The house is very nicely done; the innkeepers are
                   delightful, kind, caring, gracious and lovely." (1997)

FRISCO
(SUMMIT COUNTY)

On the south shores of Lake Dillon and the crossroads of Summit County's year-round resorts. From here, it's easy access to Breckenridge, Copper Mountain, Keystone and handy to Vail. Now undergoing restoration and a growth spurt, it's a great base camp. The Frisco Nordic Ski Center offers X-C in a pine forest along the lake shore. And for hearty souls, the Frisco Gold Rush is the biggest citizen's X-C race in the Rocky Mountains. But Frisco's Fantastic Fourth tops them all with laser light shows, live music, parades, foodfest and spactacular fireworks over Lake Dillon. From Denver, 75 miles west on I-70 and Highway 9.

THE FINN INN

PO Box 1315, Frisco, CO 80443   970-668-5108
Bill & Edith Anttila, Resident Owners
Finnish spoken.

LOCATION	One mile from I-70 exit 201.
OPEN	All year.
DESCRIPTION	A 1971 wood A-Frame with wraparound deck and rustic/antique furnishings.
NO. OF ROOMS	Three rooms share two bathrooms.
RATES	High season rates (December through March) are $80 for a single or double with shared bathroom. Off season rates are $60 for a single or double with shared bathroom. There is a two-night minimum stay during high season.
CREDIT CARDS	No
BREAKFAST	Full, hearty breakfast is served in the dining room.
AMENITIES	TV/VCR, videos in all rooms, outdoor hot tub, living room with moss-rock fireplace.
RESTRICTIONS	No smoking, the resident dog and cat are named Mustaa and Ariel.

FRISCO LODGE

321 Main Street, PO Box 1325, Frisco, CO 80443   970-668-0195
Susan Wentworth, Resident Owner   800-279-6000
                                                                                          FAX 970-668-0149

LOCATION	Corner of 4th and Main.
OPEN	All year.
DESCRIPTION	An 1885 Tyrolean with rustic furnishings.
NO. OF ROOMS	Ten rooms with private bathrooms and eight rooms with three shared bathrooms.
RATES	Winter rates are $95-100 for a single or double with private bathroom and $50-65 for a single or double with shared bathroom. Summer rates are $35-40 for a single or double with private bathroom and $30-35 for a double with shared bathroom. Inquire about minimum stay. There is a reservation/cancellation policy.
CREDIT CARDS	American Express, Discover, MasterCard, Visa
BREAKFAST	Continental is served in the dining room.
AMENITIES	Hot tub, fireplace, TV, radio and phone in rooms, complimentary apres ski, small meeting facilities.
RESTRICTIONS	Smoking limited, no pets, no children.

THE GALENA STREET MOUNTAIN INN

106 Galena Street, PO Box 417, Frisco, CO 80443   970-668-3224
Brenda McDonnell, Resident Manager   FAX 970-668-1569

LOCATION	Take the Frisco Main Street exit #201. From Main Street, turn on First Avenue and go one block to Galena Street.
OPEN	All year.
DESCRIPTION	A 1992 inn of neo-mission architecture with European interior decor.
NO. OF ROOMS	Fourteen rooms with private bathrooms. The Tower Room is the best in the house.
RATES	High-season rates (December, February and March) are $105-130 for a single or double with private bathroom and $160 for a suite. Low-season rates (October, November, January and April through September) are $69-105 for a single or double with private bathroom and $120 for a suite. There is a minimum stay during holidays and weekends. Cancellation requires 14 days' notice.

The Galena Street Mountain Inn, Frisco

CREDIT CARDS	American Express, Diners Club, Discover, MasterCard, Visa
BREAKFAST	Full breakfast is served Thanksgiving to Easter, Continental is served Easter to Thanksgiving, all breakfasts served in the dining room. Continental includes cereals, homemade granola, fruit dish, homemade pastries and breads. Winter breakfasts include the above plus one hot entree. Special meals are available for groups.
AMENITIES	Hot tub, sauna, robes, down comforters, 100% cotton sheets, TV and phone in the rooms, fireplace in common living room, complimentary refreshments, ski lockers and bike storage, two meeting rooms, handicapped access and catering for small meetings.
RESTRICTIONS	No smoking, no pets, inquire about children.
REVIEWED	*Best Places to Stay (The Rockies), The Colorado Guide*
MEMBER	Professional Association of Innkeepers International, Distinctive Inns of Colorado, Bed & Breakfast Innkeepers of Colorado
RATED	AAA 3 Diamonds
KUDOS/COMMENTS	"Gorgeous place, well-run, luxurious." ... "The best staff! Wonderful breakfasts." (1997)

LARK MOUNTAIN INN

109 Granite Street, PO Box 1646, Frisco, CO 80443 970-668-5237
Louise & Rob Moreno, Resident Owners 800-668-5275
FAX 970-668-2037

LOCATION	From Denver, take I-70 west to the Frisco Main Street exit, #201. Drive 3/4 mile down Main, turn right on First Avenue. The Lark is at First and Granite, one block off Main Street.
OPEN	All year.
DESCRIPTION	A 1972 two-story log and timber inn with hand-carved lodgepole and pinion-pine interior.
NO. OF ROOMS	Five rooms with private bathrooms, two rooms with shared bathrooms.
RATES	Seasonal rates are $60-100 for low and regular seasons and $85-160 for holiday and prime seasons. There is a reservation/cancellation policy.
CREDIT CARDS	MasterCard, Visa
BREAKFAST	Full breakfast, served in the dining room or on the sundeck, includes hot entree with fresh fruit, cereals, yogurt and fresh-baked item.
AMENITIES	Hot tub, robes, down comforters, mountain bikes for guests' use, rock gardens with native flowers, free transportation to all Summit County resorts.
RESTRICTIONS	No smoking, children over six are welcome. Well-behaved, housebroken pets are welcome. Resident Keeshound and "snow frisbee" champ is "Lexi Lopez."
MEMBER	Summit County Bed & Breakfast Association, Bed & Breakfast Innkeepers of Colorado, Colorado Hotel and Lodging Association, Professional Association of Innkeepers International
AWARDS	Won 1st Place in Frisco's 1995 Christmas Decorating Contest

MARDEI'S MOUNTAIN RETREAT

221 South 4th Avenue, PO Box 1767, Frisco, CO 80443   970-668-5337
Mike & Amy Wolach, Resident Owners

LOCATION	From I-70 exit 201, go west on Main Street, at the first four-way stop, turn south and go two blocks.
OPEN	All year.
DESCRIPTION	A 1950 two-story mountain cabin host home with comfortable furniture.
NO. OF ROOMS	Three rooms with private bathrooms and three rooms share two bathrooms. Columbine is the best room.
RATES	Holiday (Christmas, President's Day, Easter) rates are $90-120 for a double with a private bathroom, $70-90 for a single or double with a shared bathroom and $35-45 for a bed in the dorm room. Ski season rates are $70-90 for a double with a private bathroom, $50-60 for a single with a shared bathroom and $25-35 for a bed in the dorm. Off season rates are lower. There is a three-day minimum stay during holidays and two-week cancellation policy.
CREDIT CARDS	No
BREAKFAST	Continental breakfast is served in the dining room, includes granola, yogurts, cheeses, freshbaked muffins, bagels, fresh fruit and beverages.
AMENITIES	Fireplaces in common areas, one bedroom with private fireplace, hot tub on deck, cooking surprises, European down comforters and sinks in the rooms, TV and VCRs in rooms with private bathrooms, movie library, snowshoes available and horseshoes in summer.
RESTRICTIONS	No pets, no smoking. Children over three are welcome. The resident Golden Lab is Sage.
REVIEWED	*Recommended Country Inns of the Rocky Mountain Region.*
KUDOS/COMMENTS	"Excellent!" (1997)

OPEN BOX H BED & BREAKFAST

711 Belford Street, PO Box 1210, Frisco, CO 80443   *970-668-0661*
Chuck & Phyllis Hugins, Resident Owners   *FAX 970-668-0671*

LOCATION	From I-70 take exit #203. Go south on Summit Boulevard and continue through fourth stop light. Pass Main Street for a block and a half, turn right on 8th Avenue, right on Pitkin and left on 7th Avenue, left into alley.
OPEN	All year except April 20 to May 20.
DESCRIPTION	A 1988 three-level contemporary host home with contemporary furnishings.
NO. OF ROOMS	Two rooms with private bathrooms and two suites share one bathroom.
RATES	Winter rates, December 15 to April 15, are $59-79 for a single or double with a private bathroom and $99 for a suite with a shared bathroom. Summer rates, May 20 to December 14, are $48-69 for a single or double with a private bathroom and $89 for a suite with a shared bathroom. There is no minimum stay, ask about cancellation policy.
CREDIT CARDS	American Express, Discover, MasterCard, Visa
BREAKFAST	Full breakfast, served in the dining room, includes waffles, meat, eggs, cereal, corned-beef hash, French toast, muffins, home-baked bread, yogurt and beverages.
AMENITIES	Robes and fireplace in Mountain View suite, Jacuzzi in Butterfly room.
RESTRICTIONS	No smoking, no pets.
MEMBER	Summit County Bed & Breakfast Association

TWILIGHT INN

308 Main Street, PO Box 397, Frisco, CO 80443   970-668-5009
Teressa Kliegerman, Manager   800-262-1002
Spanish spoken.

LOCATION	One mile from I-70 exit, "Main Street Frisco," turn east off exit ramp and proceed one mile down Main Street. The inn is on the right-hand side between Third and Fourth Avenues.
OPEN	All year.
DESCRIPTION	The exterior of the inn is log and the interior is country with twelve individually decorated rooms accented with country antiques.
NO. OF ROOMS	Eight rooms with private baths and four rooms share two baths. Teressa suggests room 7.
RATES	High season, December through mid-April, rates are $103-128 for a single or double with a private bathroom, $90 for a single or double with a shared bathroom and the entire inn rents for $1,320-1,440. Off season, mid-April through November, rates are $60-75 for a single or double with a private bathroom, $50 for a single or double with a shared bathroom and the entire inn rents for $780-840. There is a two-night minimum on holiday weekends. Cancellation requires 14 days' notice in high season and 24 hours' in low season.
CREDIT CARDS	American Express, Discover, MasterCard, Visa
BREAKFAST	Continental Plus is served in the dining room and includes homemade breads & muffins, fresh fruit, granola, cereal, oatmeal, yogurt, bagels, juice, milk, coffee and tea.
AMENITIES	Indoor hot tub and outdoor deck, steam room, two common areas, laundry room, kitchen privileges, off-street parking, guest ski/bike storage, meeting facility for up to 12 people, and two handicapped accessible rooms.
RESTRICTIONS	None. The resident pets are one Black Lab called Erik and a Yellow Lab called Bjorn...Apologies Bjorn, we spelled your name wrong in the last edition...TI...it will never happen again.
REVIEWED	*The Colorado Guide, Recommended B&Bs in Rocky Mountain Region, The Colorado Handbook*
MEMBER	Professional Association of Innkeepers International, Summit County Bed & Breakfast Association

WOODS INN INTERNATIONAL

205 South 2nd Avenue, PO Box 1302, Frisco, CO 80443   970-668-3389
Daryn Miller & Kerrie Kelly, Resident Managers   800-668-4448
FAX 970-668-8028

LOCATION	On Frisco's main street drive 1/2 mile to 2nd Avenue, turn right and go one block.
OPEN	All year.
DESCRIPTION	A 1938 two-story pine-log inn with "homey" furnishings.
NO. OF ROOMS	Seven rooms share two bathrooms that have two showers each. Try room E, the best room in the house.
RATES	High season, November through April, rates are $60 for a single with shared bathroom and $75 for a double with shared bathroom. Off season rates are $40 for a single with shared bathroom and $50 for a double with shared bathroom. There is a minimum stay during high season and holidays. There is no refund for cancellation unless the room is rebooked.
CREDIT CARDS	American Express, MasterCard, Visa
BREAKFAST	Full breakfast is served in the dining room in the winter and Continental Plus in the summer.
AMENITIES	Outdoor hot tub, common living area with TV/VCR and fireplace. Bike paths and hiking trails nearby. All mountain sports and activities can be arranged.
RESTRICTIONS	No smoking, no pets, children are welcome.
MEMBER	Summit County Bed & Breakfast Association

FRUITA

VALLEY VIEW BED & BREAKFAST

8880 21 Road, Fruita, CO 81501   970-858-9503
Lou & Jan, Resident Owners

GARDENER

Tucked in the fertile Huerfano River Valley, just south of the Wet Mountain Valley and San Isabel National Forest. This beautiful, somewhat remote area is well-kept secret. Ranching and farming are pretty much what goes on here, but there's action in Westcliffe: Rainbow Trail Round-Up Mountain Bike Race in July is one of the best of its kind; and in August, Jazz in the Sangres attracts multitudes of fans. From Pueblo, south on I-25 to Walsenburg, then 27 miles northwest on Highway 69.

MALACHITE SCHOOL & SMALL FARM BED & BREAKFAST

8055 County Road 570, Gardener, CO 81040   *719-746-2412*
Alan Mace, Resident Owner

LOCATION	Six miles west of Gardener, take Highway 69 to Redwing turnoff, then one mile south on County Road 570.
OPEN	All year.
DESCRIPTION	An 1880s adobe homestead farmhouse with contemporary solar wing on a 260-acre, non-profit, environmental, working farm and school.
NO. OF ROOMS	Three rooms with shared bathrooms.
RATES	Year-round rates are $35, $30 for a single and $5 per person for more than two to a room.
CREDIT CARDS	No
BREAKFAST	Full breakfast is served in the dining room. Lunch and dinner are available.
AMENITIES	Join in farm chores, organic gardening, plowing with draft horses, hayrides; meeting facilities, handicapped access. Inquire about farm stay, hostel and college programs.
RESTRICTIONS	No smoking, no pets.
REVIEWED	*The Colorado Guide* (see Westcliffe)

GEORGETOWN

A remarkably restored Victorian mining town and National Historic District. In town, more than 200 of the original buildings still stand. Don't miss the Bighorn Sheep Viewing Station next to Georgetown Lake. Close to Loveland Ski area. Major event: the Georgetown Christmas Market and Santa Lucia Celebration in early December. Fifty miles west of Denver on I-70.

CREEKSIDE B&B INN

610 7th Street, PO Box 917, Georgetown, CO 80444   303-569-2664
Carol Curran, Resident Owner   800-484-9493 X-5896

LOCATION	From I-70, take exit 228, go under highway and turn right and drive to the end of the road (historic district). Turn left, go one block, make second left. As you come down the street, you are looking at the inn with the picket fence and wishing well.
OPEN	All year.
DESCRIPTION	A two-story 1940s-era Victorian host home with Victorian and Colonial furnishings.
NO. OF ROOMS	Three rooms with private bathrooms.
RATES	Year-round rates for a single or double with a private bathroom are $69-95. Ask about minimum stay and cancellation policies.
CREDIT CARDS	MasterCard, Visa
BREAKFAST	"Bountiful, old-fashioned" country breakfast is served in the dining room.
AMENITIES	Robes, deck, gift shop, games, TV, video, tapes, picnic area, fishing, trails, books and magazines.
RESTRICTIONS	No smoking, no pets, children over seven are welcome. Lady the cat "welcomes guests and then goes back to nap in 'her' room."

Creekside B&B Inn, Georgetown

HARDY HOUSE

605 Brownell Street, PO Box 15, Georgetown, CO 80444   *303-569-3388*
Carla & Mike Wagner, Resident Owners   *800-490-4802*

LOCATION	Fifty miles west of Denver on I-70. Take exit #228, head south on Argentine which turns into Brownell.
OPEN	All year.
DESCRIPTION	Located in the Historic District of Georgetown. The 1880 two-story Victorian Cape Cod is red and white with a white picket fence. The interior is Victorian with a pot-bellied stove in the parlor.
NO. OF ROOMS	Four rooms with private bathrooms. The Wagners recommend the Victoria Suite.
RATES	Year-round rates are $73-82 for a single or double with a private bathroom and $82-112 for a suite. There is no minimum stay and cancellation requires seven days' notice.
CREDIT CARDS	MasterCard or Visa only to reserve room. Payment is by cash or check.
BREAKFAST	Full formal candlelight breakfast is served. Box lunches are available in the summer. Dinner is available with Romance package.
AMENITIES	All rooms have TV/VCR, phone for guests in the hallway, hot tub outside and afternoon tea and coffee with home-baked goodies inside. The inn is an easy walk to the Historic District, shops and restaurants. Romance and other packages are available,
RESTRICTIONS	No smoking, no pets, children over 12 are welcome. Frankie is the resident Parrot and the Schnauzer is Guss.
REVIEWED	*Recommended Country Inns of the Rocky Mountain Region*
MEMBER	Colorado Hotel and Lodging Association
KUDOS/COMMENTS	"Run by friendly owners." (1996)

HILLSIDE HOUSE

1034 Main Street, PO Box 266, Georgetown, CO 80444   *303-569-0912*
Ken & Marge Acker, Resident Owners   *800-490-9012*

LOCATION	Take exit 228 from I-70. Go past the Total gas station, turn right at the stop sign. Turn left at the first street (11th), go four short blocks to Main, turn right, we are the second house on the left.
OPEN	All year.
DESCRIPTION	A 1970 Victorian with stained glass, planked floors, antiques, and a veranda that stretches across the front of the house.
NO. OF ROOMS	Two rooms with private bathrooms. Try the Columbine Suite.
RATES	Year-round rates are $70-80 for the Aspen Room and $95-105 for the Columbine Suite.
CREDIT CARDS	MasterCard, Visa
BREAKFAST	Full breakfast is served in the dining room and includes Belgian waffles with peaches or strawberries and cream, breads and cakes, juices and fruit.
AMENITIES	Coffee and cookies upon arrival, candy in rooms; TV, games and puzzles in the loft; four-foot soaking tub with skylight in the Columbine Suite.
RESTRICTIONS	No smoking, no pets. Children are welcome.
KUDOS/COMMENTS	"Wonderful hosts and a comfy home." (1996)

KIP ON THE CREEK

1205 Rose Street, PO Box 754, Georgetown, CO 80444   303-569-2923
Sue & Terry Yordt, Resident Owners   800-821-6545

LOCATION	Georgetown exit 228 off I-70. Drive straight ahead over a small bridge. Turn right on Rose Street. The inn is 1/4 mile down on the right.
OPEN	All year.
DESCRIPTION	A 1980 two-story country inn with Victorian oak wicker furnishings and teddy bears, located on the banks of Clear Creek.
NO. OF ROOMS	Three rooms with private bathrooms. The Stratford might be the room of choice.
RATES	Year-round rates are $57-77 for a single with private bath and $64-85 for a double with a private bath. Reservations guaranteed with MasterCard or Visa. Cancellation requires seven days.
CREDIT CARDS	MasterCard, Visa
BREAKFAST	Full breakfast, served in the dining room, begins with homemade breads and muffins, juice, cold cereal and hot entree, e.g., pancakes, waffles, French toast, casseroles.
AMENITIES	Common areas include solarium with hot tub, family room with wood-burning stove, TV/VCR; living room with antique fireplace; deck on the creek; Stratford room has sauna in its private bath; Creek room has balcony on the creek.
RESTRICTIONS	No smoking except in designated areas. Children over 15 are welcome.
REVIEWED	*Bed & Breakfast Coucher-Dejeuner*
MEMBER	Bed & Breakfast Innkeepers of Colorado
KUDOS/COMMENTS	"Run by friendly owners." (1994)

GLENWOOD SPRINGS

Big hotels, big natural hot springs pools, and a grand place to visit, particularly from Denver over the mountains by train. Don't miss renting a mountain bike for the Glenwood Canyon Bike Path, the (wild) Strawberry Days Festival in June or the Ski-Spree Winter Carnival in February. Get there via train or I-70, 160 miles west of Denver.

ADDUCCI'S INN BED & BREAKFAST

1023 Grand Avenue, Glenwood Springs, CO 81601   *970-945-9341*
Virginia Adducci, Resident Owner

LOCATION	Center of town, five blocks south of 1-70 exit.
OPEN	All year.
DESCRIPTION	A 1900 Victorian with antique furnishings.
NO. OF ROOMS	One room with private bathroom, two rooms that share a half bathroom and shower and two rooms that share a full bathroom.
RATES	Year-round rates are $65 for a single or double with private bathroom and $28-55 for a single or double with shared bathroom. There is a reservation/cancellation policy.
CREDIT CARDS	MasterCard, Visa
BREAKFAST	Full breakfast is served in the dining room. Breakfast is available in the Adducci's restaurant.`
AMENITIES	Hot tub during ski season, TV and radio in dining room, phone in parlor, complimentary refreshments, small meeting facilities.
RESTRICTIONS	No smoking, no pets.
REVIEWED	*The Colorado Guide, Let's Go USA*

AUNTIE'S BED & BREAKFAST

109 2nd Street, Glenwood Springs, CO 81601   *970-945-7864*
Alondra Cole, Resident Owner

BACK IN TIME BED & BREAKFAST

927 Cooper Avenue, Glenwood Springs, CO 81601   *970-945-6183*
June & Ron Robinson, Resident Owners

KUDOS/COMMENTS   "Warm, friendly innkeepers." (1997)

SUNLIGHT INN

10252 County Road 117, Glenwood Springs, CO 81601   970-945-5225
Peter Brigham, Resident Owner   800-733-4757
FAX 970-945-5225

LOCATION	Twelve miles south of I-70 Glenwood Springs exit 116, at the base of Ski Sunlight.
OPEN	All year.
DESCRIPTION	A 1946 western ranch with rustic and western furnishings.
NO. OF ROOMS	Twenty rooms with private bathrooms.
RATES	Summer rates are $49-69 for a single or double with private bathroom. Winter rates are flexible. Call for details.
CREDIT CARDS	American Express, MasterCard, Visa
BREAKFAST	Continental is served in the dining room in the summer. On-site restaurant open during winter.
AMENITIES	Hot tub, fireplace in honeymoon suite, meeting facilities, handicapped access.
RESTRICTIONS	No pets. Children are welcome.

"THE" BED & BREAKFAST ON MITCHELL CREEK

1686 Mitchell Creek Road, Glenwood Springs, CO 81601   970-945-4002
Stan & Carole Rachesky, Resident Owners
Some Spanish spoken.

LOCATION	Exit #114 from I-70, go straight to stop sign, turn left (west) and go 1/2 mile to Mitchell Creek Road, turn right (north), continue up winding country road for 1-1/4 miles, enter State Fish Hatchery, drive through hatchery for 1/4 mile and follow stream.
OPEN	All year.
DESCRIPTION	A 1993 log cabin home with contemporary furnishings.
NO. OF ROOMS	One suite with private bathroom and separate entrance.
RATES	Year-round rates are $90 for a double with private bathroom. There is a two-night minimum stay on weekends and seven-day cancellation policy.
CREDIT CARDS	Visa to hold reservation only, payment by cash or check please.
BREAKFAST	Full breakfast is served on the deck or in the main house. Lunch and special meals will be considered.
AMENITIES	Very private, large patio with campfire, facilities for small weddings or other special occasions.
RESTRICTIONS	No smoking, no pets in suite, children of all ages welcome. The resident German Shepherd is Brush, and Tigger is the Cat.

GOLDEN

The state's former territorial capitol is at the entrance to Lookout Mountain Park and Golden Gate Canyon State Park, with miles of trails. The city is home to the Colorado School of Mines and Coors Brewery. Buffalo Bill Days in July and Oktoberfest in September are funfests. Just west of Denver's metroplex via Highway 6.

ANTIQUE ROSE BED & BREAKFAST INN

1422 Washington Avenue, Golden, CO 80401   *303-277-1893*
         FAX 303-278-9747

LOCATION	On the southern end of Golden's Historic District, near the Colorado School of Mines.
OPEN	All year.
DESCRIPTION	An 1880s two-story Queen Anne Victorian with gables and dormers and Victorian furnishings.
NO. OF ROOMS	Four rooms with private bathrooms. The Victoria Suite is the best room in the house.
RATES	Year-round rates are $75-95 for a single or double with a private bathroom and $115-128 for a suite. There is no minimum stay and there is a reservation/cancellation policy.
CREDIT CARDS	MasterCard, Visa
BREAKFAST	Full "American-style" breakfast served in the dining room.
AMENITIES	Roses and candlelight dinner catered upon request, whirlpool tubs.
RESTRICTIONS	No smoking. Room occupancy limited to two people. The resident Toy Poodle is called Brandy.

ASHLEY HOUSE & BREAKFAST

30500 Highway 40, Golden, CO 80401   *303-526-2411*
Ken Martin and Tim Coursey, Resident Innkeepers   *800-308-2411*
French spoken.

LOCATION	From I-70 take exit 252, the Evergreen Parkway. At the first traffic light, turn right (west) on Highway 40. Watch for a sign on the left-hand side at approximately one mile.
OPEN	All year.
DESCRIPTION	A 1993 three-story contemporary mountain inn.
NO. OF ROOMS	Five rooms with private bathrooms. Jackie Thompson thinks the Tartan Room is her best.
RATES	Year-round rates are $69-89 for a single or double with a private bathroom. There is no minimum stay and a 14-day cancellation policy with a $20 fee.

CREDIT CARDS	American Express, MasterCard, Visa
BREAKFAST	Full breakfast, served in the dining room, includes eggs, bacon, sausage, hashbrowns, homemade cinnamon rolls, muffins and beverages.
AMENITIES	Roses for birthdays and anniversaries, afternoon tea or coffee, telephones, TV in every room, hot tub on the patio, handicapped access.
RESTRICTIONS	No smoking, no pets, well-behaved children are welcome. The local dog is called Ashley.

THE DOVE INN BED & BREAKFAST

711 14th Street, Golden, CO 80401   303-278-2209
Tim & Connie Sheffield, Resident Owners   FAX 303-278-4029

LOCATION	From I-70 take exit 265 to Highway 58 and travel six miles to Washington Street, turn left and go eight blocks to 14th, turn left half a block.
OPEN	All year.
DESCRIPTION	An 1864 two-story Victorian. The outside is stucco over original Golden brick, the interior is comfortable and a huge Blue Spruce in the front yard is over 100 years old.
NO. OF ROOMS	Six rooms with private baths.
RATES	Year-round rates are $65-90. There is a five-day cancellation policy.
CREDIT CARDS	American Express, Discover, MasterCard, Visa
BREAKFAST	Full breakfast, served in the dining room, includes a hot entree, muffins, rolls, cereal, juice, fruit, coffee and tea.
AMENITIES	TV/VCR. telephones and FAX
RESTRICTIONS	No smoking, no pets, ask about children.
MEMBER	Colorado Hotel and Lodging Association, Bed & Breakfast Innkeepers of Colorado, Professional Association of Innkeepers International
RATED	ABBA 1 Crown

A TOUCH OF HEAVEN / TALMAR BED & BREAKFAST

16720 West 63rd Place, Golden, CO 80403   303-279-4133
Kathy Bury, Resident Innkeeper

GRANBY

SHADOW MOUNTAIN GUEST RANCH

5043 Highway 125, Granby, CO 80446   970-887-9524
Jim & Dale White, Resident Owners   800-647-4236

GRAND JUNCTION

Grand Junction features wineries and a wine festival, Colorado National Monument, Grand Mesa, a dinosaur museum, river sports on the Colorado River, outdoor activities and a country music festival.

THE HOUSE ON OURAY

760 Ouray Avenue, Grand Junction, CO 81501   970-245-8452
Marlene Johnsen, Resident Owner.

LOCATION	One block off 7th and Grand in downtown Grand Junction.
OPEN	All year. Closed Thanksgiving, Christmas Day and Christmas Eve.
DESCRIPTION	A 1905 two-story Victorian with antiques and Victorian furnishings.
NO. OF ROOMS	Three rooms with private bathrooms. The best room: Molly Brown.
RATES	Year-round rates are $40-65 for a single with private bathroom and $50-75 for a double with private bathroom. There is no minimum stay and cancellation requires seven days' notice.
CREDIT CARDS	MasterCard, Visa
BREAKFAST	Full, hot breakfast is served in the dining room. Lunch, dinner and special meals are available on request.
AMENITIES	TV, game room, coffee delivered to room on request. Small gift shop with collectibles and items from around the world.
RESTRICTIONS	No smoking, no pets, children over 14 are welcome. Sam is the resident Alaskan Eskimo Dog who loves people.
MEMBER	Colorado Hotel and Lodging Association, Grand Valley Bed & Breakfast Association.

JUNCTION COUNTRY INN BED & BREAKFAST

861 Grand Avenue, Grand Junction, CO 81501   970-241-2817
Karl & Theresa Bloom, Resident Owners

LOCATION	Located at corner of 9th and Grand in the downtown Historic District.
OPEN	All year except Christmas Eve and Day.
DESCRIPTION	A 1907 two-story Classic Box Victorian with Victorian furnishings.
NO. OF ROOMS	Two rooms with private bathrooms and two rooms share one bathroom. Try the Presidential Suite if Bubba isn't in town...TI
RATES	Year-round rates are $45-64 for a single with a private bathroom, $49-69 for a double with private bathroom, $35-45 for a single with a shared bathroom and $39-49 for a double with a shared bathroom. There is a seven-day cancellation policy.
CREDIT CARDS	American Express, MasterCard, Visa
BREAKFAST	Full breakfast, served in the dining room, includes fresh-baked goods, homemade jams, hot entree and beverages. Afternoon snacks and picnic lunches are available.
AMENITIES	TV available in the suites, childcare is available (please reserve in advance) as well as assistance in planning your day, and afternoon snacks are served in the parlor.
RESTRICTIONS	No smoking! no pets, all children are welcome. Siegfried the dog has a terrific name and uncertain ancestry and Scootie is a Tabby.
REVIEWED	*Frommer's Colorado*
MEMBER	Professional Association of Innkeepers International, Grand Valley Bed & Breakfast Association, American Bed & Breakfast Association.

MT. GARFIELD BED & BREAKFAST

3355 F Road, Grand Junction, CO 81520
Todd & Carrie McKay, Resident Owners
German spoken.

970-434-8120
800-547-9108
FAX 970-434-1250

LOCATION	Take exit #37 off I-70 to the first stoplight (Patterson Road also called "F" Road). Turn left at Patterson and drive approximately one mile east. Turn right just before the gas station. The B&B is on the right.
OPEN	All year.
DESCRIPTION	A 1992, 1-1/2-story ranch-style host home with country touches "both masculine and feminine."
NO. OF ROOMS	Five rooms with private bathrooms. The best room is #5.
RATES	High season (April 1 through September 30) rates are $55-110 for a single or double with private bathroom, $90 for a suite and $370 for the entire B&B. Low season rates are $44-88 for a single or double with a private bathroom, $88 for suite and $336 for the entire B&B. No minimum stay and cancellation requires a 24-hour notice.
CREDIT CARDS	American Express, Discover, MasterCard, Visa
BREAKFAST	Full breakfast is served in the dining room and includes entrees like Belgian waffles, pancakes, a Buffalo breakfast-casserole ("the most popular item"); also homemade fruit delights, fresh bread, gourmet coffee, hot herbal or regular tea, juice or milk.
AMENITIES	All rooms have air conditioning, cable TV, robes, outdoor hot tub on deck, peach orchard, BBQ grills and picnic tables, private phone line, sunken living room and loft room, piano, 120-gallon freshwater aquarium and four American Bison on property.
RESTRICTIONS	No smoking indoors, no pets, children are welcome. Hamms the dog heads up the list of resident pets. He shares space and attention with the cats, Mattie, Tom and Hamm's Kitty. Then there are Whiskey the Quarter horse and four as-yet-unnamed American Bison.
MEMBER	Bed & Breakfast Innkeepers of Colorado, AAA
RATED	AAA 2 Diamonds
KUDOS/COMMENTS	"Great hosts, truly dedicated to guests' happiness." (1996)

GRAND LAKE

Great outdoor and recreational bonanzas surround this little mountain village at the west entrance to Rocky Mountain National Park, on the shores of the state's largest natural lake, in the Arapahoe National Forest and just up the road from Shadow Mountain Reservoir. Fun times to be here: mid-July for the Western Weekend Buffalo BBQ and Lighted Boat Parade; in early August, the nation's highest chartered yacht club hosts the Annual Lipton Cup Regatta (there's a story here); and the summer-long Fishing Derby for tagged trout is challenging, as is the local 18-hole golf course. In winter, the area is home to millions of snowmobilers. About 100 miles northwest of Denver via Highways 40 and 34.

COLUMBINE CREEK RANCH B&B

14814 US Highway 34, PO Box 1675,   970-627-2429
Grand Lake, CO 80447   FAX 970-627-2429
James & Tami Wold, Resident Owners

LOCATION	On Highway 34, 100 yards from the entrance into downtown Grand Lake.
OPEN	All year.
DESCRIPTION	A 1920s-era two-story rustic host home with lots of pinewood and country interior decor.
NO. OF ROOMS	Four rooms with private bathrooms and two rooms share two bathrooms.
RATES	Year-round rates are $80 for a double with private bathroom, $55-65 for a single or double with shared bathroom and $60-75 for guesthouse and cabins. There is a minimum stay during holiday weekends and a two-week cancellation policy.
CREDIT CARDS	MasterCard, Visa
BREAKFAST	Full, all-you-can-eat breakfast is served buffet style in the dining room.
AMENITIES	Trout ponds (fishing costs extra), guests' fresh-caught trout seasoned and grilled, hot tub, snacks available at all times, big-screen TV, fireplace, marshmallow roasts, pig roasts for groups of 30 or more.
RESTRICTIONS	No smoking, no pets (except in cabins), children are welcome
REVIEWED	Colorado Association of Campgrounds, Cabins and Lodges, Guides Unlimited
MEMBER	Colorado Association of Cabins, Campgrounds and Lodges
KUDOS/COMMENTS	"Historic, renovated log lodge." ... "Charming antiques." (1996)

HUMMINGBIRD BED & BREAKFAST

132 Lakeview Drive, Grand Lake, CO 80447   970-627-3417
Dave & Judy Case, Resident Owners

LOCATION	Two miles south of Grand Lake off County Road 465.
OPEN	All year.
DESCRIPTION	A 1992 two-story contemporary host home with a covered outside deck and country furnishings.
NO. OF ROOMS	Two rooms with private bathrooms. Try the Ruby suite.
RATES	Year-round rates are $75-95 for a double with private bathroom.
CREDIT CARDS	No
BREAKFAST	Full breakfast, served in the dining room, includes a hot entree with breakfast meats, homebaked breads, muffins, fruit and beverages.
AMENITIES	Wildflowers in the rooms, roses for special occasions, VCR/TV, private entrance, lake view, special accommodations for quilt and sewing retreats, refreshments offered on arrival or in the evening, and the innkeepers will make dinner reservations for guests.
RESTRICTIONS	No smoking, no pets, children over five are welcome.

OLDE GRAND LAKE CABINS BED & BREAKFAST

325 Vine Street, PO Box 400, Grand Lake, CO 80447   970-627-9393
Benji and Janet Bendixen, Resident Owners

LOCATION	Half block north of Main Street in Grand Lake Village.
OPEN	All year.
DESCRIPTION	A 1930s two-story peeled-log home with cabins and eclectic furnishings.
NO. OF ROOMS	Two rooms share one bathroom. Inquire about cabins.
RATES	Year-round rates are $75 for a single or double with shared bathroom. There is a reservation/cancellation policy.
CREDIT CARDS	MasterCard, Visa
BREAKFAST	Continental breakfast is served in the kitchen, sun porch or den.
AMENITIES	Robes, TV, books, laundry room, outdoor grill and complimentary coffee and tea.
RESTRICTIONS	No pets, due in part to the resident goat...we're a little vague on this caveat, so use your imagination...CH

Onahu Lodge

2096 County Road 491, PO Box 562,   970-627-8523
Grand Lake, CO 80447
Donna Lyons, Resident Owner

LOCATION	Five miles north of Grand Lake Village at the west entrance of Rocky Mountain National Park.
OPEN	All year.
DESCRIPTION	A 1969 hand-hewn log host home with comfortable antique and rustic furnishings.
NO. OF ROOMS	One room with private bathroom and one room shares a bathroom.
RATES	Year-round rates are $75 for a double with private bathroom and $125 for three or four persons with shared bath. There is a two-night minimum stay with some exceptions, and a reservation/cancellation policy.
CREDIT CARDS	No, cash or personal check.
BREAKFAST	Continental Plus is served in the dining room. Lunch for hikers and skiers with prior notice.
AMENITIES	Seclusion, views of the Never Summer Range, Colorado River and Rocky Mountain National Park, skiing out the backdoor, wildlife walk through the yard in the summer, special rates for artists or writers who need quiet, bright studio space, overnight boarding for horses.
RESTRICTIONS	No smoking inside lodge, no pets. Children over five are welcome.
KUDOS/COMMENTS	"Best location for wildlife viewing; borders Rocky Mountain National Park." (1997)

The Osprey Inn Bed & Breakfast

12685 Highway 34, Grand Lake, CO   970-627-3431

Spirit Mountain Ranch

3863 County Road 41, PO Box 942, Grand Lake, CO 80447   970-887-3551
Beth Warner & Sandy Wilson, Resident Owners   800-887-3551

LOCATION	Exit I-70 onto Highway 40 and take through Granby. Take Highway 34 east to Grand Lake and Rocky Mountain National Park. Turn left on County Road 41. Drive 3.9 miles, the ranch is on the left.
OPEN	All year.

DESCRIPTION	A 1995 timber-framed inn with cedar exterior on 72 private acres.
NO. OF ROOMS	Four rooms with private bathrooms.
RATES	Year-round rates are $100 plus tax for a single or double with a private bathroom. A minimum stay is encouraged during summer months and there is a cancellation policy.
CREDIT CARDS	Discover, MasterCard, Visa
BREAKFAST	Full breakfast includes scones or muffins, blue-corn and sour-cream waffles with pinon nuts (while they last!), fresh strawberries or raspberries, frittata with fresh herbs, bacon, home-fries and beverages. Special meals are available with prior arrangements.
AMENITIES	Hot tub in aspen grove, afternoon tea & scones, hiking and wildlife viewing on 72 mountain acres, moss-rock fireplaces, sun-drenched decks and handicapped access.
RESTRICTIONS	No smoking, no pets. Resident pets include two black Labs named Lakota & Blue, a Schnauzer named Tao and a Thoroughbred named Traveler that enjoys a nice slice of watermelon on hot afternoons..."now if he'd only spit them seeds in the sp'toon, we'd have ourselves a circus act!"...CH
MEMBER	Bed & Breakfast Innkeepers of Colorado

WINDING RIVER RESORT

1447 County Road 491, PO Box 629,
Grand Lake, CO 80447
Wes House, Resident Owners

970-627-3215
800-252-8121
FAX 970-623-1121

LOCATION	Take Highway 34 approximately 1.5 miles north of Grand Lake Village. Turn west on Country Road 491, go 1.5 miles.
OPEN	May 15th to January 1st.
DESCRIPTION	A 1989 two-story western lodge with theme rooms.
NO. OF ROOMS	Two rooms with private bathrooms. Wes recommends The Trapper room.
RATES	Year-round rates are $80 for a double with private bath. There is no minimum stay requirement and cancellation requires 30 days' notice.
CREDIT CARDS	Discover, MasterCard, Visa
BREAKFAST	Continental breakfast is served in the lodge area and includes pastries, juices, cereal, bagels and coffee or tea. Chuckwagon breakfasts and dinners are also available.
AMENITIES	Horse boarding facilities, mountain biking, hiking, fishing, birding, wildlife watching, microwave and refrigerator.
RESTRICTIONS	No smoking, no pets, children are welcome. Animal farm and 20 horses.

GREELEY

New York Tribune publisher Horace Greeley, Nathan Meeker and the Union Colonists founded this agricultural community and James Michener immortalized it in Centennial. It's the home of the University of Northern Colorado and the best public radio station in the Rockies: KUNC. From Denver, 54 miles northeast via I-25 and Highway 34.

STERLING HOUSE INN

818 12th Street Road, Greeley, CO 80631   970-351-8805
Lillian Peeples, Resident Owner
German spoken.

LOCATION	From I-25, take the Greeley exit east on Highway 34. When Highway 34 divides, take Business 34 into downtown Greeley. Turn right on 8th Avenue and go two blocks to 12th Street Road. Turn right.
OPEN	All year.
DESCRIPTION	A renovated 1885 one-story Plains Victorian with 12-foot ceilings and antique Victorian furnishings.
NO. OF ROOMS	Two rooms with private bathroom and one room shares one bathroom. The owner's favorite is the Rose Room.
RATES	Year-round rates are $46-55 for a single or double with private bathroom and $150 for the entire suite. There is a minimum stay during University of Northern Colorado graduation and a reservation/cancellation policy.
CREDIT CARDS	MasterCard, Visa
BREAKFAST	Full breakfast, served in the dining room or on front porch, includes various egg dishes, crepes, French toast, juice, fruit and beverages. Consideration is given to guests with special diets and needs. Candlelight dinners are also available.
AMENITIES	Down comforters, air conditioning, front porch swing, refreshments provided upon arrival, meeting facilities, and kitchen priviledges for longer stays.
RESTRICTIONS	Smoking restricted to enclosed back porch, no pets, children over 10 are welcome.
REVIEWED	*The Colorado Guide, Inn For the Night, The Denver Post*

GREEN MOUNTAIN FALLS

Small, pretty mountain community in the Ute Pass area. The centerpeice lake and gazebo are busy summer and winter, and Annual Christmas Yule Log Hunt is a major event. Handy to Pikes Peak toll road, about 18 miles west of Colorado Springs on Highway 24.

LAKEVIEW TERRACE HOTEL

10580 Foster Avenue, Green Mountain Falls, CO 80819   719-684-9119
Marc & Victoria Marelich, Resident Owners   FAX 719-684-8313

OUTLOOK LODGE BED & BREAKFAST

6975 Howard Street, Green Mountain Falls, CO 80819   719-684-2303
Hayley & Patrick Moran, Resident Owners

LOCATION	In the center of town, next to Church of Wildwood.
OPEN	All year.
DESCRIPTION	An 1889 Victorian built as the parsonage for the Church in the Wildwood. The Inn contains country-Victorian furnishings and is nestled in the pines near Pikes Peak.
NO. OF ROOMS	Six rooms with private bathrooms and two rooms with a shared bathroom. The Moran's pick rooms 1 and 6 as their favorites.
RATES	Year-round rates are $55 for a single or double with bath, $45-55 for a single or double with shared bath and $70 for a suite. There is no minimum stay. Cancellation requires seven days' notice and there is a $10 cancellation fee.
CREDIT CARDS	MasterCard, Visa
BREAKFAST	Full breakfast, served in the dining room, includes a hot entree, fruit, breads, muffins, juice, milk, coffee and tea.
AMENITIES	Quiet, comfortable rooms with fresh flowers. Fireplace and wood-burning stove, TV and telephone in common area. A large dining-room area serves well for meetings.
RESTRICTIONS	No smoking, no pets
MEMBER	Bed & Breakfast Innkeepers of Colorado
KUDOS/COMMENTS	"Hayley, the owner, is very friendly and helpful to guests and locals." (1994)

GROVER

Four miles from the ranch house is the Pawnee National Grasslands. Thirty miles to the east lie the Pawnee Buttes. Great location for bird watching.

WEST PAWNEE RANCH

29451 WCR 130, Grover, CO 80729   970-895-2482
Paul & Louanne Timm, Resident Owners

LOCATION	From Greeley, take Highway 85 to Road 122 (twelve miles beyond Nunn), take Road 122 until it dead ends, then turn north on Road 55 and drive to dead end, turn east on Road 126 and go to dead end, turn north on Road 57 and drive two miles to Road 130. Take Road 130 to the ranch.
OPEN	All year.
DESCRIPTION	A 1917 and 1965 one-story host home on working ranch with western and southwestern interior decor.
NO. OF ROOMS	Three rooms with private bathrooms.
RATES	Year-round rates are $50-90 for a single or double with a private bathroom and $55 for a suite. Minimum stay required during the last full week of July.
CREDIT CARDS	No
BREAKFAST	Full rancher's breakfast is served in the dining room and includes pancakes, bacon, eggs, homemade jelly, fruit and beverages. Lunch and dinner are also served, including steaks from the rancher's own cattle.
AMENITIES	Flowers in rooms, queen-sized beds, common area with picture window overlooking the prairie, refreshments served every afternoon, pictures taken of guests at the ranch and sent to them.
RESTRICTIONS	No smoking, no pets. Pebbles, the resident dog, loves kids and women. There are also numerous barn cats, four Quarter horses, several other horses and loads of cattle.
REVIEWED	*America's Wonderful Little Hotels & Inns (The Rocky Mountains & Southwest)*
MEMBER	Bed & Breakfast Innkeepers of Colorado
KUDOS/COMMENTS	"A wonderful 'old west' ranch experience in an unspoiled environment; A great getaway especially for a family." (1997)

GUFFEY

In this tiny mountain village (pop. 32), politics have gone to the cats and dogs. In a backlash against ineffective county government, the townfolk decided that critters could represent them better than humans (as this is a B&B guidebook, we won't enlarge on this subject). The first two mayoral cats were Paisley and Whiffy. Since their departure (one to cat heaven, one to Pennsylvania), the current mayor is Sandra the Golden Retriever. Stay tuned. Other claims to fame: a picture window outhouse with carpeting and mini-blinds, and a two-teacher elementary school. On the high road to Eleven Mile Canyon, about 40 miles southwest of Colorado Springs via Highways 24 and 9.

THE SPARE ROOM

1245 Canon Street, Guffey, CO 80820   *719-689-0663*
Sandra Ruvo, Owner

LOCATION	On the edge of Guffey.
OPEN	All year.
DESCRIPTION	A 1993 two-story log-sided building with southwestern and Victorian furnishings, restaurant, antique shop, art gallery and "spare room(s)." "The biggest building in the smallest town in Colorado."
NO. OF ROOMS	Three rooms share one bathroom. Try the loft.
RATES	Year-round rates are $55-65 for a double with shared bathroom. There is no minimum stay.
CREDIT CARDS	Discover, MasterCard, Visa
BREAKFAST	Full breakfast is served in the dining room and includes a choice of omelet, bacon and eggs, French Toast, Huevos Rancheros or breakfast Burrito.
AMENITIES	Quiet mountain retreat—no TV, games, etc.
RESTRICTIONS	No smoking, no pets. "This is an adult establishment; children are welcome but not recommended."

GUNNISON

This totally western town is the major escape route for Gunnison National Forest,
Blue Mesa and Taylor Park Reservoirs, Black Canyon of the Gunnison and
Curecanti National Recreation Area (bird watchers: don't miss Neversink Trail at
the eastern tip). In town the Upper Gunnison runs through it, and July's
Cattlemen's Day is the major event. For skiing, Crested Butte is a mere 30 miles
away. From Denver, 196 miles southwest via Highways 285 and Highway 50 over
Monarch Pass.

GOLD CREEK INN

8506 County Road 76, Gunnison, CO 81237   970-641-2086
Joe Benge, Resident Owner

LOCATION	Approximately 20 miles east/northeast of Gunnison. Call for directions.
OPEN	May 1 through October 15.
DESCRIPTION	An 1890 log host home on Gold Creek with log and wainscotting interior.
NO. OF ROOMS	Two rooms share one bathroom.
RATES	Seasonal rates are $45 for a single with a shared bathroom and $52 for a double with a shared bathroom. There is no minimum stay and cancellation requires two weeks' notice.
CREDIT CARDS	MasterCard, Visa
BREAKFAST	Continental Plus is served in the lounge area.
RESTRICTIONS	None.
REVIEWED	*Recommended Country Inns of the Rocky Mountain Region*

THE MARY LAWRENCE INN

601 North Taylor, Gunnison, CO 81230   *970-641-3343*
Pat & Jim Kennedy, Resident Owners

LOCATION	From Highway 50 turn north on Highway 135, go five blocks to Ruby Street, turn right and go two blocks. On corner of Ruby and Taylor.
OPEN	All year.
DESCRIPTION	An 1886 two-story Italianate Victorian inn, restored in 1988, furnished with antiques, hand-stenciled walls and colorful art work.
NO. OF ROOMS	Five rooms with private baths. Two rooms are two-room suites. Pat's favorite is the Mullin Patch.
RATES	Year-round rates are $69-74 for a double with a private bath and $89 for a suite. An additional $15-25 is charged for each person over two in the suites. There is a reservation/cancellation policy.
CREDIT CARDS	MasterCard, Visa
BREAKFAST	Full breakfast, served in the dining room, includes a main dish, meat, seasonal fruit, coffee, juices.
AMENITIES	Enclosed sun porch and large deck, robes and hand-made quilts in the rooms, TV in the suites, interesting books and magazines to read and borrow, local interest material available, maps of the area, knowledge of interesting places to go.
RESTRICTIONS	No smoking, no pets, children six and older are welcome.
REVIEWED	*America's Wonderful Little Hotels & Inns, B&Bs, Guesthouses & Inns of America, Bed & Breakfast U.S.A., The Colorado Guide, Non-Smokers Guide to Bed & Breakfasts*
MEMBER	Bed & Breakfast Innkeepers of Colorado, Colorado Hotel and Lodging Association
RATED	AAA 3 Diamond
KUDOS/COMMENTS	"Pat and Jim escaped corporate life to become innkeepers; it's a pleasure to see what they have done to make the atmosphere so comfortable and friendly." ... "A wonderful experience." ... "Gourmet food and very hospitable hosts!" (1996)

HAHN'S PEAK
(STEAMBOAT SPRINGS)

On pristine Steamboat Lake in the splendid wilderness of the Routt National Forest and Hahn's Mining District, 25 miles north of Steamboat Springs on County Road 129, just south of the Wyoming border.

THE COUNTRY INN AT STEAMBOAT LAKE

61027 County Road 129, Hahn's Peak, CO 80428   970-879-3906
Tom & Stephanie Berry, Resident Owners   800-934-7829

LOCATION	On Steamboat Lake, 25 miles north of Steamboat Springs at Hahn's Peak in the Routt National Forest.
OPEN	All year.
DESCRIPTION	A two-story log lodge with restaurant and bar.
NO. OF ROOMS	Eight rooms with private bathrooms.
RATES	Seasonal rates change according to length of stay and time of year. Please call for details.
CREDIT CARDS	MasterCard, Visa
BREAKFAST	Full breakfast is served in the dining room.
AMENITIES	Hot tub, guest lounge with satellite TV, wood-burning stove, complimentary refreshments, full-service bar, handicapped access, and meeting and conference facilities.
RESTRICTIONS	None

HEENEY

GREEN MOUNTAIN INN

7101 Summit County Road 30, Heeney, CO 80498   970-724-3812
Scott & Jeanette Astaldi, Resident Owners

HESPERUS

LA PLATA VISTA RANCH

13400 County Road 120, Hesperus, CO 81326   970-247-9062
Kathy & John, Resident Owners   FAX 970-247-5056

HOWARD

A small mountain town on the Arkansas River. From here the scenery is awesome anywhere you look and scenic byways branch in all directions. Twelve miles southwest of Salida.

THE ROBIN'S NEST BED & BREAKFAST

9134 Highway 50, Howard, CO 81233   719-942-4176
Robin & Mary McConathy, Resident Owners

LOCATION	Twelve miles east of Salida and 80 miles west of Pueblo and Colorado Springs on Highway 50.
OPEN	All year.
DESCRIPTION	A 1972 traditional country home with country furnishings set on two acres of land.
NO. OF ROOMS	Three rooms with private bathrooms and two suites share one bathroom. The best is the Shavano Room.
RATES	Year-round rates are $57-67 for a double with a private bath and $95 for the suite. There is a minimum stay on holidays. Cancellation for holidays requires 45 days' notice...dumb policy...TI—30 days' notice the rest of the season.
CREDIT CARDS	Discover, MasterCard, Visa
BREAKFAST	Full breakfast is served in the dining room. Special meals are available on request.
AMENITIES	Spa on a covered patio, fruit orchard and gardens, books and relaxation tapes, microwave and refrigerator available, fresh flowers in room.
RESTRICTIONS	No smoking, no pets, children are welcome, and the resident dog and cats are Cindy, Connie and Panther respectively.

IDAHO SPRINGS

One of the few working underground gold mines in the state is here. It's also the gateway to the nation's highest paved road to the top of Mt. Evans. A major natural attraction is the geothermal hot springs. Try an outing to Central City on the "Oh My God Road". In July, Gold Rush Days are fun. From Denver, 32 miles west on I-70.

THE RIVERSIDE BED & BREAKFAST

2130 Riverside Drive, Idaho Springs, CO 80452   303-567-9032
Theresa Gonzales, Resident Owner

LOCATION	From I-70 going west, take exit 241A into Idaho Springs, staying to the right. Take the 21st Street bridge across Clear Creek. Turn left on Riverside Drive. The B&B is west of the Argo gold mill.
OPEN	Weekends only, all year.
DESCRIPTION	A 1910 three-story country guesthouse with country and antique furnishings.
NO. OF ROOMS	One room with a private bathroom and three rooms share two bathrooms. Theresa Gonzales recommends the Hot Springs room.
RATES	Year-round rates are $74 for a double with a bathroom, $54 for a single with a shared bathroom and $64 for a double with a shared bathroom. There is no minimum stay and cancellation requires seven days' notice, 14 days' for holidays.
CREDIT CARDS	MasterCard, Visa
BREAKFAST	Full breakfast, served in the dining room, includes muffins, cinnamon rolls, egg dishes, fruit, sausages, coffee and juice. "And for those who like spicy breakfast, there's green chili!"
AMENITIES	Hot tub by a spring, robes, hot teas and homemade cookies.
RESTRICTIONS	No smoking, no pets and children over 10 are welcome. Younger children may be accepted by prior arrangement.

ST. MARY'S GLACIER BED & BREAKFAST

336 Crest Drive, Idaho Springs, CO 80452   303-567-4084
Steve, Marian & Jackie Jacquin, Resident Owners 303-914-3324 *(Denver)*
FAX 303-567-4084

LOCATION	Take Fall River Road north 9.5 miles until you reach Silver Lake. Go along the south side of the lake and bear left. Go about 50 feet and make the next right, continue 100 yards to the B&B.

EXIT 238
ST MARY
ALICE 10
MILE
TURN
RIGHT
(COUNTRY
ROAD)

OPEN	All year.
DESCRIPTION	A 1993 three-story hand-hewn log inn with country furnishings.
NO. OF ROOMS	Six rooms with private bathrooms and a cabin. The owners suggest the Honeymoon/Anniversary Suite.
RATES	Year-round rates are $85-139 for a single or double with a private bathroom. The cabin rents for $350 per week. There is no minimum stay and cancellation requires 14 days.
CREDIT CARDS	American Express, MasterCard, Visa
BREAKFAST	Full "hearty gourmet" breakfast is served in the dining room. Lunch and dinner are also available.
AMENITIES	River-rock fireplaces, hot tub, whirlpool tubs, private decks, brass beds with hand-sewn quilts, parlor and library, VCR/TV, hammock for two, facilities for weddings and seminars.
RESTRICTIONS	No smoking, no pets, no children. The resident husky/shepherd mix is called Apollo.
MEMBER	Bed & Breakfast Innkeepers of Colorado
KUDOS/COMMENTS	"Wonderful, huge log home with fireplaces." ... "Built with guests in mind in a beautiful mountain setting." ... "Hosts are friendly, caring people." (1997)

St. Mary's Glacier Bed & Breakfast, Idaho Springs

INDIAN HILLS

MOUNTAIN VIEW BED & BREAKFAST

4754 Picutis Road, Indian Hills, CO 80454   303-697-6896
Graham & Ortrud Richardson, Resident Owners

KUDOS/COMMENTS   "The best gourmet breakfast in the Rockies." (1996)

KEYSTONE

SKI TIP LODGE

PO Box 38, Keystone, CO 80435   970-468-4202
Erin Clark Gilchrist, Resident Innkeeper

LA JUNTA

THE JANE ELLEN INN

722 Colorado Avenue, La Junta, CO 81050   719-384-8445

MY WIFE'S INN

801 Colorado Avenue, La Junta, CO 81050   719-384-7911
Karen & Marty Fleischacker, Resident Owners   800-616-3642

LAKE CITY

Historic walking tour, Lake San Cristobal, Alfred Packer Massacre Site, Alpine Loop & Silver Thread National Scenic Byways, Hinsdale County Museum, near five 14'ers, local musical & theatrical productions, and the Arts and Crafts Festival during the third Tuesday in July.

ALPINE LOOP B&B

Henson Creek Road, PO Box 955, Lake City, CO 81235   970-944-2944
Dolly & Kelly Perryman, Resident Managers   FAX 505-525-2065

LOCATION	On the Alpine Loop Backcountry Byway, nine miles west of Lake City on the Henson Creek Road toward Engineer Pass in the abandoned mining townsite of Capitol City.
OPEN	All year.
DESCRIPTION	A 1987 three-story modern host home with saltillo tile kitchen and living areas, Indian pottery and country interior decor.
NO. OF ROOMS	One room with private bathroom and two rooms share two bathrooms. Managers' favorite is the Matterhorn room.
RATES	High season rates (June through August) are $112 for a single or double with a private bathroom and $77-87 for a single or double with a shared bathroom. Low season rates (September through May) are $102 for a single or double with a private bathroom and $67-77 for a single or double with a shared bathroom. There is no minimum stay requirement. Holidays and special events require 30 days' cancellation notice. Otherwise, cancellation requires eight days' notice for a refund less a $15 charge.
CREDIT CARDS	MasterCard, Visa
BREAKFAST	Full breakfast, served family style in the dining room with the innkeepers, includes ham, bacon or sausage, eggs, breakfast casseroles, homemade breads or muffins, fresh fruit and beverages. Lunch and dinner are also available.
AMENITIES	Home-baked delights, fireplace in living room, robes, large wraparound deck, bright stars and crisp Rocky Mountain spring water.
RESTRICTIONS	No pets, smoking permitted on outside deck.
MEMBER	Bed & Breakfast Innkeepers of Colorado
RATED	1995 Spectacular Location Award (Bed & Breakfast Innkeepers of Colorado)

Cinnamon Inn Bed & Breakfast, Lake City

CINNAMON INN BED & BREAKFAST

426 Gunnison Avenue, PO Box 266, Lake City, CO 81235   970-944-2641
Larry Washburn & Kathie Steele, Resident Owners   800-337-2335
Spanish and German spoken.

LOCATION	In the Village of Lake City on the southeast corner of 5th and Gunnison Avenue (Highway 149).
OPEN	All year.
DESCRIPTION	An 1878 two-story Victorian with front and back porches and Victorian and country furnishings, listed on both the National and State Historic Registers.
NO. OF ROOMS	Two suites with private bathrooms and three rooms share one bathroom. Try the Kitty Eastman Suite.
RATES	Year-round rates are $95-110 for suites with a private bathroom and $75-80 for a single or double with a shared bathroom. There is a minimum stay on the July 4th weekend and cancellation requires 14 days' notice.
CREDIT CARDS	MasterCard, Visa
BREAKFAST	Full country breakfast, served in the family kitchen, includes fruit bowl, roasted coffee and hot gourmet entree of the day.
AMENITIES	Fresh flowers in the rooms during the summer from Kathie's Victorian garden, suite with whirlpool tub & fireplace, jazz piano performed by Larry at breakfast, robes in rooms, TV in the kitchen, snowshoes available.
RESTRICTIONS	No smoking, no pets, children over six are welcome.
REVIEWED	*Rocky Mountain States* "Lonely Planet" (Colorado, Wyoming and Montana), *Recommended Country Inns (Rocky Mountain Region)*,
MEMBER	Bed & Breakfast Innkeepers of Colorado
RATED	Mobil 1 Star
KUDOS/COMMENTS	"Larry is a professional pianist; he loves 'Java Jazz', Kathie is a gourmet cook." (1997)

MONCRIEF MOUNTAIN RANCH & LODGE

PO Box 593, Lake City, CO 81235　　　　　　　970-944-2796
Jack Moncrief, Resident Owner　　　　　　　　FAX 970-944-2721
Spanish spoken.

LOCATION	Nine miles south of Lake City on County Road 30, off Highway 149.
OPEN	Open May 1 to October 31st.
DESCRIPTION	A 1984, 20,000 square-foot log lodge with western log furniture. Located on 320 acres.
NO. OF ROOMS	Ten rooms with private bathrooms. Try #5, Gimi's Room.
RATES	High season, July through September, rates are $80 for a single with private bath, $90 for a double with private bath and $25 per person for a guesthouse. There is a seven-day cancellation policy and a 15% service charge.
CREDIT CARDS	MasterCard, Visa
BREAKFAST	Continental Plus is served in dining rooms, hot entrees are served on the weekends. Dinner is available and special meals are prepared for groups.
AMENITIES	Mountain bike rentals, hot tub, fireplace, TV, ping-pong table, big screen movies, popcorn, tea and lemonade, auditorium with stage, barbeques, multi-level decks and fishing pond.
RESTRICTIONS	No smoking, no pets. Children are welcome. There are four resident dogs.
MEMBER	Lake City Bed & Breakfast Association

OLD CARSON INN

8401 County Road 30, PO Box 114, Lake City, CO 81235   970-944-2511
Judy Berry, Resident Owner   800-294-0608

LOCATION	Go south of Lake City on Highway 149, turn on County Road 30 (look for Lake San Cristobal Recreation Area sign), the inn is 8.5 miles on CR 30.
OPEN	Memorial Day through October.
DESCRIPTION	A 1990 three-story log inn filled with antiques, murals and southwestern art located in the shadow of two "fourteeners."
NO. OF ROOMS	Seven rooms with private bathrooms. Judy suggests the Big Indian Mine.
RATES	Year-round rates are $74-115 for a single or double with private bathroom. There is no minimum stay and ask about cancellation.
CREDIT CARDS	American Express, Discover, MasterCard, Visa
BREAKFAST	Full breakfast, served in the dining room, is a "very large" mountain breakfast with a hearty egg dish, meat, fruit, two kinds of homemade breads and beverages. Lunch and dinner are available.
AMENITIES	Outdoor hot tub, satellite TV, VCR, film library, books and games in large common area with wood-burning stove and beverages available anytime.
RESTRICTIONS	No smoking, no pets
REVIEWED	Recommended Inns of the Rocky Mountains, Best Places to Stay in the Rocky Mountains
MEMBER	Bed & Breakfast Innkeepers of Colorado

LAKE GEORGE

UTE TRAIL RIVER RANCH

21446 County Road 77, Lake George, CO 80827   719-748-3015
Debra Baxter & Jim Fagerstrom, Resident Owners

LA VETA

This quiet little town at the north end of the beautiful Cuchara Valley is alive with art, artists and theatrical productions. The annual Huerfano County Rodeo on July Fourth and Francisco Fort Day in August add to the fun. Adjacent to the town is a championship 18-hole golf course. From Walsenburg, 14 miles southwest via Highways 160 and 12.

1899 INN BED & BREAKFAST

314 South Main, PO Box 372, La Veta, CO 81055   719-742-3576
Marilyn Schwarz Hall, Resident Owner

LOCATION	Center of town, next to La Veta Library and Fort Francisco Museum.
OPEN	All year.
DESCRIPTION	A 1909 two-story gabled stone country inn with early American furnishings.
NO. OF ROOMS	Two rooms and cottage with private bathroom, three rooms share two bathrooms.
RATES	Year-round rates are $40 for a single with a private bathroom, $50 for a double with a private bathroom, $35 for a single sharing a bathroom, $45 for a double sharing a bathroom. The cottage is $50 for a single and $65 for a double. There is a reservation/cancellation policy.
CREDIT CARDS	No
BREAKFAST	Full breakfast is served in the sun room and may include French toast, German pancakes, popovers, muffins, eggs and beverages.
AMENITIES	Flowers, robes, piano, games, gift shop and porch swing.
RESTRICTIONS	None. Purdy the cat is confined to the back room and outside.
REVIEWED	*The Colorado Guide, Colorado Historic Inns & Hotels, Country Inns: Midwest & Rockies, Inns of the Southwest, The Old House Lover's Guide to Inns and Bed & Breakfasts and Guest Houses, Recommended Country Inns of the Rocky Mountain Region.*
KUDOS/COMMENTS	"Established, picturesque and gracious." (1994)

HUNTER HOUSE BED & BREAKFAST

115 West Grand Avenue, PO Box 427, La Veta, CO 81055   719-742-5577
Bill & Wanda Hunter, Resident Owners

LOCATION	At the five mile marker on Highway 12 out of La Veta.
OPEN	All year.
DESCRIPTION	A 1906 gabled adobe home furnished with antiques and collectibles.
NO. OF ROOMS	Three rooms share one bathroom. Choose the Collins Room with 1865 furnishings.
RATES	Year-round rates are $55-100 for a double with shared bathroom. There is no minimum stay.
CREDIT CARDS	No
BREAKFAST	Full breakfast, served in the dining room, includes biscuits & gravy, country ham, scrambled eggs, hash browns or grits and beverages. Lunch, dinner and special meals are available with advanced notice.
AMENITIES	Fifty-two inch TV in living room, library in the den, private sitting room, robes, afternoon and evening snacks and beverages, patio with outdoor fireplace, fruit orchard, homemade jelly.
RESTRICTIONS	No smoking, no pets (owners are allergic to animals and smoke), children are welcome.
KUDOS/COMMENTS	"Comfortable, gracious, nice hosts from Texas." (1995) "Huge breakfast, nice gift shop." (1996)

POSADA DE SOL Y SOMBRA

113 West Virginia, PO Box 522, La Veta, CO 81055   719-742-3159
Carroll & Betty Elwell, Resident Owners

LOCATION	Take Fourth Street south from railroad off Main Street.
OPEN	All year.
DESCRIPTION	A two-story country farmhouse built around 1880. Completely remodeled in 1993 with country furnishings.
NO. OF ROOMS	Two rooms share one bathroom.
RATES	Year-round rates for a single or double with a shared bathroom are $43-49. There is a two-night minimum stay on certain holidays, a 50% deposit reserves a room and cancellation requires five days' notice.
CREDIT CARDS	No
BREAKFAST	Full breakfast, served in the dining room or terrace, includes fruit, choice of bread, entree and condiments. Special meals on request.
AMENITIES	Robes, art gallery of local artists' work, close to golf course and shops, TV/VCR, games, library, two sitting rooms, large yard and front porch swing and wicker furniture.
RESTRICTIONS	No smoking, no pets. Resident dog, Tugger, is very gentle, and the cat is named...uh...Cat. Limited facilities for small children.
REVIEWED	*The Denver Post, Recommended Inns*
KUDOS/COMMENTS	"Great cook! Lovely gardens." (1996) "Well decorated, nice, relaxed hosts." (1997)

LEADVILLE

Once the epitome of boom-town wealth, its history is as heady as its altitude —
10,188 feet, and the ghosts of H.A.W. Tabor and Baby Doe and Matchless Mine
still fill the town. This historic mining town lies in the spactacular Arkansas Valley
in the shadow of Colorado's two highest peaks, Mt. Elbert and Mt. Massive. It is
also the home of the Leadville 100, a fairly serious ultra marathon. From Denver
103 miles to Copper Mountain, then south 24 miles on Highway 91.

THE APPLE BLOSSOM INN

120 West 4th Street, Leadville, CO 80461   719-486-2141
Maggie Senn, Resident Owner   800-982-9279
                                                FAX 719-486-0994

LOCATION	Entering Leadville from the north, take Poplar Street, which turns right at 9th Street and then becomes Harrison Avenue, take a right West 4th Street, the inn is a 1/2 block on the right side.
OPEN	All year.
DESCRIPTION	An 1879 two-story Victorian on the State Historic Register, locally known as "The Easter Egg House" for its pastel yellow, lavender and green gingerbread-cottage appearance. The inn is furnished in comfortable Victorian.
NO. OF ROOMS	Three rooms with private bathrooms and four rooms share two bathrooms. Maggie recommends The Library as her favorite room.
RATES	Year-round rates are $69-79 for a single or double with a private bathroom, $54-59 for a single or double with a shared bathroom, suites rent for $99-144 and the entire inn rents for $525. There is no minimum stay and cancellation requires seven days' notice.
CREDIT CARDS	American Express, MasterCard, Visa
BREAKFAST	Full breakfast is served in the dining room and includes bacon, sausage, homefried potatoes, an egg dish, something home-baked like cinnamon rolls or muffins, fresh fruit, yogurt, hot or cold cereal, milk, juice, coffee and tea.
AMENITIES	Robes, bubble bath, amenity basket, afternoon snacks include brownies, assorted hot and cold beverages.
RESTRICTIONS	No smoking, no pets
REVIEWED	*Recommended Country Inns of the Rocky Mountain Region*
MEMBER	Bed & Breakfast Innkeepers of Colorado, Professional Association of Innkeepers International, Colorado Hotel and Lodging Association
AWARDS	ABBA 2 Crowns
KUDOS/COMMENTS	"Maggie is a wonderful hostess with beautiful rooms, she really goes out of her way to make you feel at home." ... "Wonderful food." (1996)

The Apple Blossom Inn, Leadville

Delaware Hotel

700 Harrison Avenue, Leadville, CO 80461   719-486-1418
Scott & Susan Brackett, Resident Owner   800-748-2004
FAX 719-486-2214

LOCATION	On Harrison Avenue (main street) in the heart of greater Leadville Historic District.
OPEN	All year.
DESCRIPTION	An 1886 three-story French Mansard Victorian with "Second Empire" elements on the roof. The hotel has been renovated with oak paneling, crystal chandeliers and period antiques, listed on the National Historic Register.
NO. OF ROOMS	Thirty-six rooms with private bathrooms. The Bracketts like #2 Bridal Suite.
RATES	Year-round rates are $50-63 for a single with private bath, $55-68 for a double with private bath and $90-100 for a suite. Cancellation requires 72 hours' notice and two weeks' for holiday periods.
CREDIT CARDS	American Express, Diners Club, Discover, MasterCard, Visa
BREAKFAST	Full breakfast, served in the dining room, includes a choice of three entrees. Lunch and dinner are also available.

AMENITIES	Weekend entertainment in the lobby, hot tub, lobby bar, special theme weekends, e.g., murder mystery, medieval, etc., meeting facilities for up to 35 and banquet facilities for up to 100, full-service restaurant on site.
RESTRICTIONS	Restaurant is non-smoking, no pets.
REVIEWED	*Bed & Breakfasts and Country Inns: West, American and Canadian Bed & Breakfasts, Recommended Country Inns of the Rocky Mountain Region.*
MEMBER	Association of Historic Hotels of the Rocky Mountain West, American Bed & Breakfast Association, Professional Association of Innkeepers International, Colorado Hotel and Lodging Association
RATED	AAA 2 Diamonds
AWARDS	Colorado Historical Society, Stephen Hart Award for Outstanding Historic Preservation, 1993.

THE ICE PALACE INN & ANTIQUES

813 Spruce Street, Leadville, CO 80461   719-486-8272
Giles & Kami Kolakowski, Resident Owners   800-754-2840

THE LEADVILLE COUNTRY INN

127 East 8th Street, Leadville, CO 80461   719-486-2354
Judy & Sid Clemmer, Resident Owners   800-748-2354
                                              FAX 719-486-0300

LOCATION	Half block off Harrison Avenue, third house on the right.
OPEN	All year.
DESCRIPTION	An 1893 Queen Anne Victorian with country Victorian furnishings.
NO. OF ROOMS	Nine rooms with private bathrooms.
RATES	Year-round rates are $57-139 for a single or double with private bathroom. Rooms having more than two guests add $15 per person. There is a minimum stay during high season and a reservation/cancellation policy.
CREDIT CARDS	American Express, Diners Club, Discover, MasterCard, Visa
BREAKFAST	Full gourmet breakfast is served in the dining area. Ask about special packages and candlelight dinner with carriage or sleigh ride available at extra cost.

AMENITIES	Jacuzzi in gazebo, robes in some rooms, TV, radio in all rooms and phone in some rooms, bicycles, complimentary fresh-baked goods, wedding and meeting facilities, limited handicapped access.
RESTRICTIONS	No smoking, no pets, children over three are welcome.
REVIEWED	*America's Wonderful Little Hotels & Inns, The Colorado Guide, Inn Places for Bed & Breakfasts.*
MEMBER	Bed & Breakfast Innkeepers of Colorado, Distinctive Inns of Colorado
KUDOS/COMMENTS	"A truly elegant country inn." ... "A top-notch inn that is professionally run but still warm and friendly." ... "Afternoon snacks were elegant. The best waffles I ever tasted." (1997)

PERI & ED'S MOUNTAIN HIDEAWAY

201 West 8th Street, Leadville, CO 80461   719-486-0716
Peri & Ed Solder, Resident Owners   800-933-3715
FAX 719-486-2181

LOCATION	Follow Highway 91 to Leadville, to Harrison Avenue (main street), take the first right on 8th, the inn is one block on the left.
OPEN	All year.
DESCRIPTION	An 1879 three-story Victorian home "where you can put up your feet and feel at home," with Victorian and western decor.
NO. OF ROOMS	Seven rooms with private bathrooms. Peri recommends the Tabor Suite.
RATES	Year-round rates are $45-75 for a single or double with a private bathroom, $65-75 for a suite, $100 for two in the guesthouse and $500 for the entire B&B. The guesthouse requires a two-night minimum stay and there is a cancellation policy.
CREDIT CARDS	American Express, Discover, MasterCard, Visa
BREAKFAST	Full breakfast is served in the dining room and includes a hot dish with meat, yogurt, granola and plenty of juice and coffee. Special meals are available.
AMENITIES	Robes, telephones available in some rooms, hot tub on deck, kitchen for guest use, TV and VCR in parlor, musical instruments, games and books.
RESTRICTIONS	No smoking, no pets (Brenndan, the resident Cocker, loves kids). Children of all ages are welcome.
KUDOS/COMMENTS	"Peri, Ed and family love to share their home and lifestyle...a real breath of fresh air." (1994) "Recent renovations are wonderful." (1996)

WOOD HAVEN MANOR

809 Spruce, Leadville, CO 80461   *719-486-0109*
Jolene & Bobby Wood, Resident Owners   *800-748-2570*
                                                                FAX 719-486-0210

LOCATION	From Harrison Street (Leadville's main street) turn west on 8th Street and go two blocks, turn right on Spruce, the inn is the second and third house on the block.
OPEN	All year.
DESCRIPTION	Two side-by-side two-story 1899 Victorians with Victorian and fine antique furnishings.
NO. OF ROOMS	Seven rooms with private bathrooms. Jolene suggests the Tabor Suite.
RATES	Year-round rates are $50-85 for a single with private bathroom, $77-95 for a double with private bathroom, $119 for a suite, $350 per night for the entire inn with breakfast and $300 without breakfast. There is no minimum stay except for group arrangements and cancellation requires 10 days' notice.
CREDIT CARDS	American Express, Discover, MasterCard, Visa
BREAKFAST	Full breakfast, served in the dining room, includes an entree, fresh-fruit frappe, homemade bread and beverages. Lunch and picnics on request.
AMENITIES	Afternoon snacks, coffee and tea anytime, suite with whirlpool and candles around the tub, piano and fireplace in living room, TV/VCR in common room, robes, breakfast in bed on request, and flowers and fruit baskets for special occasions.
RESTRICTIONS	No smoking, no pets, children over three are welcome.
REVIEWED	*Non-Smokers Guide to Bed & Breakfasts*
MEMBER	Colorado Hotel and Lodging Association, Bed & Breakfast Innkeepers of Colorado, Professional Association of Innkeepers International
RATED	Mobil 1 Star
KUDOS/COMMENTS	"Bobby and Jolene make everyone feel like they've just come home." (1997)

LONGMONT

This agricultural center in Boulder County was started as the Chicago-Colorado Colony. It is much more a midwestern sort of town than anything else with beautiful old homes and wide streets surrounded by subdivisions. From Denver, 30 miles north on I-25 and five miles west on Highway 119.

ELLEN'S BED & BREAKFAST

700 Kimbark Street, Longmont, CO 80501   303-776-1676
Baldwin "Baldy" & Ellen Ranson, Resident Owners
Spanish, French & Russian spoken.   FAX 303-776-1676

LOCATION	In Longmont go one block east of Main Street; four blocks north of Third Avenue.
OPEN	All year.
DESCRIPTION	A 1910 two-story Victorian with eclectic furnishings that reflect the owners' world-wide travel.
NO. OF ROOMS	One room with private bathroom and one room with shared bathroom. Ask for the largest room with the poster bed.
RATES	Year-round rates are $70 per couple and $20 each additional guest (children). No minimum stay and no reservation/cancellation policy.
CREDIT CARDS	No
BREAKFAST	Full hearty breakfast, served in the dining room, includes stuffed croissant, fresh-fruit scones or Santa Fe quiche, on Bulgarian china and heirloom silver.
AMENITIES	Flowers, imported chocolate, beverage on arrival, rubber duck and Gary Larson 'toons in the bathroom, and conversation with well-traveled hosts.
RESTRICTIONS	None. Children welcome and there are two Miniature Schnauzers, Rufus and Rosie, whom "our guests keep wanting to take home."
AWARDS	Award for redevelopment, "Architecture and Design Excellence," City of Longmont Planning Commission.

LOVELAND

Here at the mouth of the Big Thompson Canyon lies the "Sweetheart City". Valentines from around the country (and world) are sent here to be remailed with Loveland's postmark and special chachet. Named for railroad pioneer W.A.H. Loveland, not romance, this important agricultural and recreational area includes Boyd Lake State Recreational Area. Fifty miles north of Denver on I-25 and Highway 34.

APPLE AVENUE BED & BREAKFAST

3321 Apple Avenue, Loveland, CO 80538   970-667-2665
Tom and Ann Harroun, Resident Owners

LOCATION	From Highway 34 go north on Taft Avenue 1.3 miles, right on Beech, second left on Apple, third driveway on left.
OPEN	All year.
DESCRIPTION	A 1973 contemporary ranch host home with traditional and early American furnishings.
NO. OF ROOMS	Two rooms share 1-1/2 bathrooms. Ann recommends the Green Room.
RATES	Summer rates are $55-60 for a single or double with a shared bathroom. Winter rates are $10 less. There is no minimum stay and cancellation requires seven days' notice.
CREDIT CARDS	American Express, Discover, MasterCard, Visa
BREAKFAST	Full breakfast is served in the dining room and may include blueberry pancakes, orange French toast, veggie-filled omelet or eggs benedict with bacon, ham or sausage and fresh-baked muffins. Pure Vermont maple syrup is served. Restricted diets are accommodated and afternoon tea is available by arrangement.
AMENITIES	Air conditioning, ceiling fans, robes, fresh flowers in season, laundry facilities, clock radios in bedrooms, deck off of bedrooms, living room with TV, books and games, flexible mealtimes and menus.
RESTRICTIONS	No smoking, no pets.
MEMBER	Bed & Breakfast Innkeepers of Colorado

CATTAIL CREEK INN

2665 Abarr Drive, Loveland, CO 80538   970-667-7600
Sue Buchman, Resident Owner   800-572-2466

KUDOS/COMMENTS	"Great view of the mountains, perfectly set on the edge of a golf course." ... "Close to the Sculpture Gardens and Lake Loveland, excellent wine cellar, good conversation." (1997)

DERBY HILL INN BED & BREAKFAST

2502 Courtney Drive, Loveland, CO 80537   970-667-3193
Dale & Beverly McCue, Resident Owners   800-498-8086
                                                              FAX 970-667-3193

LOCATION	In a neighborhood on the south side of Loveland about a mile from the downtown area.
OPEN	All year.
DESCRIPTION	A 1975 tri-level traditional host home in a quiet neighborhood.
NO. OF ROOMS	Two rooms with private bathrooms. Beverly likes the West Derby room.
RATES	Year-round rates for a single or double with a private bathroom are $70-85. There is no minimum stay and cancellation requires seven days' notice.
CREDIT CARDS	American Express, MasterCard, Visa
BREAKFAST	Full breakfast, served on antique china in the dining room or on the deck in the summer, includes a choice of two entrees, fresh fruit, homemade muffins and specialty breads, juice, and gourmet coffee.
AMENITIES	Fresh flowers, chocolates, early morning coffee, robes, complimentary snacks and soft drinks, air conditioning, private sitting area, television in room and FAX machine.
RESTRICTIONS	No smoking, no pets, children over 12 are welcome.
MEMBER	Professional Association of Innkeepers International, Bed & Breakfast Innkeepers of Colorado

JEFFERSON HOUSE

342 East Third Street, Loveland, CO 80537   970-669-6220
Art & Jeanne Myers, Resident Owners

LOCATION	One block from downtown and two blocks west of the Loveland Civic Center, on the southwest corner of Third & Jefferson.
OPEN	All year.
DESCRIPTION	An 1897 three-story brick Victorian filled with paintings and sculptures by Art Myers located in the heart of Loveland's art community. Highlights include the original woodwork and transoms above all doors.
NO. OF ROOMS	Three rooms share one bathroom. The Myer's favorite room is the Queen Room.

RATES	A single with shared bath is $35 and a double with shared bath is $45. There is no minimum stay and there is a one-week cancellation policy.
CREDIT CARDS	No
BREAKFAST	Continental breakfast is served in the dining room and includes muffins, croissants, juice, fruit, coffee, tea and hot chocolate.
RESTRICTIONS	No smoking, children over 10 years of age are welcome.

THE LOVELANDER BED & BREAKFAST INN

217 West 4th Street, Loveland, CO 80537   970-669-0798
Lauren & Gary Smith, Resident Owners

LOCATION	Center of town, just east of Garfield Avenue.
OPEN	All year.
DESCRIPTION	A 1902 two-story Victorian with Victorian furnishings.
NO. OF ROOMS	Eleven rooms with private bathrooms.
RATES	Year-round rates are $77-135 for a single or double with private bathroom. Cancellation requires seven days' notice.
CREDIT CARDS	American Express, Discover, MasterCard, Visa
BREAKFAST	Full gourmet breakfast is served in the dining room, garden or on the veranda.
AMENITIES	Radio and phones in rooms, complimentary refreshments, separate meeting and special events center with three-level deck, FAX and copy services, limited handicapped access.
RESTRICTIONS	No smoking, no pets, children over 10 are welcome.
MEMBER	Distinctive Inns of Colorado, Professional Association of Innkeepers International
RATED	AAA 3 Diamonds
KUDOS/COMMENTS	"Very hospitable innkeepers; Cozy retreat from everyday life." ... "Very comfortable beds and delicious breakfast." (1997)

SYLVAN DALE GUEST RANCH

2939 North County Road 31D, Loveland, CO 80537   970-667-3915
Susan Jessup, Resident Owner

Wild Lane Bed & Breakfast Inn, Loveland

WILD LANE BED & BREAKFAST INN

5445 Wild Lane, Loveland, CO 80538
Steven Wild, Resident Owner

970-669-0303
800-204-3320

LOCATION	Take Highway 34 west through Loveland and turn right on Wild Lane.
OPEN	All year.
DESCRIPTION	A 1905 two-story Victorian country inn with Victorin interior on a landscaped 200-acre estate. This historic family home is listed on the National and State Historic Registers.
NO. OF ROOMS	Five rooms with private bathrooms. The owner recommends the Blue Rose room.
RATES	Year-round rates are $89-109 for a single or double with a private bathroom. No minimum stay is required and cancellation requires five days' notice.
CREDIT CARDS	American Express, Discover, MasterCard, Visa
BREAKFAST	Full breakast with "herbal flair" is served in the dining room, guestrooms or on the sun porch. Lunch and dinner are available with advance notice and a minimum number of guests required.
AMENITIES	Three fireplaces, parlor, library, enclosed sun porch, landscaped grounds, herb farm and gift shop.
RESTRICTIONS	No smoking, no pets, children over 14 are welcome. Oliver is the resident cat.
REVIEWED	*Victoria* magazine, *Herb Companion* magazine, *Recommended Country Inns*
MEMBER	Professional Association of Innkeepers, Bed & Breakfast Innkeepers of Colorado

LYONS

A picturesque western town and designated National Historic District because of its 15 sandstone buildings. There's great antiquing here, and it's the summer's best place for square dancing. Forty-five northwest of Denver on Highway 36.

BENAM BED & BREAKFAST

18424 North St. Vrain Drive, Lyons, CO 80540   303-823-9264
Douglas & Patricia Batchelder, Resident Owners   800-820-9264
French spoken.

LOCATION	One-and-a-half miles northwest of Lyons just off Highway 36.
OPEN	All year except for Thanksgiving Day through New Year's Day.
DESCRIPTION	A 1942 log host home with country French and traditional furnishings on an eight-acre Christmas-tree farm along the St. Vrain River.
NO. OF ROOMS	One room with private bathroom.
RATES	Year-round rates are $215 for a double with private bathroom. There is no minimum stay. Ask about the reservation/cancellation policy.
CREDIT CARDS	MasterCard, Visa
BREAKFAST	Full breakfast is served in the dining room or outdoors overlooking the river. "Guests are assured of the finest French and traditional English cuisine." Special meals are available.
AMENITIES	Fresh flowers, afternoon tea, walking paths, fishing, common areas with fireplaces, "refreshing Pimms" served on the deck.
RESTRICTIONS	No smoking, no pets, no children. The resident Labs, Ridge and Drako, shake hands.
MEMBER	Bed & Breakfast Innkeepers of Colorado
RATED	AAA 3 Diamonds

INN AT ROCK 'N RIVER BED & BREAKFAST AND TROUT POND FISHING

16858 North St. Vrain Drive, Lyons, CO 80540
Barbara & Marshall McCrummen, Resident Owners

303-823-5011
800-448-4611

LOCATION	Three miles west of Lyons on Highway 36.
OPEN	From April 1 through October 31.
DESCRIPTION	A 1965 frame country inn on the river with pine furnishings. A trout farm on 18 acres along the St. Vrain River.
NO. OF ROOMS	Nine rooms with private bathrooms. Try the Carriage House.
RATES	Seasonal rates are $89 for a single with private bathroom and $129-159 for a double with private bathroom. There is a two-night minimum stay on holiday weekends. There is a cancellation policy.
CREDIT CARDS	American Express, Discover, MasterCard, Visa
BREAKFAST	Full breakfast, served in the dining room, is a choice of nine different entrees. Lunch, dinner and special meals for groups are available.
AMENITIES	Full kitchens in rooms, catch 10-to-28-inch Rainbow trout in stocked ponds (the innkeepers will cook them for you or trade for smoked trout at a small charge), hiking nearby.
RESTRICTIONS	No smoking in rooms, no pets. Children of all ages are welcome.
RATED	AAA 2 Diamonds

MANCOS

The eastern gateway to Mesa Verde National Park, one of the nation's major archeological preserves. This small rural town at the north end of Mancos River Canyon is a great place to start exploring Mancos State Park. Between Cortez and Durango on Scenic Highway 160.

ALICE ANN'S BED & BREAKFAST

209 Bauer, Mancos, CO 81328   970-533-1083
Alice Ann Saunders, Resident Owners   800-425-4234

BAUER HOUSE

100 Bauer, Mancos, CO 81328   970-533-9707
Bobbi Black, Resident Innkeeper   800-733-9707
                                                   FAX 970-533-7022

ECHO BASIN RANCH

43747 Road M, Mancos, CO 81328   970-533-7000
Lori Large, Resident Owner   800-426-1890
                                                   FAX 970-533-9103

GINGERBREAD INN BED & BREAKFAST

41478 Highway 184, Mancos, CO 81328   970-533-7892
Linda Metcalf, Resident Owner   800-617-2479

LAKE MANCOS GUEST RANCH

42688 County Road N, Mancos, CO 81328   970-533-7900
Robin Williams, Resident Owner   800-325-9462
                                                   FAX 970-533-7858

LOST CANYON LAKE LODGE

15472 County Road 353, Mancos, CO 81328　　　　970-882-4913
Beth Newman & Ken Nickson, Resident Owners　　　800-992-1098

LOCATION	Approximately 10 miles northwest of intersection of Highways 160 and 184 in Mancos.
OPEN	All year.
DESCRIPTION	A 1983 contemporary log inn on 40 acres overlooking Lost Canyon Lake Reservoir. Furnishings are eclectic and each room is decorated in a different style, e.g., southwestern, wicker, country French, antique.
NO. OF ROOMS	Five rooms with private bathrooms. Pick a room overlooking the lake.
RATES	High season, April 15 through November 15, rates are $55-75 for a single with private bathroom and $70-90 for a double with private bathroom. Off season rates are $10 less. There is a two-day minimum stay and a reservation/cancellation policy.
CREDIT CARDS	American Express, MasterCard, Visa
BREAKFAST	Full breakfast, served in the dining room, includes hot entrees, hot breads, seasonal fruits, granola and beverages. Box/picnic lunches are available.
AMENITIES	Hot tub overlooking the lake, greenhouse where the owners raise flowers, herbs and organic vegetables, wraparound decks, afternoon snacks, laundry, wedding and board retreat facilities, books and games.
RESTRICTIONS	No smoking, no pets, all children are welcome. The owners raise AKC Newfoundland dogs, Yorkies, a foundling and assorted cats, all of whom are not in the lodge.
REVIEWED	*Best Places to Stay in the Rocky Mountains, The Colorado Guide*
MEMBER	Bed & Breakfast Innkeepers of Colorado, Professional Association of Innkeepers International.
KUDOS/COMMENTS	"Friendly, homey and quite beautiful. We loved this place!" ... "We felt very welcome there with our three young boys; Beth is a delightful person." (1997)

RIVERSBEND BED & BREAKFAST

42505 Highway 160, Mancos, CO 81328　　　　970-533-7353
Gaye & Jack Curran, Resident Owners　　　　　800-699-8994

SWINGING GATE RANCH BED & BREAKFAST

8353 County Road 39, Mancos, CO 81328   970-533-7730
Vance Feast, Resident Owner   FAX 970-533-7730

MANITOU SPRINGS
(COLORADO SPRINGS)

At the foot of Pikes Peak, Manitou Springs features the Lilac Festival in May, the Emma Crawford Memorial Coffin Races in October and the Fruitcake Toss in January. Also, the Pikes Peak Cog Railway, Iron Springs Chateau Melodrama Theatre, Miramont Castle and Cave of the Winds. The natural mineral waters once made this the gathering place for the Ute and Arapahoe Indians. Now one of America's largest National Historic Districts, this small town with art colony overtones is built on steep hillsides against the foothills of the Pikes Peak. The Pikes Peak Cog Railway is a good way to get to the top.

FRONTIER'S REST

341 Ruxton Avenue, Manitou Springs, CO 80829   719-685-0588
Jeanne Vrobel, Resident Owner   800-455-0588
                                                  FAX 719-685-1519

LOCATION	From Colorado Springs, take I-25 to Highway 24 west (exit 141). Go four miles to Manitou Avenue and turn west. Go to Ruxton Avenue and turn left. Go three blocks.
OPEN	All year.
DESCRIPTION	An 1890 1-1/2-story Victorian folk home and cottage with "old west" Victorian furniture, located in the Manitou historic district at the foot of Pikes Peak.
NO. OF ROOMS	Four rooms with private bathrooms. Jeanne suggests the Settler room.
RATES	Year-round rates are $75-110 for a single or double with a private bathroom and $400 for the entire B&B. Minimum stays are required on holiday weekends or during special events. Cancellation requires seven days' notice.
CREDIT CARDS	American Express, Discover, MasterCard, Visa
BREAKFAST	Full breakfast is served in the dining room, includes one of 12 "theme" breakfasts, like Southwestern, Scandinavian immigrant or Native American. Special meals are available. A food list is given to guests at check in.

AMENITIES	Fresh-baked cookies, "Manitou" lemonade, nightly homemade desserts, rocking chairs, antique-filled theme rooms, heat-controlled bathrooms, full guest kitchen, laundry facilities, 24-hour beverage bar, Olde Fashioned Christmas, Murder Mystery weekends, and small meeting facilities.
RESTRICTIONS	No smoking, children with well-behaved adults are welcome. "Due to stairs, the inn is probably not suitable for people who have difficulty walking."
REVIEWED	*Recommended Country Inns*
MEMBER	Bed & Breakfast Innkeepers of Colorado

GRAY'S AVENUE HOTEL

711 Manitou Avenue, Manitou Springs, CO 80829
Tom & Lee Gray, Resident Owners

719-685-1277
800-294-1277
FAX 719-685-1847

LOCATION	From I-25 take exit 141 to Highway 24 and go west four miles. Take first Manitou exit to Manitou Avenue, proceed 1.2 miles west. The hotel is on the right.
OPEN	All year.
DESCRIPTION	An 1886 three-story shingled Queen Anne with antiques and family mementos. Large, old-fashioned front porch and lots of stairs offer built-in aerobics.
NO. OF ROOMS	Seven rooms with private bathrooms—that is, one three-room suite and two two-room suites. The Grays suggest The General's Room.
RATES	Year-round rates are $50-70 for a single or double with a private bathroom and $10 extra for rooms accommodating more than two persons. There is no minimum stay and cancellation requires 72 hours' notice.
CREDIT CARDS	American Express, MasterCard, Visa
BREAKFAST	Full breakfast, usually served buffet style, includes waffles, pancakes or casserole, plus bacon or ham, fresh fruit, juice and muffins.
AMENITIES	Some clawfoot tubs in bathrooms, extensive video library, afternoon refreshments, outdoor hot tub and small meeting room.
RESTRICTIONS	No smoking, no pets, children over 10 are welcome. The resident dogs are a German Shepherd named Mackeson, who "loves to play soccer with his toys," and a Golden Lab called Cody, and Kaya the Australian Cattle Dog.
REVIEWED	*The Colorado Guide, Country Inns of the Rocky Mountain Region, Non-Smokers Guide to Bed & Breakfasts*
AWARDS	1986 City of Manitou Spring Design Award, presented by the Historic Preservation Commission.

ONALEDGE BED & BREAKFAST

336 El Paso Boulevard, Manitou Springs, CO 80829   719-685-4265
Adam Kevil, Resident Owner   800-530-8253

LOCATION	From Manitou Avenue, two blocks west to Mayfair Street, right to El Paso Boulevard, top of the hill.
OPEN	All year.
DESCRIPTION	A 1912 three-story English Tudor with Victorian furnishings.
NO. OF ROOMS	Three rooms with private bathrooms, two suites with private bathrooms and hot tubs.
RATES	Year-round rates are $95-150 for a single or double with private bathroom. There is a reservation/cancellation policy.
CREDIT CARDS	American Express, Discover, MasterCard, Visa
BREAKFAST	Full gourmet breakfast is served in the dining room or on the patio.
AMENITIES	TV and air-conditioning in rooms, fireplaces in all rooms, hot tubs in three rooms, complimentary refreshments.
RESTRICTIONS	Smoking limited, no pets. Children 12 and over are welcome.
REVIEWED	*Recommended Country Inns of the Rocky Mountain Region*
MEMBER	Bed & Breakfast Innkeepers of Colorado
KUDOS/COMMENTS	"The antiques, pot-belly stoves, storybook setting, along with the stories the innkeepers tell, make us hate to leave." (1996)

RED CRAGS BED & BREAKFAST INN

302 El Paso Boulevard, Manitou Springs, CO 80829   719-685-1920
Howard & Lynda Lerner, Resident Owners   800-721-2248
     FAX 719-685-1073

LOCATION	Four miles west of Colorado Springs.
OPEN	All year.
DESCRIPTION	An 1870 four-story Victorian Mansion with Victorian furnishings on a two-acre site, listed on the National and State Historic Registers.
NO. OF ROOMS	Eight rooms with private bathrooms. The owner recommends the Teddy Roosevelt Room.
RATES	Year-round rates for a single or double with private bathroom are $75-165. There is a two-night minimum stay on holidays and special events; cancellation requires 30 days during holidays and special events, otherwise ten days.

Red Crags Bed & Breakfast Inn, Manitou Springs

CREDIT CARDS	American Express, Discover, MasterCard, Visa
BREAKFAST	Full gourmet breakfast is served just about anywhere. Special meals are available.
AMENITIES	Robes, Jacuzzi, gourmet coffees and teas and fresh-baked goods are always available, complimentary sherry, wine and port in evenings.
RESTRICTIONS	No smoking, no pets. Children 10 and older are welcome. There is a "loveable Springer Spaniel" named Jackson.
REVIEWED	*Recommended Country Inns of the Rocky Mountain Region*
MEMBER	Bed & Breakfast Innkeepers of Colorado
KUDOS/COMMENTS	"Elegant but very comfortable." ... "Wonderful grounds, excellent hosts." (1997)

RED EAGLE MOUNTAIN B&B INN

616 Ruxton Avenue, Manitou Springs, CO 80829
Stacie & Don LeVack, Resident Owners

719-685-4541
800-686-8801

LOCATION	From I-25 take exit 141 and go west on Highway 24. Take the Manitou Avenue exit, continue west to Ruxton Avenue, turn left on Ruxton, we are two blocks past the Cog Railway on the right side of the road.
OPEN	All year.

DESCRIPTION	An 1894 two-story Queen Ann with Victorian furnishings and spectacular views.
NO. OF ROOMS	Five rooms with private bathrooms. See the Red Eagle Suite.
RATES	Year-round rates are $65-85 for a single with bath and $70-90 for a double with bath. There is a two-night minimum stay from May through September and cancellation requires seven days' notice or forfeit 50% of the deposit.
CREDIT CARDS	American Express, Discover, MasterCard, Visa
BREAKFAST	Full gourmet breakfast, served in the dining room or in guest rooms, includes such things as strata or quiche, fresh breads and fruit. Homemade snacks are always available, as are special meals.
AMENITIES	Homemade cookies and cakes, one room with private sauna, hot tub outdoors, fresh flowers, robes and slippers, TV and bomb shelter...an unusual amenity, but then this is Colorado Springs...TI
RESTRICTIONS	No smoking, resident Cocker is called Dreyfus. Children are welcome
MEMBER	Bed & Breakfast Innkeepers of Colorado

RED STONE CASTLE BED & BREAKFAST

Red Stone Castle, Manitou Springs, CO 80829   719-685-5070
Cavan Daly McGrew, Resident Owners

LOCATION	Four blocks from downtown, Manitou Avenue to Pawnee, left to South Side Road, left to castle gate.
OPEN	All year.
DESCRIPTION	An 1892 small Victorian castle on 20 acres. Listed on the National Historic Register and furnished with antiques.
NO. OF ROOMS	One luxury suite called "Inspiration."
RATES	A single with private bathroom is $110 and double with private bathroom is $140. Additional guests are $25 per person. There is no minimum stay and there is a reservation/cancellation policy.
CREDIT CARDS	No
BREAKFAST	Full breakfast is served in the dining room or on the patio in the summer.
AMENITIES	Fresh and dried flowers, coffee and tea at the wet bar, telephone, robes, small reception and outdoor wedding facilities.
RESTRICTIONS	No smoking, no pets, Duke is the resident dog.

TWO SISTERS INN—A BED & BREAKFAST

Ten Otoe Place, Manitou Springs, CO 80829   719-685-9684
Sharon Smith & Wendy Goldstein, Resident Owners   800-274-7466

LOCATION	Exit 141 off I-25 in Colorado Springs. Go four miles west on Highway 24 to Manitou Avenue, exit one mile west on Manitou Avenue. Left at town clock on to Otoe Place.
OPEN	All year.
DESCRIPTION	A 1919 two-story Victorian bungalow with Victorian furnishings and garden cottage with a fireplace and skylight shower.
NO. OF ROOMS	Three rooms with private bathrooms and two rooms share one bathroom. Sharon & Wendy suggest the Honeymoon Cottage.
RATES	Year-round rates are $75 for a single or double with private bathroom, $63 for a single or double with a shared bathroom and $95 for the cottage. There is a minimum stay for some holidays and special events and a seven-day cancellation policy with a $15 fee. Non-refundable advance payment for holidays and special events.
CREDIT CARDS	Discover, MasterCard, Visa
BREAKFAST	Full "creative gourmet" breakfast, prepared by "resident, schooled chefs using inn-grown herbs and flowers from the inn's gardens," served in the dining room.
AMENITIES	Fresh flowers and home-baked treats in the rooms, beverages including Manitou's natural sparkling water, lemonade, antique piano and games in the parlor, books and maps of local points of interest and on-site parking.
RESTRICTIONS	No smoking, no pets, children over 10 are welcome.
REVIEWED	*America's Wonderful Little Hotels & Inns, Frommer's Guide to Colorado, The Colorado Guide, Recommended Country Inns*
MEMBER	Bed & Breakfast Innkeepers of Colorado, Professional Association of Innkeepers International, Tourist House Association of America, Colorado Hotel and Lodging Association
AWARDS	Manitou Springs Historic Preservation Commission, Historic Renovation Award, 1990.
KUDOS/COMMENTS	"Small B&B with cozy rooms and very hospitable hosts." (1994) "A warm and friendly inn with caring owners and wonderful food." ... "Their place is great, the Honeymoon Cottage is exquisite." ... "Gourmet breakfasts, Sharon and Wendy are the perfect hosts." (1997)

VICTORIA'S KEEP: A BED & BREAKFAST INN

202 Ruxton Avenue, Manitou Springs, CO 80829
Marvin Keith, Owner

719-685-5354
800-905-5337
FAX 719-685-5913

LOCATION	West from Colorado Springs on Highway 24 to Manitou Springs business exit, continue west through town then take a left on Ruxton, then two blocks down on the right, directly in front of the Miramont Castle.
OPEN	All year.
DESCRIPTION	A restored 1891 two-story Queen Anne Victorian with wraparound porch and antique furnishings.
NO. OF ROOMS	Six rooms with private baths and fireplaces. Marvin's favorite room is the Parlor suite.
RATES	Year-round rates are $80-95 for a single or double with private bath and $105-160 for a suite with a private bath. There is no minimum stay. Cancellation requires seven days' notice or forfeit deposit for one night.
CREDIT CARDS	American Express, Discover, MasterCard, Visa
BREAKFAST	Full (serious) breakfast, served just about anywhere in the house, might be crabmeat & eggs or frittatas or biscuits & gravy. Lunch and picnic baskets are available.
AMENITIES	Spa, mountain bikes, 24-hour beverages, TV and VCR with video library, phone, air conditioning in all rooms, flowers, candles, fireplaces, wine and cheese tasting, breakfast in bed and candy dish.
RESTRICTIONS	No smoking.
REVIEWED	*National Trust's Guide to Historic B&Bs, Inns and Small Hotels*
MEMBER	Professional Association of Innkeepers International, Bed & Breakfast Innkeepers of Colorado
KUDOS/COMMENTS	"Cozy Victorian home with spacious rooms and great breakfasts."... "Romantic getaway to die for! Personal welcome note and turndown service were special touches."... "Marvin is a marvelous gourmet chef."... "Wine and cheese tasting a definite plus." (1996)

MARBLE

The famous Yule Marble Quarry is open again, and the town's two-digit population is on the rebound. Summer do's: the Marble Art Fair and Sculptor's Symposium along the Crystal River in July. The view of Crystal Mill is worth the hike and fishin's good in town at Beaver Lake. Down the road from Redstone, and about 60 miles southwest of Aspen via Highway 133 and County Road 3.

THE INN AT RASPBERRY RIDGE

5580 County Road 3, Marble, CO 81623   970-963-3025
Gary & Patsy Wagner, Resident Owners

LOCATION	On the edge of town as you enter Marble. You can't miss us.
OPEN	All year except for the weeks of Thanksgiving, Christmas and New Years.
DESCRIPTION	A 1960 log ranch/country inn sits in a town with 55 year-round residents.
NO. OF ROOMS	Four rooms with private bathrooms. The Brass Room is the best.
RATES	Summer (April through October) rates are $70-80 for a double with private bath and off season rates are $50 for a double with private bath. There is a reservation/cancellation policy.
CREDIT CARDS	No
BREAKFAST	Full breakfast, served in the dining room or on deck, includes egg dishes, fresh-baked coffeecake and fresh fruit. Lunches are packed on request.
AMENITIES	Snacks always available, very helpful innkeepers.
RESTRICTIONS	No smoking, no pets and children over 12 are welcome.
MEMBER	Bed & Breakfast Innkeepers of Colorado
KUDOS/COMMENTS	"Great hospitality and terrific breakfast in one of Colorado's most fascinating and historic mountain communities." ... "Great breakfast beautifully presented." ... "Tastefully decorated, not cutesy." ... "Great setting, great hosts." (1996)

MEREDITH

Don't blink or you'll miss this village in the White River National Forest. Follow along the Frying Pan River 20 miles or so east of Basalt.

DOUBLE DIAMOND RANCH BED & BREAKFAST

23000 Frying Pan Road, Meredith, CO 81642   970-927-3404
Jack & Joan Wheeler, Resident Owners   FAX 970-927-3404

LOCATION	Take Frying Pan River Road 23 miles from Main Street in Basalt to Ruedi Reservoir. The driveway and ranch gate is 1/4 mile past the end of the reservoir on the right.
OPEN	All year.
DESCRIPTION	A 1987 log ranch house and cabins with "upscale traditional old west" and antique furnishings and western memorabilia.
NO. OF ROOMS	Two rooms in the ranch house with private bathrooms and two cabins. Pick the Rose Room.
RATES	Year-round rates are $85 per room in ranch house with private bathroom, $195 for two-bedroom cabin and $105 for the wilderness cabin. There is no minimum stay and a 30-day cancellation policy.
CREDIT CARDS	No
BREAKFAST	Full breakfast, served in the dining room, includes an egg dish, seasonal fruit, homemade biscuits, muffins, breads and jams with beverages. Lunch and dinner are available with prior notice.
AMENITIES	Fresh flowers in the guest rooms, hot tub in meadow, horseback trips, wilderness horseback rides, hiking and cross-country ski trails, guided fly fishing in gold medal water or high country lakes.
RESTRICTIONS	No smoking, children are welcome. There are 18 horses, five mules, an Australian Shepherd named Max and a Border Collie named Ty.
KUDOS/COMMENTS	"Delightful farmhouse and cabin...Try their dinners!" (1996)

MINTURN

This small, pretty village has a couple of great, reasonable restaurants and is handy to Vail, and the Holy Cross and Eagle's Nest Wilderness Areas. Seven miles west of Vail via I-70 exit 171.

EAGLE RIVER INN

145 North Main Street, Minturn, CO 81645   970-827-5761
Patty Bidez, Manager   800-344-1750
Some Spanish spoken.   FAX 970-827-4020

LOCATION	Seven miles beyond Vail, south two miles on Highway 24 to Minturn.
OPEN	All year except for May.
DESCRIPTION	An 1894 three-story adobe, totally remodeled with southwestern interior, overlooking the Eagle River.
NO. OF ROOMS	Twelve rooms with private bathrooms.
RATES	Winter rates, November through April, are $100-180 for a single or double with a private bathroom. Off season rates, June through October, are $100 for a single or double with a private bathroom. There is a two-day minimum stay if Saturday is involved and cancellation requires 14 days—30 days at Christmas.
CREDIT CARDS	American Express, MasterCard, Visa
BREAKFAST	Full breakfast, served in the dining room, includes fresh fruit, baked goods, homemade granola, yogurt, and a hot entree such as cream-cheese French toast, green-chili quiche or sausage polenta.
AMENITIES	Fresh flowers, TV, hot tub on the wraparound deck, meeting room, complimentary evening wine tasting and appetizer buffet, 10 mountain bikes and six pairs of snowshoes are lent to guests.
RESTRICTIONS	No smoking, no pets, children over 12 preferred. Geezer is the resident Airdale; Rosie, the resident Golden.
REVIEWED	*America's Wonderful Little Hotels & Inns, The Colorado Guide, Recommended Country Inns of the Rocky Montain Region, American Historic Inns*
MEMBER	Professional Association of Innkeepers International
RATED	AAA 3 Diamonds, Mobil 3 Stars

THE MINTURN INN

442 Main Street, Minturn, CO 81645   970-827-9647
Tom & Cathy Sullivan and Mick Kelly, Resident Owners   800-646-8876
                                                       FAX 970-827-5590

LOCATION	From I-70, take exit #171, turn right and go two miles to the town of Minturn. The inn is four blocks down on the left across from the Pasta Palace.
OPEN	All year.
DESCRIPTION	A 1915 refurbished log home with custom-made log beds, antler chandeliers, hardwood floors and a river-rock fireplace.
NO. OF ROOMS	Eight rooms with private bathrooms and two rooms share one bathroom. Try the 10th Mountain Division Room.
RATES	Winter rates, November through April, are $89-189 for a single or double with a private bathroom and $79-129 for a single or double with a shared bathroom. Summer rates are $75-125 for a single or double with a private bathroom and $65 for a single or double with a shared bathroom. There is a two-night minimum stay if one day is a Saturday. Cancellation requires 14 days' notice and a $25 fee.
CREDIT CARDS	American Express, Discover, MasterCard, Visa
BREAKFAST	Full, hot, homestyle breakfast is served in the dining room.
AMENITIES	Sauna.
RESTRICTIONS	No smoking, no pets, children over 12 are welcome. The resident dog is called Cnosis.
REVIEWED	*Denver Post, New York Times, Men's Journal.*
MEMBER	Bed & Breakfast Innkeepers of Colorado

MOFFAT

WHITE EAGLE VILLAGE

67485 County Road T, Moffat, CO 81143   719-256-4865
JoAnne Duncan, Resident Owner   800-613-2270
                                                       FAX 719-256-4868

MONARCH PASS

OLD MINE—MOUNT SHAVANO BED & BREAKFAST

16780 Highway 50 West, Monarch Pass, CO 81201   719-539-4640
M. Robins, Resident Owner

MONTE VISTA

This is the agricultural trade center for the San Luis Valley. Don't miss the Monte Vista National Wildlife Refuge for migratory birds. They are in abundant flurry between October and April. The cowboys arrive in late July for the Ski-Hi Stampede and Rodeo. From Alamosa, 17 miles west via Highways 285 and 160 and within close proximity to the Rio Grande National Recreation Area.

THE WINDMILL BED & BREAKFAST

4340 West Highway U.S. 160, Monte Vista, CO 81144   719-852-0438
Sharon & Dennis Kay, Resident Owners   800-467-3441

LOCATION	Four miles west of U.S. Highway 285 on U.S. Highway 160.
OPEN	All year.
DESCRIPTION	A 1950 one-story Spanish-style ranch home with early southwest and antique furnishings.
NO. OF ROOMS	Four rooms with private bathrooms. The owners' favorite is the Frontier Room.
RATES	Year-round rates are $65-99 for a single or double with a private bathroom. There is no minimum stay requirements. Ask about the reservation/cancellation policy.
CREDIT CARDS	MasterCard, Visa
BREAKFAST	Full breakfast, served in the dining room, includes natural-grown meats, grains and pastries, egg dishes and San Luis potatoes.
AMENITIES	Hot tub under the windmill, wildlife viewing, afternoon refreshments, fresh flowers, telephones available, TV and VCR in common area, view of the San Luis Valley and surrounding mountains, hiking, bird watching.
RESTRICTIONS	No smoking, no pets, children of well-behaved parents are welcome. Granny Rags, the resident cat, patrols the premises. Watch for Antelope on property.
MEMBER	Professional Association of Innkeepers International

MONTROSE

ANNIE'S ORCHARD: A HISTORIC BED & BREAKFAST

14963 63.00 Road, Montrose, CO 81401   970-249-0298

TRAVELER'S B&B INN

502 South 1st Street, Montrose, CO 81401   970-249-3472
Lois Straughn, Resident Owner

MONUMENT

A pastoral, country quilt of horse ranches, wide green acres and impressive homes, 20 miles north of Colorado Springs via I-25. From here it's a straight shot to the Renaissance Festival in Larkspur and the outlet shops at Castle Rock (bring endurance and money).

CROSS KEYS INN B&B

20450 Beacon Lite Road, Monument, CO 80132   719-481-2772
Rick & Suzanne Laidlaw, Resident Owners   800-250-5397
     719-481-8992

LOCATION	Three-hundred yards west of I-25 at Monument exit 163.
OPEN	All year.
DESCRIPTION	A 1984 two-story log host home with rustic/antique furnishings on five acres.
NO. OF ROOMS	Three rooms with private bathrooms.
RATES	Year-round rate for a single or double with a private bathroom is $85-120. There is no minimum stay, ask about a cancellation policy.
CREDIT CARDS	American Express, Discover, MasterCard, Visa
BREAKFAST	Full breakfast, served in the dining room, includes full egg dish or pancakes/waffles, bread, fruit and beverages.
AMENITIES	Solarium with hot tub, fireplace in living room, TV/VCR and videos, hiking, biking and horseback trails close by.
RESTRICTIONS	No smoking, no pets, children over 12 are welcome.
MEMBER	Bed & Breakfast Innkeepers of Colorado, Professional Association of Innkeepers International
KUDOS/COMMENTS	"Mountain views and gourmet breakfasts." (1997)

MORRISON

This delightful National Historic District is a terrific stay-over spot to explore the amazing red sandstone formations in the 640-acre Red Rocks Park, and the Easter Sunrise Services and summer concerts at Red Rocks Amphitheater. About 15 miles west of Denver via I-70 and State Road 74.

CLIFF HOUSE LODGE B&B INN & COTTAGES

121 Stone Street, Morrison, CO 80465   303-697-9732
Peggy Hahn, Resident Owner   FAX 303-697-0113
French and Spanish spoken.

LOCATION	From I-70 take exit 259 south along the hogback past Red Rocks Park. The Inn is the first building on the right side as you enter the village of Morrison, turn right under the archway.
OPEN	All year.
DESCRIPTION	An 1873 two-story French sandstone inn with Victorian furnishings. Includes cottages and is on the National and State Historic Registers.
NO. OF ROOMS	Ten cottages have private bathrooms. The best room is called Camelot.
RATES	Year-round rates are $129 and up.
CREDIT CARDS	MasterCard, Visa
BREAKFAST	Full candlelight breakfast for two with romance package is delivered to the cottage.
AMENITIES	Fireplaces, robes, VCR, free movies, stereo in rooms. Private hot tubs in suites, romance packages, outdoor hot tub and carriage rides to Red Rocks Park, hiking trails.
RESTRICTIONS	No pets, restricted smoking. Only two persons in cottage.
REVIEWED	*Recommended Country Inns of the Rocky Mountain Region, A Treasury of Bed & Breakfasts*
MEMBER	Bed & Breakfast Innkeepers of Colorado
KUDOS/COMMENTS	"Romantic and private." (1997)

MOSCA

Near the Great Sand Dunes at the foot of the Sangre de Cristos. Rising 700 feet tall, these are the tallest dunes in North America. Zapata Falls offers scenic waterfall with panoramic view of the valley.

INN AT ZAPATA RANCH

5303 Highway 150, Mosca, CO 81146
Angela Moses, Innkeeper

719-378-2806
800-284-9213
FAX 719-378-2428

LOCATION	Guests coming from east and west, take Highway 160 to Highway 150. Turn north and drive 12 miles. Those coming from north and south, take Highway 7 to County Road 6, turn east and drive 16 miles to Highway 150, turn south and drive one mile.
OPEN	April 1 to January 1.
DESCRIPTION	Rough-hewn log buildings of late-1800s construction, renovated in 1989 with western decor, listed on the National Historic Register.
NO. OF ROOMS	Fifteen rooms with private bathrooms. Innkeeper recommends Room 9.
RATES	Rates are seasonal and there is no minimum stay requirement.
CREDIT CARDS	American Express, Diners Club, Discover, MasterCard, Visa
BREAKFAST	Full breakfast, offered in spring and summer, includes homemade pastries, fruit, cheese, juice and granola. Lunch and dinner are also available.
AMENITIES	Outdoor pool & hot tub, sauna, exercise room, massage, hayride, horseback, tours of bison ranch, 18-hole championship golf course.
RESTRICTIONS	No smoking. The resident Bison is Amelia...Travis Ilse, the old gumshoe, solves another great mystery...we editors thought Amelia was lost over the Pacific...CH
REVIEWED	*Frommer's Colorado, Association of Historic Hotels, Distinctive Inns of Colorado, Colorado Restaurants & Recipes*

MEMBER
Association of Historic Hotels, Independent Innkeepers Association, Distinctive Inns of Colorado, Colorado Hotel & Motel Association

KUDOS/COMMENTS
"Wonderful, relaxed atmosphere, exquisite dining; tour and history of the ranch was excellent, as was the hospitality." (1997)

Inn at Zapata Ranch, Mosca

NATHROP

Here is major access to the incredible Collegiate Peaks. Pick your peak, forge the Arkansas, soak it up in the Mt. Princeton Hot Springs. Adjacent to Buena Vista, 93 miles west of Colorado Springs on Highway 24.

THE INN AT CHALK CLIFFS

16557 County Road 162, Nathrop, CO 81236   719-395-6068
Phyllis Terry, Resident Owner   FAX 719-395-6068

LOCATION	From Nathrop go five miles on County Road 162, turn right at sign and go to the end of the road. The inn is 0.6 miles west of the Mt. Princeton Hot Springs Resort.
OPEN	All year.
DESCRIPTION	A 1976 two-story frame home with contemporary furnishings. The house looks out at Mt. Antero and is nestled at the foot of Mt. Princeton.
NO. OF ROOMS	One room with a private bathroom and two rooms share one bathroom. Pick the upstairs east-side bedroom.
RATES	A single with private or shared bathroom is $50, a double with private or shared bathroom is $60. There is no minimum stay and cancellation requires 24 hours' notice.
CREDIT CARDS	American Express, Discover, MasterCard, Visa
BREAKFAST	Full breakfast, served in the dining room, includes blueberry pancakes, ham/bacon, eggs if desired, fruit cup and beverages.
AMENITIES	Use of the front room including TV/VCR and game table, dining room and kitchen in the evening. Hiking trail on property.
RESTRICTIONS	None. Three resident cats, Bruno, Shadow and Misty.

THE LANDING AT CHALK CREEK

16390 County Road 162, Nathrop, CO 81236   719-395-4150
John Record, Resident Owner

MAGPIE COTTAGE BED & BREAKFAST

13735 County Road 270, Nathrop, CO 81236   719-395-6797
Mitzi & Tom Mohr, Resident Owners

Streamside Bed & Breakfast, Nathrop

STREAMSIDE BED & BREAKFAST

18820 County Road 162, Nathrop, CO 81236   719-395-2553
Denny & Kathy Claveau, Resident Owners

LOCATION	On Chalk Creek in Chalk Creek Canyon. From Buena Vista take Highway 285 to Nathrop. Go west from Nathrop on County Road 162 for eight miles to our driveway on the left.
OPEN	All year except December 24 through 26.
DESCRIPTION	A 1975 rustic mountain home and two-story cottage with country/traditional furnishings, "a mountain paradise" located within San Isabel National Forest.
NO. OF ROOMS	Three rooms with private bathrooms. The owners recommend the Columbine Loft.
RATES	Year-round rates are $64-69 for a single or double with a private bath. There is a minimum stay on holiday weekends and a ten-day cancellation policy.
CREDIT CARDS	No
BREAKFAST	Full breakfast is served in the dining room.
AMENITIES	No phones, no TV but lots of solitude, close to hot springs, picnic table, lounge chairs and fire pit on streamside.
RESTRICTIONS	No smoking, no pets, children over six welcome on a limited basis.
MEMBER	Bed & Breakfast Innkeepers of Colorado
KUDOS/COMMENTS	"Friendly hosts, away from town." (1997)

NORWOOD

Norwood features Pioneer Day and the San Miguel Fair, plus local rodeos. Skiing is 30 miles away in Telluride.

ANNIE'S COUNTRY BED & BREAKFAST

551 County Road 44ZN, Norwood, CO 81423   *970-327-4331*
Anne Shaffer, Resident Owner

LOCATION	One mile east of Norwood, north on County Road 44ZN, 1/2 mile off Highway 145.
OPEN	All year.
DESCRIPTION	A 1917 western homestead with tin roof and low ceilings "where plumbing, electricity and central heating are the amenities"...great description, Annie, you make your place sound like a real ranch home...TI
NO. OF ROOMS	One room with private bathroom and two rooms share one bathroom.
RATES	Year-round rate for a single or double with a private bathroom is $45 and a single or double with a shared bathroom is $40. There is no minimum stay and a 60-day cancellation policy during hunting and ski seasons.
CREDIT CARDS	No
BREAKFAST	Full breakfast is served in the kitchen and includes bacon, ham, sausage or steak with eggs fixed as guest requests, sourdough pancakes, muffins, biscuits and "real" coffee. Lunch and dinner are available on request.
AMENITIES	"Peace, quite and sourdough"...and if that's not enough...line-dried linens, piano, board games and "absolutely no TV."
RESTRICTIONS	No smoking. The resident dog is Smuck, the 30 year-old burro is Ouno. There are also plenty of horses and cattle.

Lone Cone Ranch Bed & Breakfast, Norwood

LONE CONE RANCH BED & BREAKFAST

Z 42 Road, Norwood, CO 81423   970-327-4300
Bob & Sharon Hardman, Resident Owners

LOCATION	One mile west of Norwood on Z Road.
OPEN	All year.
DESCRIPTION	A 1970 two-story rustic home decorated with antiques on a working cattle and elk ranch.
NO. OF ROOMS	Four rooms share two bathrooms.
RATES	Year-round rates are $35 for a single and $40 for a double with a shared bathroom. There is no minimum stay, ask about a cancellation policy.
CREDIT CARDS	No
BREAKFAST	Full breakfast, served in the dining room, includes fruit, blueberry or buttermilk pancakes, French toast, eggs, bacon or sausage, and orange juice. Dinner and special meals are also available.
AMENITIES	Ranch living, horse boarding, hiking, elk watching, fishing, hunting elk, deer, bear and lion.
RESTRICTIONS	No smoking. Resident pets include a cow dog named Spud and various barn cats. In October, listen to the elk bugle and watch them lock horns.

OAK CREEK

A little hamlet out of the 60s tucked between the White River and Route National Forests that is 20 miles southwest of Steamboat Springs via Highways 40 and 131.

HIGH MEADOWS RANCH

20505 Routt County Road 16, Oak Creek, CO 80467   *970-736-8416*
Jan & Dennis Stamp, Resident Owners   *800-457-4453*
                              FAX 970-736-8416

LOCATION	From Steamboat Springs, go one mile on US 40 east, turn right on Highway 131 and go 6.3 miles, then turn left on County Road 14 for 7.2 miles, turn left on bridge on to County Road 16, after 1.5 miles turn left staying on County Road 16, the ranch has a large log entry on the right.
OPEN	All year.
DESCRIPTION	A 1983-91 guest ranch with Victorian main lodge and log chalets and western decor.
NO. OF ROOMS	Five rooms with private bathrooms. The best room is the front bedroom in the Elk Lodge.
RATES	Year-round rates for a single or double with a private bathroom are $105 and the entire ranch rents for $525. There is a two-night minimum stay and cancellation requires 30 days' notice with a 10% handling fee.
CREDIT CARDS	MasterCard, Visa
BREAKFAST	Full breakfast is served family style in the dining room, includes hot entree (the specialty is Belgian waffles), fresh fruit, juice and coffee. Lunch, dinner and special meals for groups, such as a BBQ at the barn, are available.
AMENITIES	Log chalets contain kitchens and laundry facilities, wood-burning stoves, outdoor hot tub, wild-flower photography and 20-kilometer groomed cross-country ski track.
RESTRICTIONS	No smoking. Resident Yellow Lab is called Jake, the Calico is called Cassidy, and there are 18 Quarter horses on the property.

OURAY

Named for Ute Chief Ouray (you Ray), this mining town and National Historic District situated in a natural mountain amphitheater deserves to be called "The Switzerland of America". Things not to miss: the 300-foot Box Canyon Falls and Park, a soak in the hugh Hot Springs Pool and the Ouray Chamber Music Concert Series in June. This is also the starting place for the 18 mile Imogene Pass run that ends in Telluride. From Montrose, 36 miles south on Highway 550.

ABOVE TIMBERLINE

803 Main Street, PO Box 378, Ouray, CO 81427   970-329-4125
Rich & Myrna Spaulding, Resident Owners   800-325-4125

LOCATION	North end of the business district, 1/4 mile south of Hot Springs Pool on Main Street above Timberline Deli.
OPEN	All year.
DESCRIPTION	"A cross between Victorian and New Orleans bordello architecture" with traditional furnishings. Private entrance to each room from a covered deck.
NO. OF ROOMS	Three rooms with private bathrooms. The Spauldings think the Boy's Room is their best.
RATES	Summer rates are $72 for a single or double with a private bathroom and winter rates are $10 less. Cancellation requires 24 hours in the summer and seven days in the winter.
CREDIT CARDS	American Express, Discover, MasterCard, Visa
BREAKFAST	Continental Plus breakfast is served in the breakfast room and includes fruit juice, fresh fruit, yogurt, granola, fresh homemade pastry, coffee, espresso or cappuccino, tea, cocoa.
AMENITIES	Hot tub, in-room TV/VCR and over 2,000 movies, half-price lift tickets to Telluride, breakfast room is open 24 hours with snacks and hot or cold drinks.
RESTRICTIONS	No smoking, no pets, children over 12 are welcome.

CHINA CLIPPER BED & BREAKFAST INN

525 Second Street, PO Box 801, Ouray, CO 81427   970-325-0565
Elaine & Earl Yarbrough, Resident Owners   800-315-0565
                                   FAX 970-325-4190

LOCATION	Enter Ouray on Highway 550 (the main street through town), turn west on Sixth Avenue, go one block and turn left onto Second Street. The inn is next to the Matterhorn Motel parking lot.

China Clipper Bed & Breakfast Inn, Ouray

OPEN	All year.
DESCRIPTION	A three-story Southern Traditional with English period and reproduction furniture.
NO. OF ROOMS	Eleven rooms with private bathrooms. Pick the Honeymoon room.
RATES	Summer, June through October, and Christmas rates are $85 to $160 for a single or double with a private bathroom. Winter rates for a single or double with a private bathroom are $65-160. There is a minimum stay on holidays and cancellation requires 30 days' notice with a $15 dollar fee.
CREDIT CARDS	MasterCard, Visa
BREAKFAST	Full breakfast is served in the dining room and may include home fries, potatoes O'Brien, eggs, pancakes or quiche, Belgian waffles, fresh fruit in season, juices, homemade bread, coffee and tea. Afternoon wine and beer and spreads.
AMENITIES	Honeymooners receive a bottle of Champagne, wedding facilities for up to 40, robes, handicapped access, ceiling fans and decks in all rooms, fireplaces and views.
RESTRICTIONS	No smoking, no pets, no children. Lacy, the resident dog, is "discreet, doesn't go into the living room, dining room or guestrooms. Loves everyone, but waits for encouragement."
REVIEWED	Opened in 1995.
MEMBER	Distinctive Inns of Colorado, Bed & Breakfast Innkeepers of Colorado, Professional Association of Innkeepers International
RATED	AAA 3 Diamond
KUDOS/COMMENTS	"Beautifully constructed new property with the feel of the past; tastefully decorated." ... "Nice location just off the main street; Elaine is charming." (1996)

Columbus House Bed & Breakfast

746 Main Street, PO Box 31, Ouray, CO 81427   970-325-4551
Jim Ludington, Resident Owner   FAX 970-325-7388

LOCATION	On Main Street at the north end of town above the Silver Nugget Cafe.
OPEN	Open from May 27 to September 30.
DESCRIPTION	An 1898 red-brick Victorian with Victorian furnishings.
NO. OF ROOMS	Six rooms share one bathroom. Pick room #7.
RATES	Year-round rates $59-69 for a single or double with shared bathroom.
CREDIT CARDS	Discover, MasterCard, Visa
BREAKFAST	Full breakfast, served at the Silver Nugget Cafe downstairs, is included in the room price.
AMENITIES	Robes, sitting room and TV room.
RESTRICTIONS	No smoking, no pets, children over 12 are welcome.

The Damn Yankee Country Inn

100 Sixth Avenue, PO Box 709, Ouray, CO 81427   970-325-4219
Mike & Marj Manley, Resident Owners   800-845-7512
English, sort of.   FAX 970-325-0502

LOCATION	Two blocks down hill from the center of town (Sixth Avenue and Main) next to the river.
OPEN	All year.
DESCRIPTION	A 1991 two-story English Cottage with slate roof and Victorian/Country English furnishings.
NO. OF ROOMS	Ten rooms with private bathrooms. Mike Manley suggests room 10.
RATES	Summer rates, June through September, are $94-165 for a single or double with a private bathroom. Winter rates, October through May, are $68-125. There is no minimum stay. There is a one-week cancellation policy.
CREDIT CARDS	American Express, Discover, MasterCard, Visa
BREAKFAST	Full "giant gourmet" breakfast, such as eggs benedict, potatoes O'Brien, fresh fruits, Danish, juice and coffee, with "doggie bags." Dinner is available in the winter.
AMENITIES	Private entrances, phones and TV, hot tub, BBQ grills and picnic tables by the river, piano in parlor.

RESTRICTIONS	No smoking, no pets, children over 12 are welcome.
MEMBER	Bed & Breakfast Innkeepers of Colorado
RATED	AAA 3 Diamonds, Mobil 3 Stars

THE EVERGREEN BED & BREAKFAST

430 Fourth Avenue, PO Box 286, Ouray, CO 81427   970-325-7318
Thad & Marti Harris, Resident Owners

LOCATION	On Fourth Avenue (not 4th Street!), 1-1/2 blocks east of Highway 550, which is the north-south main street through the middle of town.
OPEN	All year.
DESCRIPTION	An 1898 Victorian with Victorian furnishings.
NO. OF ROOMS	One room with a private bathroom.
RATES	Year-round rates are $65 plus tax for a single or double with private bathroom. There is a special rate of seven nights for the price of six and senior discounts. Cancellation requires seven days' notice.
CREDIT CARDS	No
BREAKFAST	Full breakfast, served in the dining room or kitchen, includes eggs, bacon, toast, pancakes and beverages.
AMENITIES	Portable phone available, lounge with TV, music, piano, books, senior discounts. The room is on the first floor and handicapped accessible.
RESTRICTIONS	No smoking, no pets, one child over 12 is okay (there is a flip-out bed). The three cats are Peaches, Picayune and Tara. They are not allowed in the guest room.
MEMBER	Ouray Chamber Resort Association.

HISTORIC WESTERN HOTEL

210 7th Avenue, PO Box 25, Ouray, CO 81427   970-325-4645
Gregg & Rosemarie Pieper, Resident Owners   888-624-8403
Dutch spoken.

LOCATION	Half block west of Main Street.
OPEN	All year.
DESCRIPTION	An 1891 three-story Victorian with Victorian period furnishings located in the historic district.

NO. OF ROOMS	Two rooms with private bathrooms and 12 rooms share four bathrooms. Pick Room 1.
RATES	High season rate, May 15 to October 15, for a single or double with a private bathroom is $78, a single or double with a shared bathroom is $48. Off season rate, October 15 to May 15, for a single or double with a private bathroom is $60, a single or double with shared bathroom is $40. There is no minimum stay and cancellation requires 24 hours' notice and a $10 fee.
CREDIT CARDS	Discover, MasterCard, Visa
BREAKFAST	Continental breakfast is served. Dinner is also available.
RESTRICTIONS	No smoking, no pets.
KUDOS/COMMENTS	"Very authentic." (1997)

THE MAIN STREET HOUSE

PO Box 641, PO Box 641, Ouray, CO 81427   970-325-4317
Lee & Kathy Bates, Resident Owners

THE MANOR

317 2nd Street, PO Box 745, Ouray, CO 81427   970-325-4574
Joel & Diane Kramer, Resident Owners   800-628-6946
German spoken.

LOCATION	On 2nd Street, one "quiet" block west of Main Street between 3rd and 4th Avenues.
OPEN	All year, but closed in November.
DESCRIPTION	An 1890 two-story Georgian/Victorian Inn with Victorian furnishings, listed on both the National and State Historic Registers.
NO. OF ROOMS	Seven rooms with private bathrooms.
RATES	High season rates, early June through early October, are $80-90 for a single or double with a private bathroom. Low season rates, early October through early June, are $60-75 for a single or double with a private bathroom. There is a minimum stay over Christmas and through most of the high season; cancellation requires 10 days' notice.
CREDIT CARDS	MasterCard, Visa
BREAKFAST	Full breakfast, served in the dining room, is meatless with whole grains and fresh fruit.

The Manor, Ouray

AMENITIES	Afternoon tea, fresh-baked cookies, sitting parlor, fireplace, down comforters, featherbeds for the winter, small library, fresh flowers (in season), no TV, half-price lift tickets to Telluride, hot tub in the backyard, perennial flower garden in summer, robes.
RESTRICTIONS	No smoking, no pets, children over 12 are welcome. Jack, Ryley, Charley and Larry° are very good with guests but not allowed to roam the house. °The two dogs and two cats, respectively. Oh, and Ryley loves the Texas accent... more proof that that state is going to the dogs...TI
REVIEWED	*Recommended Country Inns of the Rocky Mountain Region, Best Places to Stay in the Rockies*
MEMBER	Bed & Breakfast Innkeepers of Colorado, American Bed & Breakfast Association
RATED	ABBA 3 Crowns

OURAY 1898 HOUSE

322 Main Street, PO Box 641, Ouray, CO 81427   970-325-4871
Lee & Kathy Bates, Resident Owners

LOCATION	On Main Street, the south end of Ouray.
OPEN	May 25 until September 25.
DESCRIPTION	An 1898 renovated Victorian host home with decks and Victorian furnishings.
NO. OF ROOMS	Three rooms with private bathrooms. The Lilac Room has a large private deck.
RATES	Summer rates, July through September, are $68-88 for a double with private bath, a single is $5 less. Off season rates, May through June, are $10 less. There is no minimum stay except for holidays, and cancellation requires seven days' notice.
CREDIT CARDS	American Express, MasterCard, Visa
BREAKFAST	Full breakfast is served in the dining room and includes "variety for every appetite." Special diets are accommodated.
AMENITIES	Cable TV in each room, hot tub, queen-sized beds, candy and nuts by each bed, coffee, tea and hot chocolate in the upstairs hallway.
RESTRICTIONS	No smoking except on the decks, no pets. Children of all ages are welcome.
REVIEWED	*The Colorado Guide*
MEMBER	Bed & Breakfast Innkeepers of Colorado
KUDOS/COMMENTS	"Hosts were very warm and gracious. Rooms were spotless and in good taste. A very elegant feeling." (1997)

PLAIN JANE SACK & SNACK

3 Munn Park, PO Box 465, Ouray, CO 81427   970-325-7313
Kit and Hank Skelding, Resident Owners
Spanish, German and French spoken.

LOCATION	From Main Street go west on 6th Avenue to bottom (end), then right on Munn Court. Yellow house.
OPEN	All year except December 22 through December 27.
DESCRIPTION	A 1982 two-story "nothing specific" style of architecture with a basic and comfortable interior...now don't overstate the elegance, Kit and Hank...CH

NO. OF ROOMS	Four rooms share three bathrooms. One is a family room.
RATES	Year-round rate is $65 for a double with a shared bathroom. Stays over one day are discounted $10. The family room goes for $85 for four people. There is a cancellation policy.
CREDIT CARDS	MasterCard, Visa
BREAKFAST	Continental Plus breakfast is served in the dining room or guest rooms, includes homemade bread and muffins, cereals, fruit dish and beverages.
AMENITIES	Homey environment, snacks, lawn chairs for lounging while enjoying the beautiful view.
RESTRICTIONS	No smoking, no pets, no drinking. The resident alley cat is called Jezebel. Children of all ages are welcome.
REVIEWED	*Family Fun* magazine
KUDOS/COMMENTS	"Friendly hosts, beautiful town location." (1997)

St. Elmo Hotel

426 Main Street, PO Box 667, Ouray, CO 81427　　　970-325-4951
Dan & Sandy Lingenfelter, Resident Owners　　　FAX 970-325-0348

LOCATION	In town on the west side of Main Street.
OPEN	All year.
DESCRIPTION	A restored 1898 two-story Victorian hotel with antique furnishings and restaurant, listed on the National Historic Register.
NO. OF ROOMS	Nine rooms with private bathrooms. Ask for room 2 or 3.
RATES	Summer rates, June through October, are $88 for a single or double with bath and $95-98 for a suite. Off season rates are $62-75 for a single or double with bath and $69-85 for a suite. There is a minimum stay on certain holidays and cancellation requires seven days.
CREDIT CARDS	American Express, Discover, MasterCard, Visa
BREAKFAST	Full breakfast buffet, served in the dining room, includes a daily entree. Dinner and Sunday brunch are also available.
AMENITIES	Hot tub, sauna, social hour with wine and cheese, equipped to handle small meetings and catered parties.
RESTRICTIONS	No smoking, no pets.
REVIEWED	*Country Inns of the Southwest, Country Inns of the West and Southwest, Recommended Country Inns of the Rocky Mountain Region*

MEMBER	Bed & Breakfast Innkeepers of Colorado
RATED	Mobil 3 Stars
KUDOS/COMMENTS	"The St. Elmo was a real treat." (1995) "Very Victorian and authentic, oldest lodging establishment in town, historic, attractive, and unique in that it also houses the finest restaurant in town. More of a hotel atmosphere than a B&B." (1997)

THE VICTORIAN ROSE

637 5th Street, PO Box 9, Ouray, CO 81427　　　　　970-325-4176
Jerry & Julia Klein, Resident Owner
French and Spanish spoken.

LOCATION	Greater downtown Switzerland of the Rockies.
OPEN	All year.
DESCRIPTION	An 1883/1993 Queen Anne Victorian with Victorian furnishings, listed on the Colorado Historic Register.
NO. OF ROOMS	Two rooms with private bathrooms. The best room: Raseberry Pares Room
RATES	Summer rates are $97 for a single or double with a private bathroom and $10 less in the off season.
CREDIT CARDS	No
BREAKFAST	Full breakfast is served in the parlor.
AMENITIES	Hot tub, private parlor, common area and private deck, TV, telephone.
RESTRICTIONS	No smoking, no pets. Nicklas, the resident dog, is not allowed into guest area.

PAGOSA SPRINGS

"Pagosah," land of healing waters. This quiet, beautiful community sits on a hotbed of geothermal activity. At 153 degrees, the waters are even used to heat some of the town's buildings, so soak it up at Pagosah or Rainbow Hot Springs. The Anasazi's only mountain home at Chimney Rock Archeological Area is worth a tour and don't miss the powder at Wolf Creek Ski Area. From Durango, 60 miles east on Highway 160.

BE OUR GUEST, A BED & BREAKFAST

19 Swiss Village Drive, Pagosa Springs, CO 81147   970-264-6814
Pam Schoemig, Resident Owner

DAVIDSON'S COUNTRY INN BED & BREAKFAST

2763 Highway 160 East, Pagosa Springs, CO 81147   970-264-5863
Gilbert Davidson, Resident Owner   FAX 970-264-9276

LOCATION	Two miles east of Pagosa Springs on Highway 160. Three-story brown log house on the right-hand side that sits back in the meadow.
OPEN	All year.
DESCRIPTION	A 1980 log country inn with knotty pine interior, antique furnishings, covered porch and gazebo, sitting on 32 acres with a view of the Continental Divide.
NO. OF ROOMS	Three rooms with private bathrooms and five rooms share two bathrooms. Gilbert recommends the Ponderosa Suite.
RATES	Year-round rates are $46-70 for a single or double with private bath, $42-60 for a single or double with shared bath, $70 for a suite and the cabin rents for $400 per week. Cancellation requires a week's notice.
CREDIT CARDS	American Express, Discover, MasterCard, Visa
BREAKFAST	Full country-style breakfast is served in the dining room.
AMENITIES	Books and table games and a special indoor children's play corner. The game room includes a pool table and ping-pong table.
RESTRICTIONS	No smoking and children of all ages are welcome. The resident pets are a dog named Bear and two cats, Puff and Cally.
REVIEWED	The Colorado Guide
MEMBER	Bed & Breakfast Innkeepers of Colorado, Colorado Hotel & Motel Association

ECHO MANOR INN

3366 Highway 84, Pagosa Springs, CO 81147   970-264-5646
Maureen & John Widmer, Resident Owners   800-628-5004
German and French spoken.   FAX 970-264-4617

LOCATION	Three-and-a-half miles south of Pagosa Springs on Highway 84.
OPEN	All year.
DESCRIPTION	A 1960s three-story Queen Anne Dutch country inn with a timber and plaster contemporary Tudor interior and large art collection.
NO. OF ROOMS	Ten rooms with private bathrooms. The best room in the house is the Royal Suite.
RATES	Year-round rates for a single or double with a private bathroom are $55-100 and suites are $160-280. There is no minimum stay and cancellation requires 14 days' notice or 30 days' notice for holidays.
CREDIT CARDS	American Express, MasterCard, Visa
BREAKFAST	Full breakfast is served in the breakfast room.
AMENITIES	Hot tub, satellite TV, woodstoves, fireplace, meeting facilities and horse boarding.
RESTRICTIONS	No smoking, no pets, children over 10 are welcome upstairs, children under 10 are welcome in the suite downstairs. There are five outdoor cats, three horses and one dog on the property.
REVIEWED	*Recommended Country Inns of the Rocky Mountain Region, America's Wonderful Little Hotels & Inns.*
RATED	ABBA 3 Crowns

PALISADE

Surprise. Wine country in Colorado? Absolutely, with tours and tastings for the asking. Down here in Colorado's "fruit belt" apples and peaches reign — try the fresh-squeezed apple juice. Excellent year-round recreation can be found at Island Acres State Park, 10 miles east of town. From Grand Junction, 15 miles east via I-70.

THE ORCHARD HOUSE BED & BREAKFAST INN

3573 E 1/2 Road, Palisade, CO 81526   970-464-0529
Bill & Stephanie Schmid, Resident Owners   FAX 970-464-0681

LOCATION	Southwest of town on East Orchard Mesa.
OPEN	All year.
DESCRIPTION	A 1983 country farm house with a large porch and contemporary country furnishings.
NO. OF ROOMS	Two rooms with private bathrooms. The best room is the deluxe suite—"Sorry, no cute names."
RATES	Year-round rates are $55 for a single with private bathroom and $79 for a double with private bathroom. There is a $30 charge for each additional guest over two. There is a 14-day cancellation policy with a $10 service charge and no minimum stay.
CREDIT CARDS	MasterCard, Visa
BREAKFAST	Full breakfast, served in the dining room, is "guests' choice" with local fruit in season. Dinner and special meals are also available.
AMENITIES	Fresh flowers, local Colorado wines and hors d'oeuvres, pick your own peaches in season, winery tours, weddings, family reunions and meeting facility for small groups.
RESTRICTIONS	Smoking in limited areas.
REVIEWED	*The Colorado Guide, Frommer's Colorado*

The Orchard House Bed & Breakfast Inn, Palisade

PAONIA

COLORADO GUEST RANCH

1938 Highway 133, Paonia, CO 81428   970-929-6260
Elaine, Resident Owner   FAX 970-929-6250

PEACE & PLENTY BED & BREAKFAST

206 Rio Grande, Paonia, CO 81428   970-527-7722
Eames & Margit Yates, Resident Owners   FAX 970-527-7722

RIVER RANCH B&B, ORCHARD & STUDIO

1389 3945 Lane, Paonia, CO 81428   970-527-5443
Judy Nielson, Resident Owner

PINE

Very small and beautiful wooded community in the Pike National Forest, southwest of Denver via Highway 185.

MEADOW CREEK BED & BREAKFAST INN

13438 Highway 285,   *303-838-4167*
Berry Hill Lane @ Douglass Ranch, Pine, CO 80470
Pat & Dennis Carnahan, Don & Judy Otis, Resident Owners

LOCATION	From traffic light in Conifer (by Safeway Center) continue on Highway 285 for 5.3 miles. Exit left on 285 Frontage Road, pass the school, turn left at Douglass Ranch Drive (in to Douglass Ranch), follow paved road around to the first right at Berry Hill Lane, continue up lane to the inn.
OPEN	All year.
DESCRIPTION	A 1929 two-story stone and wood country inn with mixed antique, country and contemporary furnishings on 35 acres, listed on the State Historic Register.
NO. OF ROOMS	Seven rooms with private bathrooms. In the last edition Pat recommended The Room in the Meadow, but they have added the Colorado Sun Suite and she is confused...TI
RATES	Year-round rates are $89-180 for a single or double with private bathroom, $129-180 for a suite. There is a minimum stay on weekends and holidays and cancellation requires seven days' notice, 30 days' if more than three rooms are booked.
CREDIT CARDS	American Express, MasterCard, Visa
BREAKFAST	Full breakfast, served in the dining room or buffet on the weekends, includes eggs or casserole, bacon or sausage, homemade pastries, fruit and beverages. Dinner is available Friday and Saturday with a three-day reservation.
AMENITIES	Outdoor hot tub, all rooms have tape or CD unit and candlelight, sauna room, two large decks, hammock, gazebo, three rooms have private hot tubs, king beds and fireplaces, all rooms have robes, homemade chocolate "turtles" at bedside, fresh flowers in season, cookies, snacks and beverages available anytime.
RESTRICTIONS	No smoking, no pets, no children. The resident Shiz Tuze is called Bear and the barn cats are called Mr. Meadow and Mr. Creek.
REVIEWED	*Recommended Country Inns of the Rocky Mountain Region, Recommended Romantic Inns of America*
MEMBER	Bed & Breakfast Innkeepers of Colorado,
KUDOS/COMMENTS	"A romantic inn where your every need will be catered to" ... "Warm, delightful innkeepers." (1994) "Great food! Secluded setting. Exceptional hosts; This place is perfect—the owners have remembered all the little things like homemade cookies, tissue on both sides of the bed, etc." ... "Never wanted to leave." (1997)

PITKIN

GINGERBREAD HOUSE BED & BREAKFAST

311 South 1st, Pitkin, CO 81241   *970-641-5120*
Mark & Annie Jenkins, Resident Owners

KUDOS/COMMENTS   "Contemporary building with Pitkin country touches; lovely
                 location, warm hosts." (1997)

PONCHA SPRINGS

Nothing much to recommend this little village except some fine mountain scenery
to the west and south. Find Poncha Springs about 100 miles west of Pueblo.

JACKSON HOTEL BED & BREAKFAST

220 South Main, Poncha Springs, CO 81242   *719-539-4861*
Tammy & Ed Connolly, Resident Owners   *FAX 719-539-4861*

LOCATION   One block south from the intersection of Highway 50 east and
                    Highway 285 west on the west side of the roadway.

OPEN   All year.

DESCRIPTION   An 1878 three-story rough-cut timber and square-nail stagecoach
                    stop with authentic period furnishings.

NO. OF ROOMS   Ten rooms share two bathrooms and one room has a private
                    bathroom. The best room is The Jailhouse.

RATES   High season, June to October, rates are $37-42 for a single with
                    shared bathroom, $48 for a double with shared bathroom. Off
                    season rates for a single are $5 less and the doubles are still $48.
                    There is no minimum stay and a seven-day cancellation policy.

CREDIT CARDS   Diners Club, Discover, MasterCard, Visa

BREAKFAST   Full breakfast, served in the country kitchen, includes pancakes,
                    bacon or sausage and beverages.

AMENITIES   Banquet facility, pub on site.

RESTRICTIONS   No smoking, no pets, all children are welcome.

KUDOS/COMMENTS   "They've got a bar." (1997)

POWDERHORN

ALICE'S BED & BREAKFAST

18769 Highway 149, Powderhorn, CO 81243   970-641-2080
Alice Wilson, Resident Owner

PUEBLO

The state's third largest city is at the transition zone between mountains and plains, at the confluence of Fountain Creek and the Arkansas River. Check out the Union Avenue National Historic District, Sangre de Cristo Arts and Conference Center and the Raptor Rehabilitation and Nature Centers. Pueblo Reservoir is the place to be for water sports. Interesting summer events: The Annual Governor's Cup Regatta and Cinco de Mayo in May; National High School Rodeo Finals in July and the State and County Fairs in August. Forty-two miles south of Colorado Springs on I-25.

ABRIENDO INN

300 West Abriendo Avenue, Pueblo, CO 81004   719-544-2703
Kerrelyn Trent, Resident Owner   FAX 719-542-6544

LOCATION	I-25 to exit 97B, then west one mile.
OPEN	All year.
DESCRIPTION	A 1906 three-story Four-Square Classical manor-house furnished with antiques and period reproductions on park-like grounds. Listed on the National Historic Register.
NO. OF ROOMS	Ten rooms with private bathrooms. Kerrelyn recommends the Blake Room.
RATES	Year-round rates are $53-100 for a single with private bathroom, $58-110 for a double with private bathroom, $78-83 for a suite and $835 plus tax for the entire B&B. There is a minimum stay during special events and a reservation/cancellation policy.
CREDIT CARDS	American Express, Diners Club, MasterCard, Visa
BREAKFAST	Full breakfast, served in the dining room, varies but includes entrees like a green-chile and chorizo-sausage egg bake; also blueberry streusal coffeecake, almond and polenta coffeecake, Abriendo Inn toast, strawberry and banana fruit cup and beverages.

Abriendo Inn, Pueblo

AMENITIES	Fresh flowers and candy in the rooms, air conditioning in all rooms, modem hook-ups, telephones and TV in all the rooms, fresh fruit basket and homemade cookies all the time, snacks and beverages, off-street parking.
RESTRICTIONS	No smoking, no pets, and children over seven are welcome. Old Michelle, the outside dog, "just lays around watching the coming and going of everyone"...sort of like the owner of this publishing house...CH
REVIEWED	*The Colorado Guide, The Official Guide to American Historic Inns, America's Wonderful Little Hotels & Inns.*
MEMBER	Independent Innkeepers Association, Distinctive Inns of Colorado, Bed & Breakfast Innkeepers of Colorado, Professional Association of Innkeepers International.
RATED	AAA 3 Diamonds, Mobil 3 Stars
KUDOS/COMMENTS	"Beautiful and comfortable, warm and hospitable, Kerrelyn has done everything right." ... "The house is dressed to perfection, wonderful antiques." (1997)

Baxter Inn Bed & Breakfast

325 West 15th, Pueblo, CO 81003   719-542-7002
Lois & David Jones, Resident Owners

RED CLIFF

This little mining town is famous for its location at the base of Shrine Pass and its view of Mount of the Holy Cross. This is also the trailhead for the Tenth Mountain Trail Hut System. From Vail, seven miles west on I-70 to Minturn exit 171, then eight miles south via Highway 24.

PLUM HOUSE BED & BREAKFAST

236 Eagle Street, Red Cliff, CO 81649　　　　　　970-827-5881
Sydney Summers, Resident Owner

LOCATION	From I-70 take the Minturn exit after Vail. Drive through Minturn and approximately nine miles to Red Cliff on Highway 24.
OPEN	All year.
DESCRIPTION	A secluded 1940s two-story Victorian with comfortable furnishings.
NO. OF ROOMS	One room shares a bathroom.
RATES	Year-round rates are $50 for a single with a shared bathroom and $60 for a double with a shared bathroom. Prefer two-night stays, cancellation requires seven days' notice.
CREDIT CARDS	No
BREAKFAST	Full breakfast is "customized according to preference." Dinner is available with one week's notice.
AMENITIES	Hot tub indoors, large tape/CD/book library, wood stove, in summer a vegetable and flower garden, and in winter there are snowshoes and cross-country skis for rent.
RESTRICTIONS	No smoking, no pets, no children.

REDSTONE

Founded as a Utopian dream by industrialist John Osgood for his mine workers. His own former estate is still alive at Redstone Castle. Best things to do in this Victorian "company town" is to soak-up its spirited, arty ambiance: shop the Boulevard, picnic in the new town park on the Crystal River and wonder at the awesome red cliffs. From Glenwood Springs, 30 miles south via Highway 82 and 133.

AVALANCHE RANCH COUNTRY INN & LOG CABINS

12863 Highway 133, Redstone, CO 81623   970-963-2846
Sharon Boucher, Resident Owners   FAX 970-963-3141

LOCATION	Four miles north of Redstone.
OPEN	All year.
DESCRIPTION	A 1913 farmhouse with cabins, antique shop & restaurant on 45 mountain acres on Crystal River, with country furnishings
NO. OF ROOMS	Two rooms with private bathrooms and two rooms share one bathroom. Deerpath is the best room. There are also 11 cabins available with breakfast at an additional charge.
RATES	High season, May through October, rates are $95-155 for the rooms. Please inquire about low season rates. There is a three-day minimum stay during high season and cancellation requires 30 days' notice with a $25 fee.
CREDIT CARDS	Discover, MasterCard, Visa
BREAKFAST	Continental Plus is served in dining room or guestrooms on request.
AMENITIES	Robes, snacks, sitting and dining rooms with fireplace, volleyball, badminton, horseshoes, tree house, tire swing, gift shop, wedding/reception/meeting facilities, horse boarding, natural hot springs in the river a mile away. On site services available: serenade by guitarist, massage, facial, manicure, fishing guides and float trips.
RESTRICTIONS	No smoking inside, pets are welcome in the cabins ($10 charge per pet), children over eight are welcome in the inn. The resident critters: dog, Ripple; llama, Alex; miniature donkey, Tony; and two nubian goats, Sugar and Spice.
REVIEWED	*Best Places to Stay in the Rocky Mountain Region, Recommended Country Inns of the Rocky Mountain Region, America's Wonderful Little Hotels & Inns, Gene Kilgore's Ranch Vacations*
MEMBER	Bed & Breakfast Innkeepers of Colorado, Professional Association of Innkeepers International

Cleveholm Manor, The Historic Redstone Castle, Redstone

KUDOS/COMMENTS "Charming hostess, delightful surroundings."... "Unique B&B, fun place." ... "A joyful retreat for families." (1996)

CLEVEHOLM MANOR, THE HISTORIC REDSTONE CASTLE

0058 Redstone Boulevard, Redstone, CO 81623 970-963-3463
Cyd Lange, Resident Manager 800-643-4837

LOCATION	Take the first right after the bridge into town, drive one mile on a country road to the Manor.
OPEN	All year.
DESCRIPTION	A 1902 three-story English Tudor Manor with original antiques and museum quality interior; listed on the National Historic Register; located in the Crystal River Valley.
NO. OF ROOMS	Eight rooms with private bathrooms and eight rooms share three bathrooms. Cyd Lange recommends the Lady Bountiful Suite.
RATES	Year-round rates are $150 for a single or double with private bathroom, $95-125 for a single or double with shared bathroom and $185-225 for a suite. There is no minimum stay and a seven-day cancellation policy.
CREDIT CARDS	American Express, MasterCard, Visa
BREAKFAST	Continential Plus is served in the sun room (Loggia).
AMENITIES	No phones or TV in the rooms...bravo...TI, robes in all rooms, game room, complimentary tour with stay, spiced wine and cider in winter and lemonade and iced tea in summer, full bar available, full wine list, meeting rooms for small groups and "weddings!"
RESTRICTIONS	No smoking in the Manor.
REVIEWED	*America's Wonderful Little Hotels & Inns, Recommended Country Inns of the Rocky Mountain Region*

Distinctive Inns of Colorado, American Bed & Breakfast
Association, National Bed & Breakfast Association

KUDOS/COMMENTS "Fantastic turn-of-the-century atmosphere. Exquisite service.
Gourmet dinner a must experience." ... "A totally delightful
experience. A chance not only to live like royalty, but also to be
treated that way." ... "Wonderful setting and history." (1994) "A
national treasure! We enjoyed sitting next to a crackling fire as
snow fell outside; one of a kind." ... "The setting is beautiful. The
property is well maintained. A great wedding site." (1996)

CRYSTAL DREAMS BED & BREAKFAST

0475 Redstone Boulevard, Redstone, CO 81623   970-963-8240
Lisa & Steve Wagner, Resident Owners

MCCLURE HOUSE

22995 Highway 133, Redstone, CO 81623   970-963-1020
Judy Melby, Resident Owner   800-303-3929

KUDOS/COMMENTS "Judy is outstanding." (1997)

MOON RIDGE HAVEN

030 Elk Lane, Redstone, CO 81623   970-963-0356
Jessica McMahon, Resident Owner

RIDGWAY

A very western ranching community in the San Juan Mountains with major film credits (True Grit and How the West Was Won). Ridgway State Park offers up good fishing, boating, camping, X-C skiing and ice skating. Only 10 miles north of Ouray and 25 miles south of Montrose at the junction of Scenic Highways 62 and 550.

THE ADOBE INN

251 Liddell Drive, Ridgway, CO 81432   970-626-5939
Joyce & Terre Bucknam, Resident Owners

LOCATION	From Highway 550 take Highway 62 for 1/4 mile, first dirt street to the left after crossing river, one block off highway.
OPEN	All year except for Thanksgiving, Christmas Eve and Christmas.
DESCRIPTION	A 1984 southwestern adobe country inn and Mexican restaurant with southwestern furnishings, small patio and wonderful view of the mountains. The inn is on one-and-a-half acres with nice grounds at the edge of town.
NO. OF ROOMS	Three rooms share two baths. The best room in the house is #1.
RATES	Year-round rates are $35-45 for a single or double with a shared bathroom. There is no minimum stay. Forty-eight-hour cancellation except for holidays when five days are required.
CREDIT CARDS	American Express, MasterCard, Visa
BREAKFAST	Continental breakfast is served down the hall and includes coffee, homemade muffins and juice for children. Dinner is available in the Mexican restaurant.
AMENITIES	Patio, lounge with fireplace, TV in rooms, telephone in hallway.
RESTRICTIONS	No smoking, there is a resident Himalayan cat called Annie.
REVIEWED	*The Colorado Guide, Country Inns of the Rocky Mountain Region*
AWARDS	1990 Business of the Year, awarded by the Ouray County Chamber of Commerce

CHIPETA SUN LODGE

304 South Lena, Ridgway, CO 81432   970-626-3737
Lyle & Shari Braund, Innkeepers   800-633-5868

KUDOS/COMMENTS	"Beams with uniqueness." ... "Lyle and Shari are terrific hosts." (1997)

SALIDA

The word means "exit", but this is the entrance to scenic and recreational wealth. On the banks of the Arkansas River and at the headwaters of the Arkansas Headwaters Recreation Area, this is the jumping-off place for major white water rafting. When the spring thaw swells the Arkansas to flood stage in mid-June, celebrations surround the prestigious, championship FIB-Ark River Boat Race. Less turbulence can be found at the Salida Hot Springs Pool, and the downtown Historic District is worth a stroll. Rockhounders alert: the surrounding area offers up a richness of gems. From Pueblo, 97 miles west via Highway 50.

THE CENTURY HOUSE BED & BREAKFAST

401 East First Street, Salida, CO 81201   719-539-7064
Ruth Fisher, Resident Owner

LOCATION	Highway 291, across from the hospital.
OPEN	All year.
DESCRIPTION	An 1890 two-story Second Empire "Painted Lady" with mansard roof, transoms, high ceilings, brass lighting and antique furnishings.
NO. OF ROOMS	Two rooms have a private bath and two rooms share one bathroom. The Woodland is the best room.
RATES	Year-round rates are $55-70 for a single or double with a private bathroom and $45-60 for a single or double with a shared bathroom. Cancellation requires seven days' notice.
CREDIT CARDS	MasterCard, Visa
BREAKFAST	Full breakfast, served in the dining room, includes quiche, Canadian bacon, homemade cinnamon rolls and beverages.
AMENITIES	Robes, early morning coffee and afternoon snack.
RESTRICTIONS	No smoking, no pets, children over eight are welcome.
MEMBER	Bed & Breakfast Innkeepers of Colorado
KUDOS/COMMENTS	"Charming turn-of-the-century atmosphere; very homey and clean." ... "Ruth is a gracious hostess." (1997)

The Century House Bed & Breakfast, Salida

THE GAZEBO COUNTRY INN BED & BREAKFAST

507 East 3rd, Salida, CO 81201   *719-539-7806*
Don & BJ, Resident Owners

LOCATION	Located in downtown Salida on the corner of 3rd Street and B, five blocks east of Main Street (F).
OPEN	All year.
DESCRIPTION	A restored 1901 three-story brick Victorian with Victorian furnishings and panoramic views.
NO. OF ROOMS	Three rooms with private bathrooms. BJ suggests the "most spacious room," the Monarch Rose.
RATES	Year-round rates are $65-75 for a single or double with private bathroom and $195 for the entire B&B. Cancellation requires 14 days' notice.
CREDIT CARDS	American Express, MasterCard, Visa
BREAKFAST	Full breakfast, served in the dining room with crystal and fine china, includes a special entree (French toast, Colorado Quiche), muffins, fruit plate and beverages.
AMENITIES	Tea tray on arrival, gazebo, flowers in each room, refrigerator stocked with soft drinks, hors d'oeuvres, library, fresh-fruit tray and TV/VCR in common room. Special packages available for Valentine's Day, Mother's Day and Anniversaries.
RESTRICTIONS	No smoking, no pets, children over eight are welcome.
REVIEWED	*Bed & Breakfast Rocky Mountains, Recommended Country Inns*
MEMBER	Bed & Breakfast Innkeepers of Colorado

OLD MANHATTAN HOTEL BED & BREAKFAST

228 1/2 North F Street, Salida, CO 81201   *719-539-3138*
Peggy Witty, Ray & Penny Kitson, Resident Owners   *800-288-0675*

LOCATION	Booming downtown Salida on the Arkansas River and across from Riverside Park.
OPEN	All year.
DESCRIPTION	A 1901 Victorian with Victorian furnishings.
NO. OF ROOMS	Six rooms share three bathrooms. The best room is Room 7.
RATES	High season, June through August and major holidays, rates are $60 for a single or double with shared bathroom. Off season rates are $45. There is no minimum stay and cancellation requires 48 hours' notice.

CREDIT CARDS	MasterCard, Visa
BREAKFAST	Full breakfast, served in the dining room, includes quiche, omelets or pancakes with fresh fruit, potatoes and beverages.
AMENITIES	Main living room with TV/VCR, tickets at reduced rates for local hot springs, special rafting and mountain-bike tours. Facilities for small groups and workshops.
RESTRICTIONS	No smoking, no pets.

PIÑON AND SAGE BED & BREAKFAST INN

803 F Street, Salida, CO 81201   719-539-3227
Bill Woodul & Jocelyn Mullen, Resident Owners   800-840-3156
Some French and "decent" Spanish spoken.   FAX 719-539-3227

LOCATION	On the corner of 8th Street and F Street.
OPEN	All year.
DESCRIPTION	A 1901 two-story Victorian with casual southwestern decor.
NO. OF ROOMS	Four rooms share two bathrooms. Jocelyn recommends the Old West Room.
RATES	High season (includes the summer months, Thanksgiving, Christmas, New Year's and March) rates are $55-70 for a double with shared bathroom. Off season rates are $45-55 for a double with shared bathroom. There is no minimum stay and cancellation requires two weeks' notice.
CREDIT CARDS	MasterCard, Visa
BREAKFAST	Full breakfast is served in the dining room, guest rooms or on the balconies and is "cooked to order."
AMENITIES	Robes, hot tub on patio, business services and meeting space is available, large-screen TV, walking distance to downtown restaurants and Arkansas River.
RESTRICTIONS	No smoking, no pets, children over eight are welcome. The dog is called Sweet Pea and a potbelly pig goes by the name of Tar Baby.

RIVER RUN INN

8495 County Road 160, Salida, CO 81201   719-539-3818
Virginia Nemmers, Resident Owner   800-385-6925
                                           FAX 719-539-3818

LOCATION	Three miles east of Highway 285, just north of Highway 50. Look for B&B sign on the Highway.
OPEN	All year.
DESCRIPTION	An 1895 three-story brick Victorian country inn on the National and State Historic Registers. Victorian furnishings.
NO. OF ROOMS	Three rooms with private bathrooms and four rooms with two bathrooms. A third-floor dormitory has 13 beds and a shared bathroom. The Alpine Aster is the best room.
RATES	Year-round rates are $70 for a room with a private bathroom, $60 for a room with shared bathroom. The dorm is $25 per bed. There is no minimum stay and a 14-day cancellation policy.
CREDIT CARDS	MasterCard, Visa
BREAKFAST	Full breakfast, served in the dining room, includes beverages, fresh fruits, yogurt, egg or pancake/French-toast specialties, bacon, sausage, ham, homemade breads and coffeecakes. Lunch, dinner and special meals are available as part of a package deal.
AMENITIES	Private fishing on the Arkansas, guests' fresh-caught trout cooked, large front porch, homemade cookies, cider, lemonade, teas and occasionally wine.
RESTRICTIONS	No smoking except outside, no pets, children over 12 are welcome. Loon is the Australian Heeler. He won't beg for food, but he might request a little petting.
REVIEWED	*America's Wonderful Little Hotels & Inns, The Colorado Guide, Motorcycle B&B, Recommended Country Inns of the Rocky Mountain Region*
MEMBER	Bed & Breakfast Innkeepers of Colorado, Professional Association of Innkeepers International, Chaffee County Lodging Association

The Thomas House Bed & Breakfast, Salida

THE THOMAS HOUSE BED & BREAKFAST

307 East First Street, Salida, CO 81201   719-539-7104
Tammy & Steve Office, Resident Owners   888-228-1410

LOCATION	From historic downtown Salida, the inn is two blocks east of F Street on the corner of 1st and D Streets.
OPEN	All year.
DESCRIPTION	An 1888 two-story inn with an eclectic mix of American antiques and family heirlooms.
NO. OF ROOMS	Five rooms with private bathrooms and one powder room. Tammy and Steve think Mt. Princeton is the best room.
RATES	Year-round rates are $45-65 for a single or double with a private bathroom, $65 for a one-bedroom suite and $115 for a two-bedroom suite. There is no minimum stay and a 14-day cancellation policy.
CREDIT CARDS	MasterCard, Visa
BREAKFAST	Continental breakfast, served in the dining room, includes homebaked muffins and sweet breads, breads for toasting, yogurt, granola, cheese and fruit with beverages.
AMENITIES	Outdoor hot tub holds fourteen, robes, evening refreshments, reading room stocked with current newspapers and magazines as well as an assortment of fiction and nonfiction books, TV in the suite, shady deck and kitchenettes for light cooking.
RESTRICTIONS	No smoking, no pets. Resident pooch, Spud, and cats, BB and Stinky, are confined to private quarters.
MEMBER	Bed & Breakfast Innkeepers of Colorado, Chaffee County Lodging Association

THE TUDOR ROSE B&B

6720 Paradise Road, Salida, CO 81201   *719-539-2002*
Jon & Terre Terrell, Resident Owners   *800-379-0889*
FAX 719-530-0345

LOCATION	One-and-a-half miles southeast of Salida, a half-mile south of Highway 50 on County Road 104 at the top of the hill.
OPEN	All year.
DESCRIPTION	A 1979 three-story Tudor inn with "elegant, unique and comfortable" furnishings.
NO. OF ROOMS	Four rooms with private bathrooms and two rooms share one bathroom. The Terrells recommend the Henry Tudor suite.
RATES	Year-round rates for a single or double with a private bathroom are $60-75, rates for a single or double with a shared bathroom are $50-80 and a suite is $105. The entire B&B rents for $495 for up to 16 people. During the summer there is a two-day minimum stay on the weekends and cancellation requres 72 hours' notice, "100% refund, no fee."...great cancellation policy, sure to win you repeat guests...TI.
CREDIT CARDS	American Express, Discover, MasterCard, Visa
BREAKFAST	Full breakfast is served in the dining room or on the deck may include seasoned eggs, potato crepes with bearnaise sauce, sausage pattie, cherry crepes, orange juice, coffee and tea.
AMENITIES	Sunken hot tub on deck, robes, overnight horse boarding, outdoor dog pens, Jacuzzi suite, feather beds and sweetheart package with champagne, dinner and chocolate strawberries.
RESTRICTIONS	No smoking inside, pets outside only. The resident Keeshounds are Keesha and Chivas and the Lab is Zeus.
REVIEWED	*America's Wonderful Little Hotels & Inns, Overnight Stabling Directory, Horse Travel Guide*
MEMBER	Bed & Breakfast Innkeepers of Colorado, Professional Association of Innkeepers International
RATED	AAA 2 Diamonds, Mobil 2 Stars
KUDOS/COMMENTS	"Perfect for a romantic getaway; Jon and Terre pay a lot of attention to detail." (1995) "The inn backs up to a national forest." ... "A welcome change of pace for those needing a weekend away from noise and traffic." (1997)

THE YELLOW HOUSE AT MAYSVILLE

16665 West Highway 50, Salida, CO 81201   719-539-7531
Erik & Cheri Moore, Resident Owners

LOCATION	Six miles west of Poncha Springs on Highway 50 at the foot of Monarch Pass.
OPEN	All year.
DESCRIPTION	A renovated 1888 two-story rural Victorian at an altitude of 8,200 feet beside the headwaters of the Arkansas River.
NO. OF ROOMS	Three rooms share three bathrooms. Ask for the south bedroom.
RATES	Year-round rates are $45 for a single or double with a shared bathroom.
CREDIT CARDS	MasterCard, Visa
BREAKFAST	Full breakfast, served in the breakfast room, is made to order.
AMENITIES	Two private outdoor hot tubs beside the Arkansas River, art and craft shop/gallery.
RESTRICTIONS	None. There is a resident Newfoundland called Sumo and a Chow/Retriever called Scoobie. The cats are Beau & Marilyn.

SAN ACACIO

A sleepy little village located in the San Luis Valley that is 35 minutes from Dunes National Park, east eight miles to the Cumbres Toltec Narrow Guage Railroad and south 35 minutes to Ski Rio. From Alamosa, 22 miles south on Highway 285, turn east on Highway 142 for 25 miles.

THE DEPOT

Route 1, Box 186, San Acacio, CO 81150 719-672-3943
Neil Fletcher, Resident Owner 800-949-3949
Some Spanish is spoken.

LOCATION	Eight miles west of San Luis on Highway 142, the largest building on the east end of town.
OPEN	All year.
DESCRIPTION	A 1910 historic train depot with stucco frame construction, Victorian furnishings and large converted freightroom that is the private dining room for guests.
NO. OF ROOMS	One room with a private bathroom and three rooms share one full and two half bathrooms. There is a large bedroom loft for children. The Family Suite has a fireplace.
RATES	Seasonal rates are $49 for a single with private bathroom, $59 for a double with a private bathroom, $29.50 for a single with shared bathroom, $39 for a double with a shared bathroom. There is no minimum stay but deposit is forfeited with cancellation.
CREDIT CARDS	No, cash or personal checks.
BREAKFAST	Full breakfast of omelets and hashbrowns is served in large open-freight dining room or outside in warm weather. Cooking facilities are available upon request.
AMENITIES	Terrific view, large lawns, flower and vegetable gardens in a country setting, fresh strawberries and asperagus served in season.
RESTRICTIONS	No smoking in the building (smoking areas outside). The resident critters include guinea fowl, chickens and goats.

SAN LUIS

The oldest town in Colorado is built around its adobe plaza, 50 miles south of Fort Garland on Highway 59.

EL CONVENTO BED & BREAKFAST

512 Church Place, San Luis, CO 81152   719-672-4223
Connie Morrell, Resident Manager

LOCATION	Two blocks west of Main Street.
OPEN	All year.
DESCRIPTION	A 1905 two-story adobe convent with southwestern furnishings.
NO. OF ROOMS	Four rooms with private bathrooms.
RATES	Year-round rates are $60 for a single and $10 more for each additional adult and $5 for each additional child under 12.
CREDIT CARDS	MasterCard, Visa
BREAKFAST	Full breakfast is served in the dining room.
AMENITIES	Library, house available for families with fireplace and kitchen (inquire about rates), skiing at Ski Rio in New Mexico (about 20 miles away), small meeting room.
RESTRICTIONS	No smoking in rooms, pets with prior approval, $25 deposit for pets (resident dog). Children of all ages are welcome.
REVIEWED	*The Colorado Guide*

SILVER PLUME

BREWERY INN BED & BREAKFAST

238 Main Street, Silver Plume, CO 80476   303-569-2284
Greg Hein, Resident Manager   800-500-0209

SILVERTHORNE
(SUMMIT COUNTY)

Tucked at the base of Buffalo Peak in the Lake Dillon area, the Gold Medal Blue River winds through town. Try hiking to Cataract Lake and Falls or visiting National Historic Factory Stores District. West of Denver, 70 miles via I-70.

ALPEN HUTTE

PO Box 91, Silverthorne, CO 80498   970-468-6336

MOUNTAIN VISTA BED & BREAKFAST

358 Lagoon Lane, Silverthorne, CO 80498   970-468-7700
Sandy Ruggaber, Resident Owner   800-333-5165

LOCATION	From I-70 take exit 205. At Wendy's in Silverthorne turn right and then take another right at the next stop sign. Pass the Village Inn and turn left on Lagoon Lane to the sixth house on the right with a flagpole in the driveway.
OPEN	All year.
DESCRIPTION	A 1976 two-story contemporary mountain-style host home with contemporary interior.
NO. OF ROOMS	One room with private bathroom and two rooms share one bathroom. The best room is Bedroom C with the private bath.
RATES	Winter rates, November through April, are $65-85 for a single or double with private bathroom and $60-80 for a single or double with a shared bathroom. Summer rates, May through October, are $55 for a single or double with a private bathroom and $50 for a single or double with a shared bathroom. There is a minimum stay over Christmas and there is a non-refundable deposit.
CREDIT CARDS	No
BREAKFAST	Full breakfast is served in the dining room during the winter and Continental Plus during the summer.
AMENITIES	Robes in each room, guest kitchen with snacks and drinks. Fireplace and TV on each level. Discount ticket to community recreation center.
RESTRICTIONS	Smoking is restricted, no pets. The resident "mostly Samoyed" is called Mogul "and believes everyone comes just to see her." Children over six are welcome.
MEMBER	Summit County Bed & Breakfast Association
KUDOS/COMMENTS	"Nice, clean, contemporary B&B, close to bus route, in town location, good arrangement of space." (1996)

SILVERTON

This national Historic Landmark in the San Juan Skyway is ornate Victorian at its grandest. Evidence of its opulent past is reflected in the gold-domed courthouse. Fun events: The Jubilee Folk Music Festival in late June attracts outstanding musicians, and it's oompha-time at the Great Western Rocky Mountain Brass Band Festival in mid-August. The Durango & Silverton Narrow Guage Railroad, operating since 1882, terminates here. Forty-five miles north of Durango via the awesome Million Dollar Highway 550.

ALMA HOUSE HOTEL

220 East 10th Street, Silverton, CO 81433   970-387-5974
Leanne Walls, Resident Manager   800-267-5336
                                                  FAX 970-387-5974

LOCATION	Enter Silverton on Greene Street, turn right at 10th Street. The inn is on the left in the second block.
OPEN	May 15 to October 20.
DESCRIPTION	An 1897 three-story Victorian with antique furnishings and silk Victorian wallpaper, listed on the National and State Historic Registers. Rooms are named after local mines.
NO. OF ROOMS	Six rooms with private bathrooms and four rooms share two bathrooms. The best room is the Silver Queen suite.
RATES	High season (June 15 through September) rates are $75 for a single or double with private bathroom, $60 for a single or double with shared bathroom, $90-100 for suites, and $650 for the entire B&B. Low season (May, except for Labor Day weekend, through June 15th and October) rates are $70 for a single or double with a private bathroom, $55 for a single or double with a shared bathroom, $85-90 for suites, and $575 for the entire B&B. There is no minimum stay and cancellation requires 48 hours' notice.
CREDIT CARDS	American Express, MasterCard, Visa
BREAKFAST	Full breakfast is served in the dining room and includes homemade pastries, an egg dish, fruit and beverages.
AMENITIES	Free mineral and crystal museum, historic photos and sketches of local mining activity.
RESTRICTIONS	No smoking. Well-behaved, clean pets are welcome.
RATED	Mobil 3 Stars

WINGATE HOUSE BED & BREAKFAST

1045 Snowden Street, Silverton, CO 81433   970-387-5520
Judy Graham, Resident Owner

SNOWMASS AND SNOWMASS VILLAGE

Part of the Aspen complex, but just far enough away from the glitz to offer tranquil skiing, and ski-in, ski-out everything. Also multitudes of restaurants and spendy shops. Summer activities are on the rise and center around the Village Music Series and the Anderson Ranch Arts Center (and Aspen, of course). From Glenwood Springs, 23 miles southeast.

AT HOME IN SNOWMASS

31 Martindale, Snowmass Village, CO 81615   970-923-2488
Nancy & Wolf Gensch, Resident Owners   FAX 970-923-3467

CONNABLES' GUEST HOME

3747 Brush Creek Road, Snowmass Village, CO 81615   970-923-5034
Ce Ce & Bruce Connable, Resident Owners   FAX 970-923-5034
French and Spanish spoken.

LOCATION	From Highway 82 take Brush Creek Road 3.6 miles. The B&B is on the right. There is a sign on the fence at the bottom of the driveway.
OPEN	Winter: Thanksgiving to mid-April; summer: June 15 to September 30.
DESCRIPTION	A 1991 contemporary two-story wood- and log-accented home with eclectic furnishings and southwestern flavor.
NO. OF ROOMS	One room with a private bathroom and two rooms share one bathroom. The best room has a fireplace and panoramic view.
RATES	Winter rates are $100-125 per room, except at Christmas when they are $150-175 per room; summer rates are $50-75 per room. Cancellation requires 30 days' notice.
CREDIT CARDS	No
BREAKFAST	Full breakfast is served in the winter and Continental Plus in the summer.
AMENITIES	Terry robes, outdoor hot tub, afternoon wine, juices and daily goodies, game table, three fireplaces in great room, dining room, den.
RESTRICTIONS	No smoking, no pets, resident Persian cat goes by the name of Noni.

POKOLODI LODGE BED & BREAKFAST

25 Daly Lane, Snowmass Village, CO 81615   970-923-4310
Stacy Carskaden, Resident Manager   FAX 970-923-2819

STARRY PINES BED & BREAKFAST

2262 Snowmass Creek Road, Snowmass, CO 81654   970-927-4202
Shelley Burke, Resident Owner   800-527-4202

LOCATION	Turn off Highway 82 at Snowmass, go 1.5 miles to stop sign, bear left on Snowmass Creek Road, first mailbox on the left (horses on the mailbox).
OPEN	All year.
DESCRIPTION	A 1982 contemporary ranch home with white-ash wood and natural stone interior on a trout stream and 70 acres.
NO. OF ROOMS	Two rooms with private bathrooms and one suite.
RATES	Year-round rates are $80-95 for a single or double with private bathroom and $100-120 for a suite. There is a two-night minimum stay during high season and cancellation requires two weeks' notice in high season, one weeks' in low season.
CREDIT CARDS	No
BREAKFAST	Continental Plus is served in the dining room. Special meals can be catered on request.
AMENITIES	Flowers and robes in rooms, outdoor hot tub, fireplace, TV/VCR, balconies overlooking private pond and trout stream, picnic area with hammock, horses boarded.
RESTRICTIONS	No smoking, no pets, children over six are welcome.
MEMBER	Bed & Breakfast Innkeepers of Colorado

SPRINGFIELD

PLUM BEAR RANCH

29461 County Road 21, Springfield, CO 81073   719-523-4344
Wendy Lynch, Resident Manager   FAX 719-523-4324

STEAMBOAT SPRINGS

"Ski Town USA" is a world-class resort and cowboy-populated ranching area with two major hot springs, one in Strawberry park and one feeds the Hot Springs Pool. Standout events include the Cowboy Downhill in January (must be seen to be believed), the week-long Winter Carnival in February and the month-long Strings in the Mountains Festival and the hot air balloon Rainbow Weekend in July. In the Yampa Valley, 166 miles northwest of Denver via I-70 and Highway 40.

CLERMONT INN

917 Lincoln Avenue, PO Box 774927,	*970-879-3083*
Steamboat Springs, CO 80477	*800-851-0872*
Tonya Dean, Manager	*FAX 970-879-8645*

LOCATION	Center of town, between 9th and 10th Streets.
OPEN	All year.
DESCRIPTION	A 1948 Victorian motor inn.
NO. OF ROOMS	Twenty-two rooms with private bathrooms and shared tubs and showers.
RATES	Holiday rates are $134-169 for a single or double with private bathroom. Winter rates are $64-80. Spring rates are $64-79 and Summer rates are $49-69. There is a reservation/cancellation policy. Please call for details.
CREDIT CARDS	American Express, Diners Club, Discover, MasterCard, Visa
BREAKFAST	Full breakfast is served in the on-site, full-service restaurant called Mazzola's. Lunch and dinner are also available.
AMENITIES	Hot tub in game room, fireplace in library, cable TV and phones in rooms, ski lockers, city bus service with bus stop on the corner, meeting facilities, full-service restaurant and bar, pizza served until midnight, handicapped access, off-street parking.
RESTRICTIONS	No pets, some rooms are none smoking. Children of all ages are welcome.
REVIEWED	*The Colorado Guide*

ELK RIVER ESTATES

PO Box 5032, Steamboat Springs, CO 80477   *970-879-7556*
Bill Fetcher, Resident Owner

LOCATION	Five miles northwest of Steamboat Springs on County Road 129, phone for specific directions.
OPEN	All year.
DESCRIPTION	A 1972 suburban-ranch host home that is attractive, neat and well maintained. Heated in winter by a wood-fired fireplace insert and supplemental electric heat.
NO. OF ROOMS	One room with private bathroom.
RATES	Year-round rates are $35 for a single with bath and $40 for a double with bath. The room also has a sleeper sofa.
CREDIT CARDS	No
BREAKFAST	Full breakfast, served in the kitchen, includes sourdough pancakes. Lunch and dinner at guests' option.
AMENITIES	High tea (or other beverages) offered in late afternoon, mangled linens...Wow, an innkeeper unconcerned about matching sheets and towels! Thanks, Bill...CH, TV, videos and extensive classical record collection available. Ski-guide service to Steamboat and trips to Strawberry Park Hot Springs at no charge other than admission.
RESTRICTIONS	No smoking, no pets (resident cat, Winnie), no children.

THE HOME RANCH

54880 RCR 129, Clark, CO 80428   *970-879-1780*
Ken & Cile Jones, Resident Owners   *FAX 970-879-1795*

LOCATION	Highway 40 from Steamboat Springs, exit onto County Road 129 and take it 18 miles to Clark. Ranch entrance is 1/4 mile past the Clark General Store on the right.
OPEN	December 20 through March and June to October.
DESCRIPTION	A traditional western-style ranch with main lodge and cabins with eclectic furnishings on a 1,500 acre working cattle ranch bordering the Routt National Forest.
NO. OF ROOMS	Six rooms with private bathrooms in the main lodge and eight cabins.
RATES	Seasonal rates start at $430 for lodge rooms and $480 for cabins. Minimum stay of seven nights in the summer and three nights in the winter and a 90-day cancellation policy.
CREDIT CARDS	American Express, Discover, MasterCard, Visa
BREAKFAST	Full breakfast, served in the dining room, includes hot and cold buffet and á la carte items. Lunch and dinner are also included in the rates.
AMENITIES	Horseback riding, fly fishing, hiking, cross-country skiing, shuttle for downhill skiing, hayrides, BBQs, barn dances, gourmet cuisine; each cabin has a hot tub, down comforters, pillows and a wood stove; there is a hot tub, heated pool and a sauna near the main lodge.
RESTRICTIONS	No pets, no cellular phones. Children over six are welcome. The resident dogs are Dancer, Bronco and Sugar Bear, and the cats are called Barney and Cheese.
REVIEWED	*Amex/Departures, Travel & Leisure, Town & Country, Bon Appetit, Ranch Vacations, The Colorado Guide, Relais & Chateaux*
RATED	Mobil 4 Stars, Relais & Chataux Green Rating

THE INN AT STEAMBOAT

3070 Columbine Drive, PO Box 775084,   *970-879-2600*
Steamboat Springs, CO 80477   *800-872-2601*
Tom & Roxane Miller-Freutel, Resident Owners   *FAX 970-879-9270*

LOCATION	Take Highway 40 southeast from downtown, turn left on Walton Creek Road, go 3/4 mile and turn left on Columbine Drive, third building on the left.
OPEN	All year except for mud season (mid-April to mid-May).
DESCRIPTION	A 1972 two-story European lodge with country-theme furnishings and nautical accents.
NO. OF ROOMS	Thirty-two rooms with private bathrooms.
RATES	Winter rates are $49-139 for a single or double with private bathroom. Off season rates are $39-85 for a single or double with private bathroom. The minimum stay and cancellation policies are complex and variable.
CREDIT CARDS	American Express, Discover, MasterCard, Visa
BREAKFAST	Continental Plus is served in the dining room.
AMENITIES	Phone, TV, turndown service, outdoor heated pool (104 degrees in the winter), sauna, game room, mountain bikes, ski tuning, full concierge service, complimentary beverages and desserts and private ski shuttle.
RESTRICTIONS	No smoking, no pets. Children 12 and under are free.
RATED	AAA 2 Diamonds, ABBA 2 Crowns

MARIPOSA BED & BREAKFAST

855 North Grand Street, PO Box 2302,   970-879-1467
Steamboat Springs, CO 80477   800-578-1467
Paul Greco, Resident Owner

LOCATION	Right on Sixth Street, go three stop signs. Sixth becomes Laurel at the elementary school. Stay on Laurel past the big white house on the left. Grand Street is the first left past the big white house.
OPEN	All year.
DESCRIPTION	A 1992 southwestern-style inn with log-beamed ceilings and Santa Fe-style handcrafted doors. On the banks of Soda Creek.
NO. OF ROOMS	Four rooms with private bathrooms. Paul Greco's favorite room is the Pine Room.
RATES	Seasonal rates are $65-$85 for a single or double with a private bathroom. There is no minimum stay and cancellation requires 21 days' notice and a $25 fee.
CREDIT CARDS	MasterCard, Visa
BREAKFAST	Full breakfast, served in the dining room, is different every day.
AMENITIES	Greenhouse/sunroom overlooking the pond.
RESTRICTIONS	No smoking, no pets, children of any age are welcome with notification.
REVIEWED	*Recommended Country Inns*
KUDOS/COMMENTS	"Open, low-keyed southwest feel, ask for the Pine room, you will sleep in a handmade (by the owner) pine bed about three feet off the floor. Sit in the sunroom and overlook a field of horses and a pond." (1995)

OLD TOWN INN

702 Oak Street, Steamboat Springs, CO 80477   970-870-0484

SKY VALLEY LODGE

PO Box 3132, Steamboat Springs, CO 80477   970-879-7749
Steve Myler, Resident Owner

STEAMBOAT BED & BREAKFAST

442 Pine Street, PO Box 772058,   970-879-5724
Steamboat Springs, CO 80477   FAX 970-879-5724
Gordon Hattersley, Resident Owner

LOCATION	Two blocks north of Main Street.
OPEN	All year.
DESCRIPTION	A renovated 1889 three-story Victorian with Victorian furnishings.
NO. OF ROOMS	Seven rooms with private bathrooms.
RATES	Winter rates are $95-135 for a single or double with private bathroom and summer rates are $75-85 for a single or double with private bathroom. Prices are about $10 higher on weekends. There is no minimum stay. Cancellation requires two weeks' notice for full refund.
CREDIT CARDS	Discover, MasterCard, Visa
BREAKFAST	Full breakfast, served in the dining room, includes hot entree, homebaked breads and fresh fruit, cereals and beverages.
AMENITIES	Hot tub and deck, complimentary fruit and beverages, music conservatory with piano, TV and movies, large yard nice for weddings and family reunions, walking distance to restaurants and shops of downtown Steamboat.
RESTRICTIONS	No smoking, no pets, no children. The resident Golden Retriever is Josh—he loves to play fetch. Jazz is the resident cat.

Steamboat Valley Guest House, Steamboat Springs

STEAMBOAT VALLEY GUEST HOUSE

1245 Crawford Avenue, PO Box 773815,   970-870-9017
Steamboat Springs, CO 80477   FAX 970-879-0361
George & Alice Lund, Resident Owners

LOCATION	From Denver, take I-70 west to Dillion/Silverthorne (Exit 205). Head north on Highway 9 to Kremmling. Then west on Highway 40 to Steamboat Springs. Go through downtown and turn north on 12th Street. Go two short blocks to Crawford. Look for sign.
OPEN	All year.
DESCRIPTION	A remodeled 1957 three-story log guesthouse with English and Scandinavian decor, built with logs from the town mill and bricks from the old flour mill.
NO. OF ROOMS	Four rooms with private bathrooms.
RATES	High season (January, February, March, June, July, August and September) rates are $93-132 for a single or double with private bathroom. Low season (April, May, October, November and early December) rates are $80-108 for a single or double with private bathroom. Rates are higher during Christmas holiday. There is a minimum stay on most weekends and holidays and a reservation/cancellation policy.
CREDIT CARDS	American Express, Diners Club, Discover, MasterCard, Visa
BREAKFAST	Full breakfast is served in the dining room, includes "always something hot," like Swedish pancakes with lingon berries, green-chili and cheese souffle or a steaming bowl of Irish oatmeal topped with cinnamon, brown sugar and walnuts.
AMENITIES	Outdoor hot tub, covered parking, fireplace and grand piano in Great Room, wild-flower garden, free town bus.
RESTRICTIONS	No smoking, children over 10 are welcome. The official greeter is Bergen the Newfoundland Landseer, a year-round outdoor dog.
REVIEWED	*Best Places to Stay in the Rocky Mountains, The Colorado Guide*
MEMBER	Bed & Breakfast Innkeepers of Colorado, Professional Association of Innkeepers International
KUDOS/COMMENTS	"George and Alice run a lovely business!" (1997)

STONEHAM

Pawnee National Grasslands and Pawnee Buttes, Stoneham Days during the last Saturday in September, New Raymer Fair and Rodeo at the end of July, the Texas-Montana Trail route.

ELK ECHO RANCH COUNTRY B&B

47490 WCR 155, Stoneham, CO 80754   970-735-2426
Craig & Noreen McConnell, Resident Owners   FAX 970-735-2427

LOCATION	Twenty miles west of Sterling, then five miles north on Country Road 155.
OPEN	All year.
DESCRIPTION	A 1994 three-story contemporary log home with lodge-style interior including trophy heads and log beds on a 2,000 acre elk ranch.
NO. OF ROOMS	Four rooms with private bathrooms. The owners suggest the Pheasant Landing room.
RATES	Friday and Saturday rates are $89 for a single and $99 for a double with a private bathroom. There is a two-night minimum stay at Thanksgiving.
CREDIT CARDS	MasterCard, Visa
BREAKFAST	Full breakfast, served in the dining room, includes French toast served with homemade syrup or strawberries and whipped cream, ham, light Kielbasa sausage, grape clusters and beverages. Dinner and a special, traditional Thanksgiving Day meal are available.
AMENITIES	Homemade pie and coffee or tea in the evening, soap and shampoo, fresh ice-water carafe, mints, guest journal in rooms, elk and bison tour, elk boarding, air conditioning, stone fireplace in great room, meeting facility, gift shop, handicapped access on main floor.
RESTRICTIONS	No pets; smoking limited to wraparound deck, balcony and patio areas; well-behaved children are welcome. KJ is the tame elk cow "you can pet" and Remington is the bull elk "you can see close-up." In addition, there are 300 elk and 20 bison on the property.
REVIEWED	*Country magazine's Farm Vacations Guide, Denver Post*
MEMBER	Bed & Breakfast Innkeepers of Colorado, Professional Association of Innkeepers
KUDOS/COMMENTS	"Beautiful lodge and interesting tours of the elk they raise." (1996)

TELLURIDE

This tiny Victorian gem set in a box canyon high in the San Juan Mountains once was a brawling mining supply camp and site of Butch Cassidy's first bank robbery. Now it's a major ski area, and THE festival capitol of the universe. Its most famous events: the Film Festival in September; Bluegrass Festival in June; the acclaimed Chamber Music Festival and Jazz Celebration in August; and the Hang Gliding Festival (the largest in the world) in September. Getting to this National Historic Landmark on the San Juan Skyway is half the fun: 66 miles south of Montrose via Highways 550, 62 and 145.

ALPINE INN BED & BREAKFAST

440 West Colorado Avenue, PO Box 2398,	*970-728-6282*
Telluride, CO 81435	*800-707-3344*
Denise & John Weaver, Resident Owners	*FAX 970-728-3424*

LOCATION	On Colorado Avenue (main street) about three blocks from the edge of town on the right.
OPEN	All year.
DESCRIPTION	A 1903 two-story Victorian Inn, furnished with antiques.
NO. OF ROOMS	Six rooms with private bathrooms and two rooms share one bathroom. Try the suite with the whirlpool tub.
RATES	Winter rates, December through March, are $135-165 for a single or double with a private bathroom, $110-140 for a single or double with a shared bathroom and $145-220 for a suite. Summer rates (except for festivals) are $80-95 for a single or double with private bathroom, $70-85 for a single or double with a shared bathroom and $135-155 for a suite. There is a minimum stay during winter and festivals and there is a reservation/cancellation policy.
CREDIT CARDS	MasterCard, Visa
BREAKFAST	Full breakfast, served in the dining room, includes one hot entree, fruit, cereals, breads and beverages.
AMENITIES	TV in most rooms, sunroom with fireplace, large deck/veranda with hot tub, parlor with fireplace, on-site massage, apres-ski refreshments during the winter, two blocks from ski lifts.
RESTRICTIONS	No smoking, no pets, children over 10 are welcome. Justin is the resident Border Collie.
REVIEWED	*Non-Smokers Guide to Bed & Breakfasts*
MEMBER	Bed & Breakfast Innkeepers of Colorado, Professional Association of Innkeepers International
RATED	AAA 2 Diamonds

BEAR CREEK BED & BREAKFAST

221 East Colorado Avenue, PO Box 2369,
Telluride, CO 81435
Colleen & Tom Whiteman, Resident Owners

970-728-6681
800-338-7064
FAX 970-728-3636

LOCATION	On Telluride's main street.
OPEN	All year.
DESCRIPTION	A 1984 three-story brick Victorian inn with mountain-style contemporary furnishings.
NO. OF ROOMS	Ten rooms with private bathrooms. Colleen suggests room 16.
RATES	High seasons rates, December through March and mid-June through September, are $85-180 for a single or double with private bathrooms. Off season rates are $70-105 for a single or double with private bathroom. There is a minimum stay during major festivals, holidays and mid-December through mid-March.
CREDIT CARDS	Discover, MasterCard, Visa
BREAKFAST	Full breakfast is served in the dining room.
AMENITIES	Phone, cable TV/HBO in the rooms, fireplace in the common areas, steam room, sauna, rooftop deck, ski lockers, complimentary apres ski, parking and ski shuttle.
RESTRICTIONS	No smoking, no pets, children over 10 are welcome.
REVIEWED	*The Colorado Guide*
MEMBER	Bed & Breakfast Innkeepers of Colorado, Professional Association of Innkeepers International

THE JOHNSTONE INN

403 West Colorado, PO Box 546, Telluride, CO 81435   970-728-3316
Bill Schiffbauer, Resident Owner   800-752-1901
FAX 970-728-0724

LOCATION	Near center of town on main (Colorado) street.
OPEN	All year except for mud season and mid-October to Thanksgiving.
DESCRIPTION	A restored 1891 two-story Victorian boarding house on the National and State Historic Registers, with Victorian furnishings.
NO. OF ROOMS	Eight rooms with private bathrooms. Bill recommends the Columbine room.
RATES	Winter rates are $110 for a double with private bathroom and $125-170 during holidays. Summer rates are $70 for a double with private bathroom and $70-160 during festivals. There is a four-day minimum stay during festivals and a reservation/cancellation policy.
CREDIT CARDS	American Express, MasterCard, Visa
BREAKFAST	Full breakfast is served in the dining room.
AMENITIES	Apres-ski refreshments during winter, sitting room with fireplace, outdoor hot tub, phones and fresh flowers in the rooms.
RESTRICTIONS	No smoking, no pets, children over 10 are welcome.
MEMBER	Bed & Breakfast Innkeepers of Colorado

MANITOU BED & BREAKFAST HOTEL

333 South Fir, PO Box 100, Telluride, CO 81435   970-728-4011
Steve Hilliard, Resident Manager   800-538-7754
FAX 970-728-6160

PENNINGTON'S MOUNTAIN VILLAGE INN

100 Pennington Court, PO Box 2428, Telluride, CO 81435   *970-728-5337*
Michael & Judy MacLean, Resident Managers   *800-543-1437*
FAX 970-728-5338

LOCATION	Just outside Telluride, stay on Highway 145 toward Ophir, turn right two miles west of town, continue another two-to-three miles, turn left at our sign.
OPEN	Closed May 1st to May 23rd and November 1st through November 23rd.
DESCRIPTION	Contemporary French country with Victorian furnishings on the 12th fairway of the Telluride Golf Course.
NO. OF ROOMS	Twelve rooms with private bathrooms.
RATES	Winter rates are $160-210 for a single or double and summer rates are $185-210 for a single or double. Off season rates are $140-165. Christmas and festival rates are higher. There is a reservation/cancellation policy.
CREDIT CARDS	American Express, Discover, MasterCard, Visa
BREAKFAST	Full breakfast is served in the dining room.
AMENITIES	Complimentary happy hour, library lounge, indoor Jacuzzi and steam room, game room with TV, entry level lockers, laundry facilities, small meeting facilities, handicapped access.
RESTRICTIONS	No smoking, no pets. Well-behaved and well-supervised children are welcome.
MEMBER	Distinctive Inns of Colorado
KUDOS/COMMENTS	"The most beautiful mountain setting I have ever seen! This is a first-class, high-end inn in every way!" ... "Luxurious rooms with bountiful amenities. Lovely, peaceful, great food." (1996)

THE SAN SOPHIA INN

330 West Pacific Avenue, PO Box 1825, Telluride, CO 81435   *970-728-3001*
Keith Hampton & Alicia Bixby, Innkeepers   *800-537-4781*
                                                    FAX 970-728-6226

LOCATION	Half block from Oak Street ski lift.
OPEN	Closed October 21st through November 26th and early April to mid-May.
DESCRIPTION	A 1988 contemporary Victorian with country furnishings.
NO. OF ROOMS	Sixteen rooms with private bathrooms.
RATES	Bargain season rates are $130-185 for a single or double with private bathroom. Winter rates are $165-210 and summer rates are $114-164. Christmas and festival rates are higher, so call for details. There is a five-night minimum stay during Christmas and two-to-three-night minimum stay during festivals. There is a $25 charge per person over a double occupancy. There is a reservation/cancellation policy.
CREDIT CARDS	American Express, MasterCard, Visa
BREAKFAST	Full gourmet breakfast is served in the dining room or on the deck.
AMENITIES	Complimentary cocktail hour in the evening, in-room beverage service, "extensive apres ski," cable TV/VCR and phones in the room, tubs for two, robes, covered parking, gazebo with sunken Jacuzzi, observatory, library with fireplace, concierge service and English garden.
RESTRICTIONS	No smoking, no pets, and children over 10 are welcome.
REVIEWED	*Recommended Country Inns of the Rocky Mountain Region*
MEMBER	Distinctive Inns of Colorado, American Bed & Breakfast Association
RATED	AAA 4 Diamonds, ABBA 5 Crowns, Mobil 4 Stars

TRINIDAD

This busy railroad and coal mining district is a straight shot south on I-25 from Denver, just 19 miles from the New Mexico border. The Corazon de Trinidad National Historic District is a charmer and there are some good museums too, including Mitchell Memorial Museum & Gallery; don't forget Baca House and Bloom Mansion.

CARRIAGE HOUSE INN

119 North Walnut, Trinidad, CO 81082   719-846-2281
Tom Murphy, Resident Manager

CHICOSA CANYON BED & BREAKFAST

32391 County Road 40, Trinidad, CO 81082   719-846-6199
Keena Unruh, Resident Owner   FAX 719-846-6199

INN ON THE SANTA FE TRAIL

402 West Main Street, Trinidad, CO 81082   719-846-4636
Evelyn Keys, Resident Owner

LOCATION	On the historic Santa Fe Trail, take the Main Street exit off I-25, follow Main Street for three blocks; house sits on the southwest corner of Main and Animas.
OPEN	All year.
DESCRIPTION	A 1900 two-story brick Victorian with mix-matched and southwest furnishings, several verandas with gardens.
NO. OF ROOMS	Five rooms with private bathrooms and two rooms share one bathroom. Try room #3.
RATES	High season rates are $45 for a single with bathroom, $65 for a double with bathroom and $85 for a group of four. Off season rates are $10 less. Reservations are requested but not required. There is a cancellation policy.
CREDIT CARDS	American Express, Diners Club, Discover, MasterCard, Visa
BREAKFAST	Full menu breakfast is served in the dining room.
AMENITIES	The inn has fresh flowers in season, two rooms with fireplaces, air-conditioning downstairs and ceiling fans upstairs, two TVs in common areas, a glass of wine or hot chocolate upon check-in, candies and cookies for children, fresh fruit in season.
RESTRICTIONS	Mostly non-smoking. House-broken, well-behaved pets are allowed. Children are welcome.

Mount Elbert Lodge, Twin Lakes

TWIN LAKES

In the shadow of Mt. Elbert at 14,433 feet. Mid-February is the Ice Carnival with a Victorian ball and a snoeshoe race up Elbert. In August bring your Burro for the Mosquito Pass Marathon or trash yourself in the Leadvill 100, an ultra marathon that never drops below 9,000 feet and tops out at over 12,000 on Hope Pass south of here...Remember Hope Pass Bowers, and what you did on my shoes?...TI. From Leadville, go south on Highway 24 for 14 miles, turn right on Highway 82.

MOUNT ELBERT LODGE

Highway 82, PO Box 40, Twin Lakes, CO 81251   719-486-0594
Laura Downing & Scott Boyd, Resident Owners   800-381-4433
                                                      FAX 719-486-0594

LOCATION   From Twin Lakes go west 4 miles west. From Aspen take Highway
                82 east over Independence Pass for 34 miles (summer only).

OPEN   All year.

DESCRIPTION	A 1920 two-story half-log stage stop with simple country furnishings on Lake Creek surrounded by San Isabel National Forest.
NO. OF ROOMS	Six rooms share 2½ bathrooms. Housekeeping cabins do not include breakfast. Laura suggests the Mt. Elbert Room.
RATES	Year-round rates are $46-59 for a single or double with a shared bathroom. The cabins are $75-140 and have a two-night minimum stay. The entire lodge rents for $336. There is no minimum stay in the lodge and cancellation requires seven days' notice.
CREDIT CARDS	American Express, Discover, MasterCard, Visa
BREAKFAST	Continental Plus is served in the dining room and includes freshly prepared fruit dish, muffins, scones or cinnamon rolls, yogurt, oatmeal, dry cereals, bagels and cream cheese, breakfast toast, coffee, milk, juice, cocoa and an assortment of teas. Dinners by request October through May.
AMENITIES	Quiet; views; flannel robes; common area with fireplace; ice skating in the winter; in the summer, stocked fishing pond for children; back-door access to the "Black Cloud Trail" up Mt. Elbert.
RESTRICTIONS	No smoking in B&B, no pets. Fargo the canary "loves to sing especially November through May."...I don't remember that tune, could you sorta hum a few bars for me there Fargo?...TI
MEMBER	Bed & Breakfast Innkeepers of Colorado

TWIN LAKES MOUNTAIN RETREAT B&B

129 Lang Road, PO Box 175, Twin Lakes, CO 81251　　　719-486-2593
Roger & Denny Miller, Resident Owners

LOCATION	From I-70 take the Copper Mountain exit south through Leadville on Highway 24 for 17 miles to Highway 82. Go west seven miles to Twin Lakes Village. Turn right at the general store and go one block.
OPEN	May first through October 31st.
DESCRIPTION	An 1889 two-story Victorian country inn totally refurbished with floor-to-ceiling windows, country and antique furnishings.
NO. OF ROOMS	Three rooms with private bathrooms and two rooms share one bathroom. The Millers recommend Interlaken.
RATES	Seasonal rate for a single or double with a private bathroom is $78 and a single or double with a shared bathroom is $74. There is no minimum stay and cancellation requires 24 hours' notice, seven days' for holidays.
CREDIT CARDS	No
BREAKFAST	Full breakfast is served in the dining room. Frittatas, omelets, stuffed French toast, and carrot/pecan pancakes are just a few of the main courses accompanied by ham, sausage or bacon, plus fresh fruit, homemade biscuits, juice and potato dishes. "Please leave your diet at home."
AMENITIES	Quiet, fresh wildflowers in each room, glycerine soaps, lotions and shampoo. Old-fashioned swing and telescope available on front porch. Home-baked goodies are out all day along with over 50 hot chocolates, teas and coffees. Benches in the yard for bird watching and turndown service with chocolates.
RESTRICTIONS	No smoking, no pets (resident Springer Spaniel Molly), and children over 10 are welcome.
REVIEWED	*Distinguished Country Inns, Country Inns and Bed & Breakfasts*
MEMBER	Bed & Breakfast Innkeepers of Colorado
KUDOS/COMMENTS	"Roger & Denny have a lovely small B&B in one of the original miner's homes in Twin Lakes. Charmingly decorated and with breathtaking views from the front porch." (1996)

Black Bear Inn, Vail

VAIL

In the Gore Creek Valley, surrounded by three wilderness areas, this world class resort is the largest ski complex in the nation, famous for its back bowls and its serious glitz. Jerry Ford is around a lot, too, especially during the American Ski Classic in March and his Invitational Golf Tournament (Fore! Jerry) in August.

BLACK BEAR INN

2405 Elliott Road, Vail, CO 81657   970-476-1304
Jessie & David Edeen, Resident Owners   FAX 970-476-0433
German spoken.

LOCATION	West Vail exit 173 to South Frontage Road and then west 0.1 mile to Elliot Road.
OPEN	All year except for mud season (mid-April through May).
DESCRIPTION	A 1991 two-story hand-crafted log inn with contemporary furnishings on Gore Creek.
NO. OF ROOMS	Twelve rooms with private bathrooms.

RATES	The inn has seasonal rates. Winter rates (mid-November to mid-April) run $115-215 for a single or double with private bathroom. Summer and fall rates are $95-105 for the same accommodations. There is a minimum stay during the winter season and cancellation requires 14 days' notice, 30 days' for Christmas holiday plus a $25 fee.
CREDIT CARDS	Discover, MasterCard, Visa
BREAKFAST	Full breakfast, served in the dining room, includes a "gourmet chef's creation," fresh-baked breads, rolls, muffins and fruit in season.
AMENITIES	Handcrafted log or brass beds, down comforters, afternoon hors d'oeuvres, ski and boot storage, game room with pool table, game table, TV and pinball, and an executive conference room.
RESTRICTIONS	No smoking, no pets. The resident dog is named Fozzie.
REVIEWED	*Best Places to Stay in the Rocky Mountain Region, America's Wonderful Little Hotels & Inns, Recommended Country Inns: Rocky Mountain Region.*
MEMBER	Distinctive Inns of Colorado
KUDOS/COMMENTS	"Beautiful, hand-crafted log inn, rustic with elegance. The happy hour appetizers and food are superb." ... "Relaxing atmosphere, close to the slopes yet out of the way of the hustle and bustle of Vail, David and Jessie are exceptional innkeepers." ... "Best log structure as a B&B in Colorado, rustic with elegance." ... "Happy hour and food are great." (1996)

VICTOR

This 1890s gold mining boomer at the base of Battle Mountain is part of the Cripple Creek-Victor National Historic District. The Lowell Thomas Museum tells about it famous resident. Take a ride on the Cripple Creek-Victor narrow Gauge Railroad. From Colorado Springs, 50 miles southwest via Highway 24.

THE KESSEY HOUSE BED & BREAKFAST

212 South 3rd Street, Victor, CO 80860   719-689-2235
Carol & Robert James, Resident Owners

LOCATION	South 1-1/2 blocks from Victor and 3rd.
OPEN	All year.
DESCRIPTION	An 1899 three-story Victorian with intergenerational furnishings. Owned by the Kessey family for 60 of the last 95 years.
NO. OF ROOMS	Four rooms share one bathroom. The best room is The Attic on the third floor.
RATES	Year-round rates are $45 for a single with shared bathroom and $55 for a double with a shared bathroom. There is no minimum stay and there is a reservation/cancellation policy.
CREDIT CARDS	MasterCard, Visa
BREAKFAST	Full breakfast, served in the dining room, includes Belgian waffles or special French toast or baked sausage, egg and cheese dish, and beverages.
AMENITIES	Many books on the history of this mining town, gambling six miles away in Cripple Creek, shared TV in the parlor, and "we know the local fishing and hiking."
RESTRICTIONS	None.
KUDOS/COMMENTS	"Very beautiful and the innkeepers are very friendly; Carol is a wonderful resource of local history." (1996)

MIDNIGHT INN

305 South 4th Street, Victor, CO 80860	719-689-3711

David McCormick, Resident Owner
Some Spanish spoken.

LOCATION	Six miles from Cripple Creek on Highway 67.
OPEN	All year.
DESCRIPTION	A restored 1894 two-story Victorian with classic Victorian interior decor.
NO. OF ROOMS	Four rooms share two bathrooms. David recommends the back apartment (full kitchen and loft).
RATES	Year-round rates are $35-50 for a single or double with shared bathroom. There is no minimum stay and a 24-hour cancellation policy.
CREDIT CARDS	No
BREAKFAST	Full American or Mexican breakfast is served in the dining room. Lunch, dinner and special meals, including vegetarian, are available.
AMENITIES	Private fishing club, mountain-bike tours, secluded hiking.
RESTRICTIONS	None. The resident dog is called Barney.

MOUNTAIN MEMORY LODGE

119 South First, Victor, CO 80860	719-689-3411

Bill & Nancy Belei, Resident Owners

POTTERS INN

305 Victor Avenue, Victor, CO 80860	719-689-0440

John & Elizabeth Mills, Resident Owners

VICTOR MALL HOTEL

4th & Victor Avenue, Victor, CO 80860	719-689-3347

The Brandts, Resident Owners

WALDEN

WINDING RIVER GUEST RANCH
BED & BREAKFAST

PO Box 37, Walden, CO 80480   970-723-4587
Darleen West & Debbie Holsinger, Resident Owners   FAX 970-723-4771

WESTCLIFFE

This idyllic location is between the Wet Mountains and the Sangre de Cristo Mountains in a valley very few know about and even less visit. Don't tell anyone that you know about it. From Pueblo, 45 miles west on Highway 50, then go south 25 miles on Highway 69.

PURNELL'S RAINBOW INN

104 Main Street, Westcliffe, CO 81252   719-783-2313
David & Karen Purnell, Resident Owners

LOCATION	On the very west end of town, south side of street.
OPEN	All year.
DESCRIPTION	A 1988 two-story contemporary western inn located at the base of the Sangre de Cristo mountains.
NO. OF ROOMS	Two rooms with private bathrooms and two rooms share two bathrooms. The Florida room may be the best in the house.
RATES	Summer rates are $65 for a single or double with a private bathroom and $55 for a single or double with a shared bathroom. Winter rates for a single or double with a private bathroom are $60 and $50 for a single or double with a shared bathroom. There is no minimum stay. Ask about the cancellation policy.
CREDIT CARDS	Discover, MasterCard, Visa
BREAKFAST	Gourmet breakfast, served in the dining room, includes fresh fruit, home-baked muffins, special entree, juice and coffee.
AMENITIES	Game area, big-screen TV, stereo, large hot tub, fly-fishing lessons available and snowshoe rentals.
RESTRICTIONS	No Smoking, no pets, children of any age are welcome.
REVIEWED	The Colorado Guide
MEMBER	Bed & Breakfast Innkeepers of Colorado
RATED	AAA 2 Diamonds

WINDSOR

Once a mason center for sugar beet processing, Windsor remains a farming community. Labor Day week-end in Windsor features the annual "Harvest Days" celebration with a parade and baazar. Windsor is also home to numerous antique shops and old fashioned ice cream and confectionery parlors.

PORTER HOUSE BED & BREAKFAST INN

530 Main Street, Windsor, CO 80550   *970-686-5793*
Tom & Marni Schmittling, Resident Owners   *FAX 970-686-7046*

Porter House Bed & Breakfast Inn, Windsor

LOCATION
Located 55 miles north of Denver and 10 miles southeast of Fort Collins. Take I-25 to exit 262, then head east for 4.5 miles to 6th and Main Street. The Inn is on the northeast corner.

OPEN
All year.

DESCRIPTION
A restored 1898 two-story Queen Ann Victorian inn with turret and gabled roof and period antique furnishings.

NO. OF ROOMS
Four rooms with private bathrooms. The owner's favorite is the Hobbit Room.

RATES	Year-round rates are $75-90 for a single or double with a private bathroom. There are no minimum stay requirements. Ask about cancellation policy.
CREDIT CARDS	American Express, MasterCard, Visa
BREAKFAST	Full breakfast is served in the dining room and includes homemade muffins and bread, freshly squeezed juice, stuffed French toast, omelets, eggs Durango, fresh fruit and coffee. Lunch, dinner and special meals (heart-healthy and box lunches) are available with 24 hours' notice.
AMENITIES	Fresh flowers, robes, homemade truffles, bottomless cookie jar, afternoon wine and tea served in parlor, down comforters, hammock, air conditioning, FAX, copier.
RESTRICTIONS	No smoking, no pets. Children over 12 are welcome.
REVIEWED	*Recommended Country Inns of the Rocky Mountain Region*
MEMBER	Bed & Breakfast Innkeepers of Colorado, Professional Association of Innkeepers International
KUDOS/COMMENTS	"This charming doll-house-like inn is one of the best kept secrets in northern Colorado." (1996)

WINTER PARK AND FRASER

Skis and bikes are passports here in this winter and summer resort: three interconnected mountains and the world's largest mountain bike trail system — 600 miles. Competitive events fill the seasons, but summer is special: Jazz and Music Festivals in July are a time to schmooze on your blanket and revel; Alpine ArtFair, the Rocky Mountain Wine and Food Festival, and weekend rodeos all happen in July and August. Or mush with the huskies and watch for moose on the loose (everywhere). From Denver 67 miles northwest via I-70 and Highway 40. or try the Denver & Rio Grande Ski Train on Winter Weekends.

ALPEN ROSE

244 Forest Trail, Winter Park, CO 80482   970-726-5039
Robin & Rupert Sommerauer, Resident Owners   800-531-1373
German spoken.   FAX 970-726-0993

LOCATION	In Winter Park, turn west on Vasquez Road, cross the railroad tracks, take the first right on Forest Trail, second house on the left, 0.5 miles from Highway 40, just two miles from the ski area.
OPEN	All year.
DESCRIPTION	A 1965 mountain-cabin lodge with Austrian-American furnishings and a spectacular view of the Continental Divide. Just two miles from the ski area.
NO. OF ROOMS	Five rooms with private bathrooms. Check out the Alpen Rose room with the tub for two.
RATES	Winter rates, December 1 through April 15, are $80-100 for a single with private bath and $85-115 for a double with private bath. The off season rates are $55-65 for a single with private bath and $65-75 for a double with private bath. There is a minimum stay during Christmas and March.
CREDIT CARDS	American Express, Discover, MasterCard, Visa.
BREAKFAST	Full breakfast, served in the dining room, includes an egg and meat dish, fresh fruit, homemade yogurt, granola, bread and coffeecake. There is also an afternoon snack.
AMENITIES	Robes, one room has a fireplace and two rooms have a tub for two, outdoor hot tub with a view of the Continental Divide.
RESTRICTIONS	No smoking, no pets (there is a resident Chow mix called Teddy), children over 10 are welcome.
REVIEWED	*Non-Smokers Guide to Bed & Breakfasts*
MEMBER	Bed & Breakfast Innkeepers of Colorado, Bed & Breakfast Winter Park, Colorado Hotel and Lodging Association.

ANNA LEAH BED & BREAKFAST

1001 County Road 8, Fraser, CO 80442
Patricia Handel, Resident Owner

970-726-4414
800-237-9913

KUDOS/COMMENTS "Pat does an excellent job of providing a beautiful, comfortable atmosphere for her guests. Each detail is attended to! A gorgeous home filled with antiques." ... "Large property with spectacular views." (1996)

BEAR PAW INN—871 BEAR PAW DRIVE

PO Box 334, Winter Park, CO 80482
Sue & Rick Callahan, Resident Owners

970-887-1351
800-474-0091
FAX 970-887-1351

KUDOS/COMMENTS "Very friendly hosts, very comfortable and beautifully decorated rooms." ... "Somewhat remote location with spectacular views." (1996)

BEAU WEST BED & BREAKFAST

148 Fir Drive, Winter Park, CO 80482
Robert Goins, Resident Owner

970-726-5145
800-473-5145
FAX 970-726-8607

LOCATION Turn at the main entrance to the Winter Park Resort, follow around past base area, turn left after going under tracks, turn left just past Slope Restaurant, top of the hill on left.

OPEN All year.

DESCRIPTION A 1968 contemporary mountain host home at the base of Winter Park ski area, decorated with southwestern furnishings.

NO. OF ROOMS Three rooms with private bathrooms. Owner recommends a soak in the Jacuzzi in the San Francisco suite.

RATES Winter rates are $99-149 for a double with private bathroom. Summer rates are $85-100 for a double with private bathroom. There is a minimum stay required for holidays and special events and a reservation/cancellation policy.

CREDIT CARDS MasterCard, Visa

BREAKFAST Full breakfast, served in the dining room, includes various egg dishes served buffet style, fresh-baked muffins, seasonal fruit and beverages.

AMENITIES	TV in rooms, down comforters and feather beds, robes, hot tub in solarium, fireplace in living room.
RESTRICTIONS	No smoking, no pets.
MEMBER	Bed & Breakfast Innkeepers of Colorado, Colorado Hotel and Lodging Association

CANDLELIGHT MOUNTAIN INN

PO Box 600, Winter Park, CO 80482   970-887-2877
Kim & Tim Onnen, Resident Owners   800-546-4846

ENGELMANN PINES BED & BREAKFAST

1035 Cranmer Avenue, Winter Park, CO 80482   970-726-4632
Margaret & Heinz Engel, Resident Owners   FAX 970-726-5458
German spoken.

LOCATION	Go north two miles on US 40 from Winter Park towards Fraser. Turn right at the traffic light at Safeway, follow to the top of the hill, turn right on Cranmer, follow Cranmer 0.5 mile, the B&B is on the left just past the Lookout Village Condos.
OPEN	May 1 to December 15
DESCRIPTION	A 1985 tri-level contemporary mountain inn with European and American antiques decorated to be "elegant but comfortable."
NO. OF ROOMS	Five rooms with private bathrooms and two rooms share one bathroom. Pick the King Queen room.
RATES	High season, November through April, rates are $95-115 for a single or double with a private bathroom and a single or double with a shared bathroom is $75-85. Off season rates are $15 less. There is a minimum stay at Christmas and during March, ask about the cancellation policy.
CREDIT CARDS	American Express, Discover, MasterCard, Visa
BREAKFAST	Full breakfast, served in the dining room, includes a fresh fruit plate, Bircher Muesli and pastries, followed by an entree that may be German pancakes, quiche, eggs benedict, crab or raspberry crepes.
AMENITIES	Wine and hors d'oeuvres, apres-ski refreshments, Jacuzzi tubs in bathrooms, champagne for honeymooners, full kitchen for guest use, piano room.
RESTRICTIONS	No smoking, no pets, the Black Lab-mix is called Bear.

REVIEWED

REVIEWED   *Recommended Country Inns, The Colorado Guide, Frommer's Colorado*

MEMBER   Bed & Breakfast Innkeepers of Colorado, Bed & Breakfasts of Winter Park

GASTHAUS EICHLER

76768 US Highway 40, Winter Park, CO 80482   970-726-5133
Timothy Luksa, Resident Owner   800-543-3899
                                                      FAX 970-726-5175

LOCATION   In the town of Winter Park within walking distance of downtown. It is two miles from the ski area.

OPEN   All year.

DESCRIPTION   A 1987 Stucco/Bavarian lodge with classic German furnishing and restaurant with Bavarian decor on a mountain stream.

NO. OF ROOMS   Fifteen rooms with private baths. The owner's favorite room is #2.

RATES   November through April, rates are $149 for a single or double with private bathroom. May through October, rates are $59-79 for a single or double with a private bathroom. Rate includes breakfast and dinner in the winter and just breakfast in the summer.

CREDIT CARDS   MasterCard, Visa

BREAKFAST   Full breakfast is served in the restaurant.

AMENITIES   Down comforters, Jacuzzi tubs, telephone, cable TV, and lodge van to ski area.

RESTRICTIONS   No pets.

RATED   AAA 3 Diamonds

HEARTHSTONE B&B

23306 County Road 50, Fraser, CO 80442   970-726-9710
Barbara & Robert King, Resident Owners

LOCATION   Take the first left out of Fraser onto County Road 5, take the first left which is County Road 50, the house is 1.5 miles on the left from County Road 5.

OPEN   All year.

DESCRIPTION   A 1989 mountain home with country and antique furnishings.

NO. OF ROOMS	One room with private bathroom and two rooms share one bathroom. The best room is the one with the view of the Continental Divide.
RATES	High season, November 15 to April 15, rates are $65 for a single with private or shared bathroom, $85 for a double with private or shared bathroom. Off season rates are $10 less and holiday rates may be more. There is a minimum stay during Christmas and spring break and a reservation/cancellation policy.
CREDIT CARDS	MasterCard, Visa
BREAKFAST	Full breakfast is served by the cookstove in the country kitchen or in the dining room.
AMENITIES	Hot tub in solarium, deck, refreshments, fireplace, TV/VCR in great room, cross-country and mountain-bike trails at doorstep, full-moon cross-country ski tours.
RESTRICTIONS	No smoking, no pets, children over 10 are welcome. Heidi is the resident cat.
MEMBER	Bed & Breakfast Innkeepers of Colorado, Bed & Breakfasts of Winter Park

---

HIGH MOUNTAIN LODGE AND RANCH

425 County Road 5001, Fraser, CO 80442 970-726-5958
Chris & Sue Felts, Resident Owners 800-772-9987
FAX 970-726-5513

LOCATION	From Winter Park, go through Fraser, take the first left past town on County Road S; take the first left on County Road 50; go 2.8 miles and turn right at our sign.
OPEN	All year.
DESCRIPTION	A 1983 three-story European lodge with European/Swiss furnishings.
NO. OF ROOMS	Thirteen rooms with private bathrooms. Pick room 9.
RATES	Winter, November through April, rates are $100 for a single with private bathroom and $150 for a double with private bathroom. Off season rates are $60 for a single with private bathroom and $65 for a double with private bathroom. There is a $10 charge for each additional person over the double occupancy. There is a minimum stay during Christmas week and cancellation requires 30 days' notice.
CREDIT CARDS	American Express, MasterCard, Visa

BREAKFAST	Full breakfast is served in the dining room. Dinner and vege⟨ meals are also available in winter.
AMENITIES	Heated indoor swimming pool, Jacuzzi, sauna, TV, pool table, ping-pong table, treadmill, laundry facilities, horseback rides, most rooms with private fireplaces, handicapped accessible.
RESTRICTIONS	No pets during winter, summer okay. Ready for this? In addition to Ben, one of the largest horses in Colorado (23.2 hands), there are three dogs, Sadie, Tilly and Mindy, two cats, Midnight and Missy, plus 20 horses and a herd of longhorn cattle.

MORNINGSTAR RANCH BED & BREAKFAST

933 County Road 8, Fraser, CO 80442   970-726-4895
David Zink & Karen Waeschle, Resident Owners   FAX 970-726-0117
French spoken.

LOCATION	From Winter Park, go north on Highway 40 through Fraser, turn right after the Post Office in Fraser onto County Road 8. Drive one mile to the top of the hill, the ranch is on the left.
OPEN	All year.
DESCRIPTION	A 1978 two-story contemporary cedar-sided lodge with southwestern casual furnishings and encircled by a large deck. The lodge sits on 80 wooded acres.
NO. OF ROOMS	Eight rooms share four bathrooms. The Silverheels is the owner's favorite.
RATES	High season, November through April, rates for a single or double with shared bathroom are $55-75. The entire B&B rents for $600. Off season, May through October, rates for a single or double are $35-55. The entire B&B rents for $450. There is a minimum stay over holiday weekends and cancellation requires 30 days' written notice.
CREDIT CARDS	MasterCard, Visa
BREAKFAST	Continental Plus is served in the dining room and includes hearty homemade breads, muffins, hot and cold cereals, fruit and yogurt. Snacks are served in the afternoon.
AMENITIES	One-hundred kilometers of groomed hiking and cross-country trails and over 600 miles of mapped mountain-bike trails, hosts will help with routes. Outdoor hot tub, wax room, bike storage, dinner sleigh rides and summer barbeque dinner and wagon ride are also available.
RESTRICTIONS	No smoking, no pets, children over 10 are welcome. The resident English Setters are Siri and Murphy.
REVIEWED	*The Colorado Guide, Fodor's Ski Guide*
MEMBER	Winter Park Bed & Breakfast Association

NEWTON'S NEST BED & BREAKFAST

54 Icicle Way, Fraser, CO 80442   970-726-9398
Karen Newton, Resident Owner   888-726-9398

LOCATION	Two miles west of Fraser in Ice Box Estates.
OPEN	All year.
DESCRIPTION	A 1982 two-story cedar with contemporary furnishings.
NO. OF ROOMS	One room with private bathroom and two rooms share one bathroom.
RATES	Winter rates are $85-120 for a single or double and summer rates are $75-100 for a single or double.
CREDIT CARDS	No
BREAKFAST	Full breakfast is served in the dining room.
AMENITIES	Hot tub on deck, robes, complimentary refreshments.
RESTRICTIONS	No smoking, no pets, children are welcome.
MEMBER	Bed & Breakfast of Winter Park

THE PINES INN OF WINTER PARK

115 County Road 716, Winter Park, CO 80482   970-726-5416
Jan & Lee Reynolds, Resident Owners   800-824-9127
                                                      FAX 970-726-1062

LOCATION	One-quarter mile off Highway 40, just north of the Winter Park Ski Area in Old Town Winter Park.
OPEN	All year.
DESCRIPTION	A 1958 alpine country inn with knotty pine and rustic furnishings.
NO. OF ROOMS	Six rooms with private bathrooms and two rooms share one bathroom. The Reynolds suggest #6 as their best room.
RATES	Winter rates are $70 for a single with private bathroom, $110 for a double with private bathroom, $60 for a single with shared bathroom and $100 for a double with shared bathroom. Summer rates are $50 for a single with private bathroom and $80 for a double with a private bathroom, $40 for a single with a shared bathroom and $70 for a double. There is a two-night minimum stay on the weekends and there is a reservation/cancellation policy.
CREDIT CARDS	American Express, Discover, MasterCard, Visa

BREAKFAST	Full breakfast, served in the dining room, includes a hot entree, breads, cereals, yogurt and fruit.
AMENITIES	Outdoor Jacuzzi, telephone and TV in common area, afternoon refreshments, meeting facilities, game room.
RESTRICTIONS	No smoking, no pets. Children of all ages are welcome.
MEMBER	Professional Association of Innkeepers International, Winter Park Bed & Breakfast Association, Bed & Breakfast Innkeepers of Colorado

WHISTLE STOP BED & BREAKFAST

PO Box 418, Winter Park, CO 80482
Warren Watson, Resident Owner

970-726-8767
888-829-2632

WOODLAND PARK
(COLORADO SPRINGS)

The largest of a chain of mountain communities west of Colorado Springs via Highway 24. Frun time to be here: Ute Trail Stampede and Old Fashioned Fourth of July and December's month-long Magic of Lights Celebration.

PIKES PEAK PARADISE

236 Pinecrest Road, Woodland Park, CO 80866   719-687-6656
Tim Stoddard, Martin Meier & Priscilla Arthur,   800-728-8282
Resident Owners   FAX 719-687-9008

Pikes Peak Paradise, Woodland Park

LOCATION
Take Highway 24 from I-25 to Woodland Park. From the signal light at Highway 67 travel 0.9 mile to Trout Creek Road. Right on Trout Creek Road 1.9 miles to the Aspen Hills & Coyote Trail sign. Right on Coyote Trail 0.9 mile to 236 Pinecrest Road (follow signs).

OPEN
All year.

DESCRIPTION
A 1988 three-story Georgian-Greek Revival overlooking Pikes Peak, with spacious rooms.

NO. OF ROOMS
Six rooms with private bathrooms. The owners suggest the Sage Room.

RATES	Year-round rates are $95 for a single or double with private bath, suites are $135-195. The entire B&B rents for $865. There is no minimum stay. Cancellation policy: "Refunded if cancelled within seven days of making reservation. Otherwise gift certificates." Better ask for an explanantion...TI
CREDIT CARDS	American Express, Discover, MasterCard, Visa
BREAKFAST	Continental Plus is served in the dining room or guest room and includes cheese souffle, blueberry croissant, fresh fruit, juice, and coffee. Breakfast in bed costs an additional $15.
AMENITIES	In-room hot tubs, fireplaces, snacks, mountain views, and handicapped accessible.
RESTRICTIONS	No smoking, pets are OK, children over 12 are welcome. There are three Pomeranians in residence, Bear, Tiffany and Scarlett.

WOODLAND INN BED & BREAKFAST

159 Trull Road, Woodland Park, CO 80863
Frank & Nancy O'Neil, Resident Owners

719-687-8209
800-226-9565
FAX 719-687-3112

LOCATION	From Highway 24 west take the first right past the Woodland Park city limits sign and the Swiss Chalet Restaurant and drive 0.2 miles to the first house on the left.
OPEN	All year.
DESCRIPTION	A 1965 two-story brick-and-cedar contemporary country inn with "country comfortable" furnishings.
NO. OF ROOMS	Seven rooms with private bathrooms. The best room is Blue Lilac.
RATES	High season, Memorial Day weekend through September, rates are $50-90 for a single or double with a private bathroom. Low season, October through May, rates for a single or double with a private bathroom are $60-80. There is no minimum stay and cancellation requires seven days' notice.
CREDIT CARDS	American Express, Discover, MasterCard, Visa
BREAKFAST	Full breakfast, served in the dining room or patio in the summer, includes seafood omelet with freshly squeezed orange juice, fresh fruit, muffins and breads, blueberry pancakes, waffles, spinach crepes, shrimp or mushroom quiche. Box lunches for day trips are available for $5 each.
AMENITIES	Robes, snacks, teas, wine, fresh flowers in rooms, in-room coffee service in the morning, TV/VCR, rosebud bouquet for anniversaries and special occasions, hot-air ballooning with the host for $25 per person.
RESTRICTIONS	No smoking, no pets, the resident mixed Border Collie is called Ginger and the cat is called Sam. Sam loves laps but is not allowed in guest quarters.
REVIEWED	*Recommended Country Inns of the Rocky Mountain Region, America's Wonderful Little Hotels & Inns, Colorado Off the Beaten Path*
MEMBER	Bed & Breakfast Innkeepers of Colorado, Professional Association of Innkeepers International
KUDOS/COMMENTS	"Lovely, quiet setting." ... "Wooded acreage, deer grazing nearby. Helpful hosts." (1997)

YELLOW JACKET

This agricultural area in the Four Corners Region has one of the most scenic and important Anasazi archeological sites in the southwest. Check out the Yellow Jacket Ruin west of Yellow Jacket Canyon and Creek. There is no town here as such, so look for the historic Post Office as a landmark. Fifteen miles northwest of Cortez on Highway 666.

WILSON'S PINTO BEAN FARM

PO Box 252, Yellow Jacket, CO 81335   970-562-4476
Arthur & Esther Wilson, Resident Owners

LOCATION	Drive 15 miles northwest on Highway 666, turn left on Road Y and go two miles to a left turn on Road 16, first house on the left.
OPEN	First of April to last of October.
DESCRIPTION	A 1946 two-story farm home with painted stucco walls and country furnishings located on 320 acres surrounded by mature trees, an orchard and mountains on all sides.
NO. OF ROOMS	Two rooms with private bathrooms and one room with a shared bathroom. Mrs. Wilson suggests the west bedroom.
RATES	Seasonal rates are $45 for a single with a private bathroom and $35 for a double with a shared bathroom. A family of four stays for $50. There is no minimum stay.
CREDIT CARDS	No
BREAKFAST	Full breakfast, served in the dining room, can be ham, bacon or sausage and eggs, hash browns, toast or muffins, pancakes, sausage & gravy, eggs benedict and always cereal and fruit.
AMENITIES	A wonderful collection of over 2,000 books, old and new children's toys, flowers and fruit in season, TV/radio and large deck. Guests can gather eggs.
RESTRICTIONS	None ("However we would rather that guests don't smoke"). Children of any age are welcome. There are three dogs, Moby Dick, Clancy and Rowdy, and a cat called Champagne.
REVIEWED	*Non-Smokers Guide to Bed & Breakfasts*

BED & BREAKFAST INDEX

About the Publisher

TRAVIS ILSE PUBLISHERS is a traditional publishing house with a slight twist. In the lexicon of business writers, Travis Ilse Publishers is a virtual corporation. There is one principal and crew of independent freelancers who run their own companies or work for other companies and sell their skills to Travis Ilse Publishers.

When we speak of sitting around the publishing house, it might mean our occasional meetings in Boulder, but more than likely it means each of us sitting at a Mac at our various offices talking to each other or sending data via the Internet, working the FAX or talking on the phone. The advantages of a virtual corporation are psychological and practical. Each of us can live exactly where we want, work when we want and be truly responsible for our own fate. Practically speaking, we are extraordinarily flexible and responsive to the marketplace. The B&B industry is volatile, but by constantly updating our databases we can revise our books every two years making the *Absolutely Every** series of B&B books current.

Alan Bernhard is the production manager, programmer and scheduler for TIP. He is the president of Argent Associates, which produces books for eight other publishers, the executive director of the Rocky Mountain Book Publishers Association, and lives in Boulder with his son and daughter.

Carl Hanson is a free-lance editor and writer. He has been the ghost writer on a book about "lone eagles," people who are no longer tied to their offices. He lives in Seattle with a relatively chubby cat and his best friend Sarah, who is a marketing manager at a Seattle publishing conglomerate.

Travis Ilse is the senior editor and owner of the house. He was neither caught in the 1968 Chicago police riot nor was he on the last chopper out of Saigon. He did not inhale. And while he is a conscientious letter writer, he does not return phone calls, make appointments or fly commercial airlines if he can help it. He lives in the Front Range with a younger woman and looks down on Boulder.

Alan Stark is the publisher. He has worked for just about every trade publisher in the West that he has wanted to and considers himself a passable cook and sea kayaker. He has served on the boards of both The Colorado Center for the Book and the Rocky Mountain Book Publishers Association. He lives in Seattle with Sam the old mountain dog and his best friend Linda who is the director of sales and marketing at a well-known Cascadian publishing enterprise.

All of us can be reached by letter at PO Box 583, Niwot, Colorado 80544 or, if it's urgent, at saltybear@aol.com. Write us anytime.

ORDERING INFORMATION

I f you would like additional copies of this book or other books in the series, please contact your local bookstore and give them all the information listed with each title. If the bookseller doesn't have the book in stock, she or he can get it for you in about a week to ten days from Publishers Group West or a trade book wholesaler.

THE ROCKY MOUNTAIN SERIES

Absolutely Every° Bed & Breakfast in Arizona (°Almost), Alan Stark, editor, ISBN 1-882092-12-0, $14.95.

Absolutely Every° Bed & Breakfast in California, Monterey to San Diego (°Almost), Toni Knapp, editor, ISBN 1-882092-10-4, $15.95

Absolutely Every° Bed & Breakfast in Northern California (°Almost), Toni Knapp, editor, ISBN 1-882092-13-9, $16.95

Absolutely Every° Bed & Breakfast in Colorado (°Almost), Alan Stark, editor, ISBN 1-882092-19-8, $16.95

Absolutely Every° Bed & Breakfast in New Mexico (°Almost), Alan Stark, editor, ISBN 1-882092-17-1, $12.95

Absolutely Every° Bed & Breakfast in Texas (°Almost), Alan Stark, editor, ISBN 1-882092-15-5, $18.95

Absolutely Every° Bed & Breakfast in Washington (°Almost), Alan Stark, editor, ISBN 1-882092-16-3, $18.95

THE MISSISSIPPI RIVER SERIES

Absolutely Every° Bed & Breakfast in Illinois (°Almost), Toni Knapp, editor, ISBN 1-882092-14-7, $15.95.